W9-DHY-480

PEANUTS COLLECTION

It's a Dog's Life, Snoopy

It's a Big World, Charlie Brown

Peanuts 2000

BY CHARLES M. SCHULZ

Ballantine Books * New York

A Ballantine Book
Published by The Random House Publishing Group

This 2014 edition is published in the United States by Ballantine Books, an imprint of Random House, a division of Random House LLC, a Penguin Random House Company, New York, and simultaneously in Canada by Random House of Canada Limited, Toronto. The comic strips in this book were originally published in newspapers worldwide. These titles were originally published separately by Ballantine Books, an imprint of Random House, a division of Random House LLC, New York, in 2000 and 2001.

www.ballantinebooks.com
www.snoopy.com

ISBN-13: 978-0-385-36442-3

Printed in China

10 9 8 7 6 5 4 3 2 1

Contents

IT'S A DOG'S LIFE,
SNOOPY
BY CHARLES M. SCHULZ

It's a Dog's Life, SNOOPY

1-1-98
DAD WANTS TO KNOW IF YOU'VE SEEN HIS NINE-IRON..
TELL HIM I'LL ASK AROUND..
SCHULZ

SEE HOW GENTLY THE SNOWFLAKES FLOAT TO THE GROUND?

1-2-98
BONK!

WELL, MOST OF THEM..
SCHULZ

Dear Pen Pal,
How is the weather where you live?

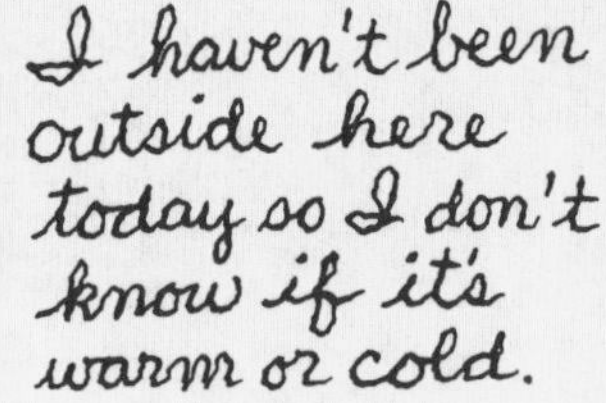
I haven't been outside here today so I don't know if it's warm or cold.

1-3-98

I think maybe it's cold.
SCHULZ

PEANUTS
by SCHULZ

© 1997 United Feature Syndicate, Inc.

LOOK OUT!
www.unitedmedia.com

GOOD GRIEF!

1-4-98
YOU SHOULDN'T HAVE YELLED..YOU MADE ME NERVOUS..
SCHULZ

1-5-98
AND NO LOVE LETTERS CAME TUMBLING OUT..
SCHULZ

BOY, THE SNOW IS COMING DOWN HEAVIER THAN EVER..

WHAT WE NEED IS SOMEONE TO GO OUT TO THE MAILBOX...

1-6-98
SOMEONE WHO DOESN'T MAKE A BIG DEAL OUT OF EVERYTHING..
SCHULZ

AND STOP YELLING!

I WASN'T YELLING..I NEVER SAID A WORD..

1-7-98

STOP NEVER SAYING A WORD!
SCHULZ

WOW! WHAT A PROJECT!

COLOR THESE PICTURES! CUT AND PASTE! DRAW THOSE TREES! MORE CUTTING! MORE PASTING!

WHAT A LEARNING EXPERIENCE! YES, MA'AM, YOU'VE DONE IT AGAIN!

WHEN SHE'S HAPPY, WE'RE HAPPY..
SCHULZ

YES, MA'AM.. I'D LIKE TO SEE THE PRINCIPAL..

I WANT TO SHOW HIM THIS PICTURE I COLORED..
1-9-98
SCHULZ

HE DOESN'T SEE ENLISTED MEN?

ANYBODY HOME?
1-10-98

THAT'S A GOOD IDEA... WHEN IT'S COLD, STAY IN YOUR IGLOO, AND BAKE CHOCOLATE CHIP COOKIES..
SCHULZ

PEANUTS
by SCHULZ

1-11

YARDSALE!
www.unitedmedia.com
SCHULZ

1-12
THIS IS A HARD TEST..

THIS ISN'T A TEST, SIR.. THEY JUST WANT TO KNOW WHEN YOU WERE BORN..

TOO LATE.. I ALREADY PUT DOWN 1492!

AND THEY SAY NO TWO SNOWFLAKES ARE EVER ALIKE..
1-13

THAT'S RIDICULOUS.. I'VE SEEN FOUR ALREADY THIS MORNING THAT WERE EXACTLY ALIKE...

THEY WERE EVEN THE SAME COLOR!
SCHULZ

HELLO?

HI, SALLY.. THIS IS PATRICIA.. I'M CALLING ABOUT A SCHOOL DANCE..
1-14

I DON'T SUPPOSE CHUCK WOULD GO WITH ME, WOULD HE? NO, I SUPPOSE NOT..

ANYWAY, TELL HIM I WAS THINKING OF HIM..

YOU ALMOST WENT TO A SCHOOL DANCE..
SCHULZ

IS CHARLES HOME? I CAME OVER TO ASK HIM TO GO TO A SCHOOL DANCE..

I DOUBT IF HE'D EVER GO WITH SOMEONE LIKE ME, THOUGH, SO I WON'T BOTHER HIM..
© 1998 United Feature Syndicate, Inc.
www.unitedmedia.com

FOR SOMEBODY WHO NEVER GOES ANYPLACE, YOU LEAD A VERY ACTIVE LIFE..
SCHULZ
1-15

PATTY? THIS IS CHARLIE BROWN..I HEAR YOU WANTED TO INVITE ME TO A SCHOOL DANCE..

THE DANCE WAS LAST NIGHT, CHUCK.. MAYBE NEXT YEAR, HUH?
1-16
www.unitedmedia.com

NEXT YEAR FOR SURE.. SAVE ME THE WALTZ
"SAVE ME THE WALTZ"?
© 1998 United Feature Syndicate, Inc.

YOU'RE PRETTY SMOOTH, BIG BROTHER..
IT'S EASY TO BE SMOOTH WHEN YOU'RE OFF THE HOOK..
SCHULZ

1-17
HOW DID THINGS GO IN COURT TODAY?
www.unitedmedia.com

I ASKED THE JUDGE IF I COULD APPROACH THE BENCH..
© 1998 United Feature Syndicate, Inc.

HE SAID, "NO!" HE SAID I SHOULD STAY IN THE BACK YARD..
SCHULZ

PEANUTS
by SCHULZ

CHARLIE BROWN! TELL YOUR DOG TO STOP STARING AT ME!

IF YOU'LL SHARE WHATEVER YOU'RE EATING, MAYBE HE'LL GO AWAY..

© 1998 United Feature Syndicate, Inc.
www.unitedmedia.com

1-18

YOU AGAIN?
HOW DID YOU KNOW IT WAS ME?
SCHULZ

1-19
THIS IS AN ARTICLE ON SCHOOLS AND EDUCATION..
© 1998 United Feature Syndicate, Inc.

IT SAYS SMALL CLASSES ARE BETTER..
IF I STAYED HOME, OUR CLASS WOULD BE EVEN SMALLER..
SCHULZ

" RED IN THE MORNING, BEAGLES TAKE WARNING"
1-20
www.unitedmedia.com

" RED AT NIGHT, BEAGLES DELIGHT"
© 1998 United Feature Syndicate, Inc.

?
SOMETHING ABOUT BIRDS AND WORMS, BUT I NEVER BELIEVED IT..
SCHULZ

" INDICATIONS OF POSSIBLE LEARNING DISABILITY.. HAS A SLOW RECALL OF FACTS.. MAKES SPELLING ERRORS.. HAS AN UNSTABLE PENCIL GRIP..."
1-21
© 1998 United Feature Syndicate, Inc.
SCHULZ

AND IT SAYS THE ANDROMEDA GALAXY IS SPEEDING TOWARD OUR GALAXY AT 300,000 MILES PER HOUR..

SCHULZ
1-22

I HEARD THE COYOTES HOWLING AGAIN LAST NIGHT, CHARLIE BROWN..

THAT'S THE LONELIEST SOUND IN THE WORLD..
LIKE A TRAIN WHISTLE AT MIDNIGHT..
OR A LONE CAN OPENER..
SCHULZ

1-24

SCHULZ

PEANUTS
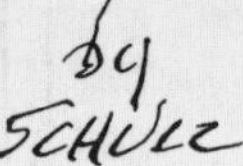
by SCHULZ

WHOOPS! I FORGOT THE PARSLEY

I GOT THE PARSLEY.. WHOOPS! NOW I FORGOT YOUR DINNER!

© 1998 United Feature Syndicate, Inc.

WAIT A MINUTE.. THIS ISN'T YOUR DINNER..THIS IS MY DINNER!

I'LL BE RIGHT BACK..
1-25

OKAY, HERE WE GO..

?
www.unitedmedia.com

IT WAS PRETTY GOOD ALTHOUGH IT COULD HAVE USED SOME PARSLEY..
SCHULZ

I'M NOT GOING TO SCHOOL TODAY..I'M GOING TO HIDE HERE UNDER MY BED UNTIL SUPPERTIME..
1-26

WHAT SHALL I TELL YOUR TEACHER?

TELL HER I SAW HER NEW BOYFRIEND YESTERDAY, AND I'M SURE SHE CAN DO BETTER THAN THAT..
SCHULZ

I TOLD YOUR TEACHER WHAT YOU SAID ABOUT HER NEW BOYFRIEND..

SHE SAID YOU WERE RIGHT.. HE'S REALLY STUPID, AND SHE'S NEVER GOING TO SEE HIM AGAIN..
1-27

I COULD RUN THE WHOLE WORLD RIGHT HERE FROM UNDER MY BED!
SCHULZ

RERUN, WHERE WERE YOU YESTERDAY?
I HID UNDER MY BED ALL DAY..

I THINK IT'S SOMETHING EVERYONE SHOULD DO ONCE IN A WHILE..
1-28

WHAT DOES YOUR DAD THINK ABOUT ALL THIS?
HE DIDN'T GO TO WORK TODAY... HE'S HIDING UNDER THE BED..
SCHULZ

IT'S TOO BAD YOU'RE NOT A HAWK..

SOME PEOPLE BELIEVE THAT HAWKS HAVE "ACCESS TO THE HEAVENS"
www.unitedmedia.com
© 1998 United Feature Syndicate, Inc.
1-29

WELL, YES.. ACCESS TO THE MALL IS PRETTY GOOD..
SCHULZ

SOMEONE AT SCHOOL TODAY ASKED ME IF I HAD AN OLDER BROTHER WHO DRAGGED A BLANKET AROUND.. "NO," I REPLIED, "I'M AN ONLY CHILD!" THEN SOMEONE SAID, "BUT DON'T YOU HAVE A WEIRD OLDER SISTER?" "NO," I INSISTED, "I'M AN ONLY CHILD!" AND SO I GO, DAY AFTER DAY, DODGING QUESTIONS FROM CURIOUS OUTSIDERS..
1-30
© 1998 United Feature Syndicate, Inc.

SCHULZ

I HAVE TO DO A REPORT ON CLOUDS..
WHAT KIND OF CLOUDS?
www.unitedmedia.com

I DON'T KNOW..YOU TELL ME..
HOW ABOUT RAIN CLOUDS?

THAT'S GOOD.. HERE, YOU WRITE IT..
I CAN'T DO YOUR HOMEWORK FOR YOU..
© 1998 United Feature Syndicate, Inc.

I HOPE IT RAINS ON YOU
SCHULZ
1-31

PEANUTS
by SCHULZ
WHERE ?!

ALL RIGHT, WHERE ARE MY COMIC BOOKS ?!
WHAT COMIC BOOKS?

MY COMIC BOOKS THAT YOU'RE ALWAYS TAKING! WHERE ARE THEY ?!

FOR YOUR SAKE, YOU'D BETTER HOPE I FIND THEM..

NEVER MIND.. I FOUND THEM UNDER THE COUCH..

I THOUGHT WE WERE GOING OUTSIDE.. WHAT ARE YOU DOING?
www.unitedmedia.com © 1998 United Feature Syndicate, Inc.

I'M NEVER MINDING..
2-1
SCHULZ

JUST BECAUSE YOU'RE SMALL, YOU DON'T ALWAYS HAVE TO BE AFRAID..

LEARN TO FIGHT BACK! DON'T LET ANYONE PUSH YOU AROUND!
© 1998 United Feature Syndicate, Inc.

IF YOU'RE THE THIRD CHILD IN A FAMILY, AND YOUR BROTHER AND SISTER ARE DEFINITELY WEIRD, I WONDER IF IT'S POSSIBLE FOR THAT THIRD CHILD TO DEVELOP AN IMMUNITY TO ALL THE UNFORTUNATE THINGS THAT OCCUR IN A FAMILY TO THAT INNOCENT THIRD CHILD WHO...
© 1998 United Feature Syndicate, Inc.

CAN A PIANO PLAYER SUPPORT A WIFE WHO IS USED TO ALL THE NICE THINGS IN LIFE?
2-4

YOU KNOW, CARS, CLOTHES, A BEACH HOUSE..THINGS LIKE THAT..

ABSOLUTELY! PIANO PLAYERS MAKE ENORMOUS AMOUNTS OF MONEY! THEIR WIVES CAN BUY ANYTHING THEY WANT!
© 1998 United Feature Syndicate, Inc.

I'LL PROBABLY MARRY A VIOLA PLAYER..

© 1998 United Feature Syndicate, Inc.
QUICK, MARCIE..I NEED AN ERASER!

BONK!
www.unitedmedia.com

2-5

HERE YOU ARE, SIR.. GLAD TO BE OF ASSISTANCE
EVENTUALLY, MARCIE, YOU'RE GOING TO DRIVE ME CRAZY..
SCHULZ

I'M GLAD TO SEE YOU'RE WALKING A LOT..IF YOU FLY TOO MUCH, YOU'LL WEAR OUT YOUR WINGS..
www.unitedmedia.com
THAT'S WHY DOGS DON'T HAVE WINGS..OUR ANCESTORS WORE THEM OUT..
© 1998 United Feature Syndicate, Inc.

?
NO, YOU CAN BELIEVE SOME THINGS I TELL YOU..
SCHULZ
2-6

I SEE WOODSTOCK IS DOING REPAIR WORK ON HIS NEST AGAIN..
© 1998 United Feature Syndicate, Inc.
2-7
SCHULZ

PEANUTS
by Schulz
DID THE MAILMAN COME?

A PERSON HAS TO BE VERY CAREFUL WITH VALENTINES..

A PERSON COULD BE SERIOUSLY INJURED WHEN HE OPENS THE MAILBOX, AND A FLOOD OF VALENTINES COMES POURING OUT...

STAND BACK! STAND BACK!

2-8
AND EVEN IF YOU ONLY RECEIVED ONE VALENTINE, YOU COULD GET A BAD PAPER CUT WHEN YOU OPENED IT..

Z

I'M AWAKE! YES, MA'AM! DID YOU CALL MY NAME?

I'M HERE! DID YOU CALL THE ROLL? DO YOU NEED VOLUNTEERS? PUT ME DOWN! I'LL BRING THE DESSERT!
www.unitedmedia.com
© 1998 United Feature Syndicate, Inc.

THE ANSWER IS "TWELVE"
THAT'S SORT OF, PROBABLY, WHAT I WAS MAYBE GOING TO SAY..
SCHULZ
2-9

IF YOU KNOW YOU'RE NOT GOING TO GET A VALENTINE, WHAT SHOULD YOU DO?
2-10
www.unitedmedia.com

PUT ON A GOOD MOPING FACE SO EVERYONE WILL KNOW YOU'RE MOPING..
© 1998 United Feature Syndicate, Inc.

HOW'S THIS?
VERY GOOD
SCHULZ

HEY, SWEET BABBOO! I BROUGHT YOU A VALENTINE!
www.unitedmedia.com

DOES IT HAVE ANY MONETARY VALUE?

I DOUBT IT..
2-11

I'M NOT YOUR SWEET BABBOO!
SCHULZ
© 1998 United Feature Syndicate, Inc.

TELL MY SWEET BABBOO I'M HERE TO PICK UP MY VALENTINE..

I'M NOT HER SWEET BABBOO, AND I WOULDN'T GIVE HER A VALENTINE IF SHE WERE THE LAST PERSON ON EARTH!

WAIT HERE..I'LL GO KICK HIM FOR YOU..
www.unitedmedia.com

OW!
2-12
© 1998 United Feature Syndicate, Inc.

THANK YOU..
NO PROBLEM.. THAT'S WHAT SISTERS ARE FOR..
SCHULZ

WHAT ARE YOU WRITING, MARCIE?
www.unitedmedia.com

I'M SENDING A VALENTINE TO CHARLES
YOU CAN'T DO THAT..HE'LL THINK YOU LIKE HIM..

I DO..I'M VERY FOND OF CHARLES
WHY DON'T YOU SIGN MY NAME, TOO?
© 1998 United Feature Syndicate, Inc.

OH, SURE! HITCH A RIDE ON MY VALENTINE!
SCHULZ
2-13

HI, CHARLES..DID YOU LIKE OUR VALENTINE?
2-14

YES, THANK YOU..IT WAS NICE
NICE?
www.unitedmedia.com

HE SAID IT WAS "NICE."
ASK HIM IF WE CAN HAVE IT BACK..
© 1998 United Feature Syndicate, Inc.

THE DAY ISN'T OVER.. WE CAN STILL GIVE IT TO SOMEONE ELSE..
SCHULZ

PEANUTS
by
SCHULZ

WELL, HOW DOES OUR BALL FIELD LOOK THIS YEAR, CHARLIE BROWN?
2-15

I THINK OUR GROUNDSKEEPER IS DOING A GOOD JOB..

THE INFIELD LOOKS GREAT AND THE GRASS IN THE OUTFIELD HAS NEVER LOOKED BETTER..

I THINK IT'S BECAUSE WE HAVE A NEW AUTOMATIC SPRINKLER SYSTEM...
www.unitedmedia.com

© 1998 United Feature Syndicate, Inc.

SCHULZ

OLAF, YOU KNOW WHAT?
© 1998 United Feature Syndicate, Inc.

SCHULZ
WHAT?
I THINK WE MADE ANOTHER WRONG TURN..
2-16

Four weeks went by...

Andy and Olaf still hadn't found our brother Spike who lives in the desert.
www.unitedmedia.com

I'VE BEEN LOOKING AT THIS MAP, AND I THINK I KNOW WHERE WE ARE..
THAT'S GREAT.. WHERE ARE WE?
2-17
© 1998 United Feature Syndicate, Inc.

RIGHT WHERE YOU'RE SITTING..
SCHULZ

HERE'S MY IDEA.. SPIKE IS A FRIEND OF MICKEY MOUSE, RIGHT?
2-18

WELL, AT LEAST HE SAYS HE IS..
AND MICKEY MOUSE IS VERY WEALTHY, RIGHT?
www.unitedmedia.com

WHY DON'T WE CALL HIM ON THE PHONE, AND ASK HIM TO SEND US A LIMO?
© 1998 United Feature Syndicate, Inc.

THAT'S YOUR IDEA?
MAYBE EVEN A STRETCH LIMO..
SCHULZ

WE'RE GOING TO CALL MICKEY MOUSE ON THE PHONE?
AND WE'LL ASK HIM TO SEND US A LIMO..

OKAY, IT'S YOUR IDEA.. YOU TALK TO HIM..

WOOF!

HAVE YOU EVER TALKED ON A PHONE BEFORE?

WOOF!

WOOF!

MAYBE HE'S NOT HOME..

Andy and Olaf never reached Mickey Mouse on the phone.

So, of course, Mickey never sent the limo.

In the meantime, Spike was still waiting for them out on the desert.

YOU'RE TALLER THAN I AM..CAN YOU SEE ANYONE?

PEANUTS
by SCHULZ

2-22

© 1998 United Feature Syndicate, Inc.

www.unitedmedia.com

BONK!

AND THEN I THREW THE BALL SO HARD, IT FLEW CLEAR AROUND THE WORLD AND BACK AGAIN, AND HIT ME ON THE HEAD!
WHAT ARE YOU LAUGHING AT?!
SCHULZ

© 1998 United Feature Syndicate, Inc.
SCHULZ 2-23
WHAT ARE THE WORDS YOU HATE MOST TO HEAR?
"YOU STAY HOME NOW, AND BE A GOOD DOG"

WHAT ARE YOU PAINTING?
THIS IS GOING TO BE MY GREATEST WORK..

I'M PAINTING A HUGE LANDSCAPE WITH TWO MIGHTY ARMIES FACING EACH OTHER ACROSS AN ENORMOUS VALLEY BENEATH A WIDE SKY WITH DARK STORM CLOUDS GATHERING IN THE DISTANCE..
2-24
© 1998 United Feature Syndicate, Inc.

IT LOOKS MORE LIKE A DUCK LANDING ON THE WATER..
THAT'S WHAT I CALL IT... "DUCK LANDING ON THE WATER"
SCHULZ

2-25
OUR NEIGHBORS HAVE BEEN COMPLAINING..
www.unitedmedia.com

THEY SAY THE DOG DOWN THE STREET BARKS ALL NIGHT..
© 1998 United Feature Syndicate, Inc.

HOW UNPROFESSIONAL..
SCHULZ

GRAMPA WISHES HE HAD HIS OLD CAR BACK..

WHEN THE MILEAGE MADE A BIG CHANGE, IT WAS FUN TO WATCH ALL THE NUMBERS ON THE ODOMETER ROLL UP..

HE SAYS THAT WAS HIS FAVORITE PROGRAM..
SCHULZ
2-26

2-27
WHEN YOU'RE A PUPPY, ONE OF THE FIRST THINGS THEY TEACH YOU IS TO "SHAKE HANDS"

THEN YOU KNOW WHAT MOM ALWAYS SAID?

MAKE SURE YOU WASH YOUR PAWS AFTERWARD..
SCHULZ

I THOUGHT YOU WERE GOING OUTSIDE..
I CAN'T..THEY SAID TO STAY TUNED FOR SCENES FROM NEXT WEEK'S EPISODE..
2-28

WELL, I'M GOING OUTSIDE..
I'D SURE LIKE TO GO WITH YOU..

I HAVE TO STAY TUNED FOR SCENES FROM NEXT WEEK'S EPISODE..
SCHULZ

PEANUTS
by SCHULZ

FLY, YOU STUPID KITE! GET UP THERE! GO!

FLY! FLY! GET UP THERE! GET UP THERE!
3-1

YOU STUPID KITE! WHAT'S WRONG WITH YOU?! YOU'RE A DISGRACE TO KITEDOM!

www.unitedmedia.com

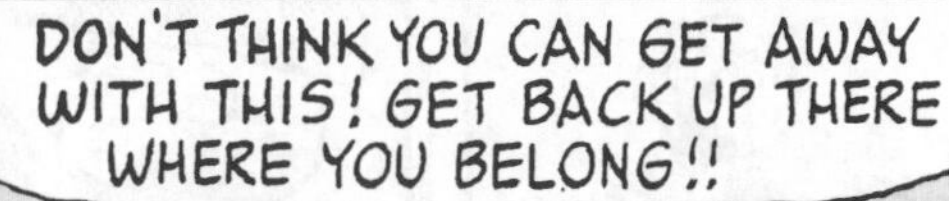
DON'T THINK YOU CAN GET AWAY WITH THIS! GET BACK UP THERE WHERE YOU BELONG!!

© 1998 United Feature Syndicate, Inc.

HOW DID YOUR KITE FLYING GO TODAY?
WELL I THINK I LEARNED SOMETHING, BUT I'M NOT SURE WHAT IT WAS..
SCHULZ

ALL RIGHT, I DON'T HAVE TO REMIND YOU HOW IMPORTANT THIS GAME IS TODAY...
3-2

REMIND ME ANYWAY..

THIS GAME TODAY IS VERY IMPORTANT!

THANKS FOR REMINDING ME!
SCHULZ

HEY, MANAGER! HOW COME I ALWAYS HAVE TO PLAY RIGHT FIELD?

BECAUSE YOU'RE NOT ONLY THE WORST PLAYER ON OUR TEAM, YOU'RE ALSO THE WORST PLAYER IN THE HISTORY OF THE GAME!

YOU LOOK LIKE YOU'VE BEEN GAINING A LITTLE WEIGHT..
SCHULZ
3-3

HEY, MANAGER..

NOW WHAT?
WE HAD TORTELLINI FOR DINNER LAST NIGHT..
3-4

SOME OF IT WAS WHITE, SOME GREEN, AND SOME KIND OF ORANGE..ISN'T THAT SOMETHING?

HOW'S THE GAME GOING?
SCHULZ

IT'S NOT RAINING HARD..

REMEMBER, "THE RAIN FALLS ON THE JUST AND THE UNJUST"

AND ANYONE PLAYING RIGHT FIELD..

IT'S ONLY A LITTLE SHOWER! IT'S LETTING UP! WHERE'S EVERYBODY GOING?
IS THIS ANY REASON TO QUIT? WHY SHOULD WE STOP PLAYING?!
BECAUSE YOUR DOG IS GETTING WET..

IT STARTED TO RAIN, AND EVERYONE RAN HOME..THEN IT STOPPED RAINING, AND EVERYONE CAME BACK..THEN WE STARTED PLAYING AGAIN..THEN WE LOST

MAYBE SOMEDAY YOU'LL GET USED TO LOSING..

WELL, MAYBE NOT..

PEANUTS®
by SCHULZ

HE'S MELTING! QUICK! DIAL "NINE-ONE-ONE"!

THE "NINE" LOOKS LIKE A SMALL "ZERO" WITH A TAIL..

© 1998 United Feature Syndicate, Inc.
www.unitedmedia.com

3-8

WOOF!

IT'S TOO LATE.. CANCEL THE CALL

WOOF!
SCHULZ

? ? ? ? ? ? ?

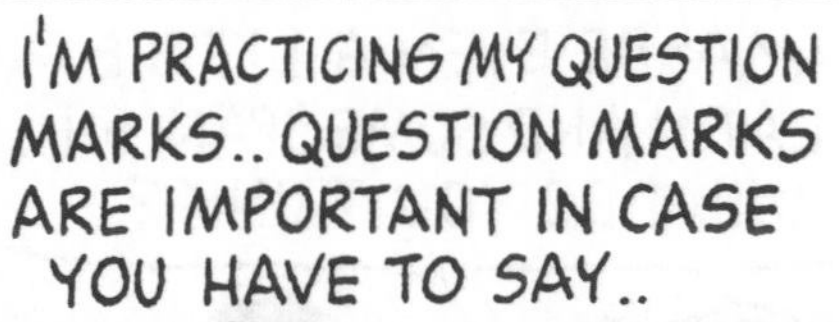
I'M PRACTICING MY QUESTION MARKS.. QUESTION MARKS ARE IMPORTANT IN CASE YOU HAVE TO SAY..

3-9
WHAT?
© 1998 United Feature Syndicate, Inc.

3-10
NO, THANKS.. I'M WITH HIM, AND HE'S JUST LOOKING..
© 1998 United Feature Syndicate, Inc.

WHEN I GET BIGGER, I'M GOING TO BE A NEWSBOY, AND STAND ON THE CORNER, AND SHOUT, "EXTRA! READ ALL ABOUT IT!"

"LINDBERGH FLIES ACROSS THE OCEAN!"
THAT'S RIGHT..
© 1998 United Feature Syndicate, Inc.
3/11

YOU NEED A BLANKET LIKE YOUR BROTHER!

I'VE BEEN THINKING OF TAKING A SPECIAL COURSE IN FRENCH..

MAYBE EVEN A LITTLE LATIN AND SOME SPANISH.. WHAT DO YOU THINK?
www.unitedmedia.com

"D-MINUS" SPOKEN HERE..
SCHULZ
3-12

NO, MA'AM.. I DON'T KNOW THE ANSWER..
3-13

ACTUALLY, I DON'T KNOW ANYTHING..
www.unitedmedia.com

SCHULZ
I'M JUST HERE TO DRESS THE SET..

I'M ALWAYS CURIOUS ABOUT STRATEGY
WHEN YOU AND YOUR OPPONENT COME TO THE LAST HOLE, AND YOU'RE TIED, WHAT'S YOUR STRATEGY?
HOPE HE HITS IT IN THE WATER..
SCHULZ
3-14
© 1998 United Feature Syndicate, Inc.

PEANUTS
by SCHULZ
MADAM LUCY SEES YOUR FUTURE

GUESS WHAT, MANAGER! I'VE DISCOVERED SOMETHING! IF I STARE AT THIS BALL, I CAN SEE THE FUTURE!

IF I CONCENTRATE ON THE BALL, I CAN SEE ALL THE GAMES WE'RE GOING TO PLAY..

I CAN SEE YOU BECOMING A GREAT PITCHER..
3-15

I CAN SEE OUR TEAM WINNING MANY CHAMPIONSHIPS! I CAN SEE...

I HATE TO INTERRUPT YOU, BUT WHILE YOU WERE SEEING EVERYTHING, THEIR RUNNER SCORED ALL THE WAY FROM FIRST BASE!

© 1998 United Feature Syndicate, Inc.
www.unitedmedia.com

I SEE A GREAT FUTURE FOR YOU, KID!
SCHULZ

SOMETIMES I LIE AWAKE AT NIGHT, AND I WORRY, AND WORRY, AND WORRY...
3-16
THEN A VOICE COMES TO ME OUT OF THE DARK THAT SAYS, "WE UNDERSTAND YOUR PROBLEM..DETAILS AT ELEVEN"
SCHULZ

THIS IS A HOE..
YES, I'VE SEEN PICTURES..

EVERY PERSON IN THIS WORLD WHO HAS EVER AMOUNTED TO SOMETHING STARTED BY USING A HOE!

3-17
SUDDENLY, I'M ON THE ROAD TO GREATNESS..
SCHULZ

THIS IS GOING TO BE OUR GARDEN..
SO?

SO YOUR JOB IS TO TAKE THAT HOE AND DIG OUT ALL THE WEEDS AND ROCKS..

I CAN DO THAT..WHEN DO YOU WANT IT FINISHED?
THIS AFTERNOON
3-18

I WAS THINKING MORE LIKE MAYBE IN FIFTY YEARS..
SCHULZ

THIS HOEING IS HARD WORK.. I'M NOT GETTING ANYWHERE..
THAT'S BECAUSE YOU'RE HOEING ON THE SIDEWALK.. YOU'RE SUPPOSED TO HOE IN THE YARD..
3-19

MY MOTHER DIDN'T RAISE ME TO BE A FARMER!
SCHULZ

I SEE YOU'VE GOT RERUN OUT THERE WORKING WITH A HOE..

IT'S GOOD FOR HIM.. ALL GREAT PEOPLE GOT THEIR START WORKING WITH A HOE..

3-20
HERE'S TIGER WOODS HITTING A 3-WOOD TO THE EIGHTEENTH GREEN..
SCHULZ

I CHANGED MY MIND.. I DECIDED I DON'T WANT A GARDEN..
WHAT ABOUT ALL THE WEEDS I DUG UP?

PUT 'EM BACK WHERE THEY WERE..
3-21

I SHOULD HAVE NUMBERED THEM..
SCHULZ

PEANUTS
by SCHULZ
"SLEEP TIGHT.. DON'T LET THE BEDBUGS BITE"

OKAY, BRING IN THE SHEEP..

ONE, TWO, THREE, FOUR, FIVE...

A GOAT! WHERE DID THAT GOAT COME FROM?
© 1998 United Feature Syndicate, Inc.
3-22

GEESE! WHO LET IN ALL THOSE GEESE? THERE'S ANOTHER GOAT! WHO LET IN THE GOATS? AND THAT HORSE! WHERE DID THAT HORSE COME FROM?!

BAM! BAM! BAM!

SOMETIMES WHEN I HAVE TROUBLE GOING TO SLEEP, I COUNT SHEEP..
TWENTY-FIVE SHEEP, TWO GOATS, FOURTEEN GEESE, A HORSE, AND I'M STILL AWAKE!
www.unitedmedia.com
SCHULZ

WELL, TIME FOR SCHOOL AGAIN..
3-23

I GUESS THAT DOESN'T MEAN MUCH TO YOU..YOUR LIFE IS MORE SIMPLE..

EDUCATION ISN'T THAT IMPORTANT..

ANYWAY, I'LL SEE YOU LATER..
AU REVOIR
SCHULZ

HERE'S THE WORLD WAR I FLYING ACE WALKING OUT ONTO THE AERODROME..

AS HE SETTLES INTO THE COCKPIT OF HIS SOPWITH CAMEL, HE SURVEYS THE DARKENING SKY..LIGHTNING FLASHES IN THE EAST..

ONLY THE BRAVEST AND MOST DEDICATED PILOT WOULD FLY IN WEATHER LIKE THIS..

3/24

LOOK AT THIS CUTE PICTURE OF A BOY AND HIS DOG IN FRONT OF A FIREPLACE..
WHERE'D HE GET A DOG LIKE THAT?
SCHULZ

ASK YOUR DOG IF HE WANTS TO GO OVER TO THE PARK AND PLAY..

3-25

WILL THEY BE GIVING OUT AWARDS?
SCHULZ

EVERYBODY IN THE WORLD HAS A DOG..WHY WON'T MOM LET ME HAVE A DOG?

A LOT OF PEOPLE IN THE WORLD DON'T HAVE DOGS..
© 1998 United Feature Syndicate, Inc.

WHY WON'T MOM LET THEM HAVE A DOG?
SCHULZ
3-26

WHAT I THINK I'LL DO TODAY IS TAKE SOME MONEY OUT OF MY COLLEGE TRUST FUND, AND GO BUY A DOG..

YOU DON'T HAVE A COLLEGE TRUST FUND
I DON'T?
3-27

PLEASE PASS THE GRAPE JELLY..
WE'RE ALL OUT OF GRAPE JELLY..
© 1998 United Feature Syndicate, Inc.

HOW CAN ANYONE NOT HAVE A DOG, A COLLEGE TRUST FUND AND GRAPE JELLY?
SCHULZ

SO THE FAMILY GOES INTO THE MALL, AND I'M LEFT ALONE IN THE CAR...

HERE'S THE WORLD FAMOUS BIG-RIG OPERATOR TOOLING HIS WAY TOWARD OMAHA..

ONE MINUTE HERE WHILE WE TAKE THE MAP OUT OF THE GLOVE COMPARTMENT..
© 1998 United Feature Syndicate, Inc.
3/28

ONE MINUTE HERE WHILE WE TRY TO GET THE MAP BACK INTO THE GLOVE COMPARTMENT..
SCHULZ

PEANUTS
by SCHULZ

3-29

READY TO GO..

© 1998 United Feature Syndicate, Inc.

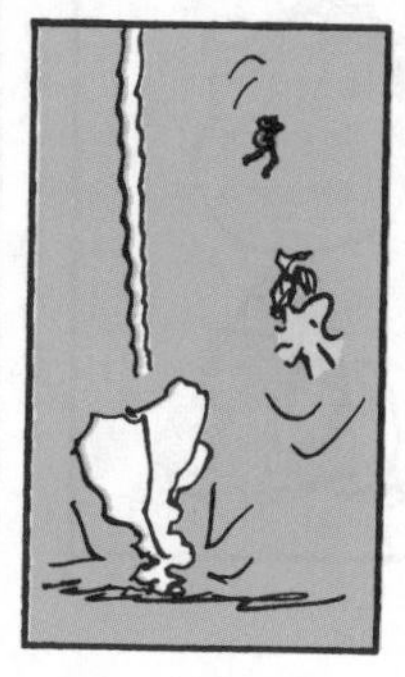

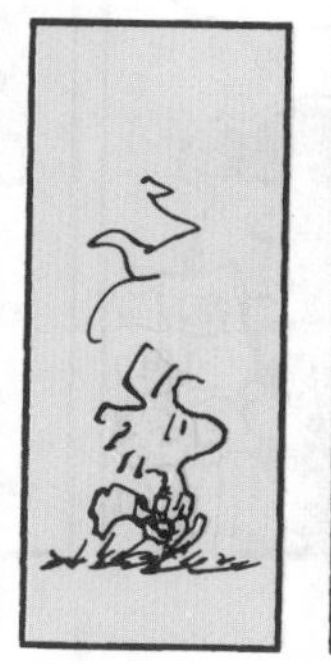

www.unitedmedia.com

NO, IF YOU'D RATHER NOT BE A TEST PILOT, YOU COULD ALWAYS GET A DESK JOB..
SCHULZ

© 1998 United Feature Syndicate, Inc.
SCHULZ
ONE HUNDRED AND ONE.. ONE HUNDRED AND TWO.. ONE HUNDRED AND THREE...
HOW MUCH IS THAT IN DOG YEARS?
3-30

YES, MA'AM..REQUEST PERMISSION TO GO OUT FOR A DRINK OF WATER..
3/31
www.snoopy.com

YES, MA'AM..REQUEST PERMISSION TO COPY ALL THE ANSWERS FROM MARCIE'S PAPER WHILE SHE'S OUT OF THE ROOM..
© 1998 United Feature Syndicate, Inc.

I'M BACK.. WHY IS THE TEACHER FROWNING?
I DON'T KNOW..SHE FROWNS A LOT..
SCHULZ

"APRIL FOOL!"
YOU DON'T SAY "APRIL FOOL" UNTIL YOU SAY SOMETHING ELSE FIRST..
www.snoopy.com

WHAT SHOULD I SAY?
SAY ANYTHING YOU WANT

© 1998 United Feature Syndicate, Inc.

4-1
THIS IS TOO HARD..
SCHULZ

THERE'S A GREAT BIG ALLIGATOR SNEAKING UP BEHIND YOU..
www.snoopy.com

"APRIL FOOL!"
"APRIL FOOLS' DAY" WAS YESTERDAY..
4/2
© 1998 United Feature Syndicate, Inc.

IT TOOK ME ALL NIGHT TO THINK OF THAT..
SCHULZ

AFTER YOU'RE DONE SAILING, YOU SHOULD TIE UP YOUR BOAT SO IT DOESN'T DRIFT AWAY..
© 1998 United Feature Syndicate, Inc.

SCHULZ
4-3

HEY! WHO SAID YOU CAN PITCH? YOU THROW LIKE MY GRANDMOTHER!
4-4
www.snoopy.com

YOUR GRANDMOTHER IS LEFT-HANDED!
© 1998 United Feature Syndicate, Inc.

YOU THROW LIKE MY AUNT MARIAN!
SCHULZ

PEANUTS
by SCHULZ
RERUN! TIME TO GET UP!

4-5

I'M SORRY, MA'AM.. I COULDN'T STUDY MY SUNDAY SCHOOL LESSON..

THE ZIPPER ON MY BIBLE IS STUCK..
SCHULZ

WHY DO DOGS EAT SO FAST?
www.snoopy.com

WE HAVE TO EAT FAST BEFORE THE HYENAS COME TO TRY TO TAKE AWAY THE KILL..

INCIDENTALLY, IF YOU'RE WORRIED ABOUT HYENAS, THERE AREN'T ANY AROUND HERE..
© 1998 United Feature Syndicate, Inc.

DID YOU LOOK IN THE TREES?
SCHULZ
4-6

SOME KID OVER AT THE PLAYGROUND PUSHED ME OFF THE SWING..I WANT YOU TO TEACH HIM A LESSON..
www.snoopy.com

WHERE IS HE NOW?
© 1998 United Feature Syndicate, Inc.
4/7

HERE..I BROUGHT HIM HOME SO YOU CAN HIT HIM..
SCHULZ

HERE, TEACH THIS KID A LESSON! HE PUSHED ME OFF THE SWING.. I'LL HOLD HIM WHILE YOU HIT HIM!
www.snoopy.com

I CAN'T HIT A LITTLE KID LIKE THAT..

© 1998 United Feature Syndicate, Inc.
TELL YOUR DOG TO BITE HIM..
4-8
SCHULZ

HE PUSHED ME OFF THE SWING..TEACH HIM A LESSON..HIT HIM!

DID YOU REALLY PUSH HER OFF THE SWING?

IT WAS A MISTAKE..I THOUGHT SHE WAS MY SISTER..
4-9
SCHULZ

FIRST HE PUSHES ME OFF THE SWING, THEN HE SAYS HE THINKS I'M CUTE..
4-10

IF SOMEONE TELLS YOU YOU'RE CUTE WHEN YOU KNOW YOU'RE NOT CUTE, WHAT DO YOU DO?

NEVER MIND.. I ALREADY KNOW

STUPID KID!!
SCHULZ

I HATE TO TELL YOU, BUT DINNER WILL BE A LITTLE LATE TONIGHT..

ACTUALLY, I'M NOT SURE JUST HOW LATE..MAYBE TEN MINUTES..MAYBE TWO MINUTES..MAYBE THREE SECONDS..

ANYWAY, JUST SO YOU KNOW..

THREE SECONDS IS A LONG TIME..
SCHULZ
4-11

PEANUTS®
by SCHULZ

AND IF A FLY BALL COMES YOUR WAY, YELL "I GOT IT!"
LET ME WRITE THAT DOWN..

I HAVE EVERYTHING YOU'VE TOLD ME WRITTEN RIGHT HERE IN MY NOTEBOOK..

© 1998 United Feature Syndicate, Inc.
4-12

"DON'T BUNT ON THE THIRD STRIKE"

"TAG UP ON AN OUTFIELD FLY" "BACK UP THE CENTER FIELDER"

WHAT IN THE WORLD..
"TRY TO HIT THE CUT-OFF MAN" "MAKE THEM PITCH TO YOU"

HERE IT IS..
www.unitedmedia.com

I GOT IT!
SCHULZ

4-13
MORNING FOG..
www.snoopy.com

INCREASING WINDS.. HIGH WAVES..
© 1998 United Feature Syndicate, Inc.

SMALL CRAFT WARNINGS..
SCHULZ

ALL RIGHT, THERE'S ONE COOKIE LEFT..WE'LL VOTE TO DECIDE WHO GETS IT...
www.snoopy.com

I VOTE FOR ME SO I GET IT!
© 1998 United Feature Syndicate, Inc.

4-14
VOTER FRAUD!
SCHULZ

I'VE OFTEN WONDERED.. HAVE YOU EVER BEEN INVITED TO PLAY IN A PRO-AM?
I'VE NEVER EVEN BEEN INVITED TO A PRO-DOG..
© 1998 United Feature Syndicate, Inc.
SCHULZ
4-15

I HEARD THE COYOTES HOWLING AGAIN LAST NIGHT.. THEY ALWAYS SOUND SO MOURNFUL..
THERE AREN'T ANY COYOTES AROUND HERE..

4-16
ALL I KNOW IS IT MADE ME FEEL VERY LONELY..
WERE YOU HOWLING LAST NIGHT?
SCHULZ

GOOD MORNING.. WOULD YOU LIKE TO BUY SOME COOKIES?
YOU'RE NOT A GIRL SCOUT..

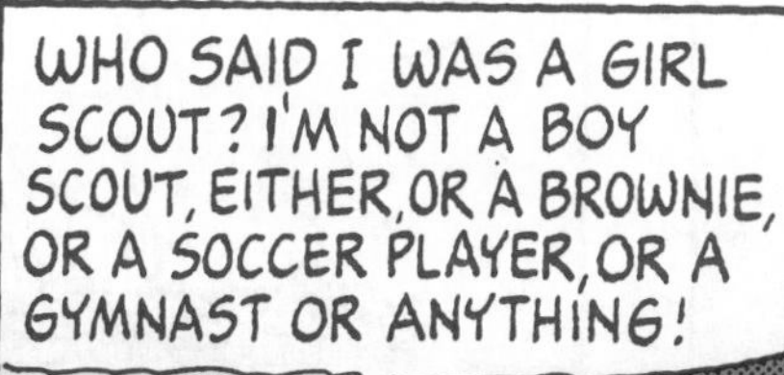
WHO SAID I WAS A GIRL SCOUT? I'M NOT A BOY SCOUT, EITHER, OR A BROWNIE, OR A SOCCER PLAYER, OR A GYMNAST OR ANYTHING!

4-17
WHERE'D YOU GET THE COOKIES?

THEY WERE LEFT OVER FROM MY LUNCH..
SCHULZ

ALL RIGHT, TROOPS..ANSWER WHEN I CALL YOUR NAME..

ROY..
4-18

JUST SAY, "HERE"...YOU DON'T HAVE TO EXPLAIN WHY..
SCHULZ

PEANUTS®
by SCHULZ
"TOUCH AND GO" FLIGHT SCHOOL

GOOD LANDING..
4-19

NOW WHEN YOU TAKE OFF AGAIN, DO YOU PUSH WITH YOUR FEET?

OR DO YOU FLAP YOUR WINGS FIRST?

DO YOU FLAP YOUR WINGS AND SORT OF LEAN INTO IT, OR DO YOU...

KLUNK!

IF YOU THINK ABOUT IT, YOU CAN'T DO IT..
SCHULZ

THIS IS MY REPORT ON WHAT'S HIS NAME..

HE WAS BORN SOMETIME BETWEEN SEVENTEEN AND EIGHTEEN HUNDRED.. VERY LITTLE IS KNOWN ABOUT HIM..
4-20
www.snoopy.com

IN FACT, WE DON'T EVEN KNOW WHO HE WAS, OR SHE WAS, OR WHATEVER..

YES, MA'AM.. THANK YOU..
© 1998 United Feature Syndicate, Inc.

ANOTHER ONE OF THE GREAT REPORTS OF ALL TIME, SIR
GOING TO BE HARD TO FOLLOW, HUH, MARCIE?
SCHULZ

"WHO LEFT THE DOOR OPEN?" THAT'S MY NEW PHILOSOPHY..
www.snoopy.com

I'M SURE IT WILL BE A GREAT SOURCE OF COMFORT DURING TIMES OF STRESS..
4-21
© 1998 United Feature Syndicate, Inc.

I SEE YOU USED ALL THE MILK AGAIN..
WHO LEFT THE DOOR OPEN?
SCHULZ

HERE'S THE WORLD WAR I FLYING ACE HOME ON LEAVE..
4-22
www.snoopy.com

IT'S NICE TO BE BACK AMONG OLD FRIENDS WHERE YOU'RE APPRECIATED..
© 1998 United Feature Syndicate, Inc.

PLEASE TAKE YOUR ROOT BEER GLASS OFF MY PIANO..
SCHULZ

HERE'S THE WORLD WAR I FLYING ACE HOME ON LEAVE..
4-23

HOW GOOD IT IS TO BE FAR FROM THE FRONT LINES
www.snoopy.com

HOW GOOD IT IS TO BE BACK IN THE PEACEFUL COUNTRYSIDE AGAIN..
© 1998 United Feature Syndicate, Inc.

IF YOU'RE NOT PLAYING, GET OFF THE FIELD!
SCHULZ

HEY, CHARLES..MOM SAYS TO COME GET YOUR DOG..
www.snoopy.com

HE'S IN OUR KITCHEN AGAIN DRINKING ROOT BEER... ALL RIGHT, I'LL TELL HIM..

GENERAL PERSHING JUST CALLED..ALL LEAVES HAVE BEEN CANCELED..YOU'RE TO GET BACK TO THE AERODROME IMMEDIATELY!

4-24
WITH OR WITHOUT A KISS?
© 1998 United Feature Syndicate, Inc.

WITHOUT..
SCHULZ

I DON'T UNDERSTAND YOU..
www.snoopy.com

YOU CAN'T JUST WALK INTO SOMEONE'S KITCHEN, AND START DRINKING ROOT BEER!
4-25

WHAT IF THEY DON'T WANT YOU? IT'S NOT AS IF YOU WERE INVITED! THERE ARE SOME THINGS YOU JUST DON'T DO!
© 1998 United Feature Syndicate, Inc.

WAS HE TALKING TO ME?
SCHULZ

LUNCH TIME?
PEANUTS
by SCHULZ

THERE SHE IS, CHARLIE BROWN..THERE'S THE LITTLE RED-HAIRED GIRL..

OF ALL THE PLAYGROUND BENCHES ON ALL THE PLAYGROUNDS IN ALL THE WORLD, SHE HAS TO SIT THERE..

PLAY IT, LINUS..IF SHE CAN STAND IT, I CAN... PLAY IT..

© 1998 United Feature Syndicate, Inc.

SHE'S LEAVING, CHARLIE BROWN..
4-26

HERE'S LOOKING AT YOU, KID..

HEY! I THINK SOMEBODY STOLE MY LUNCH BOX..
www.unitedmedia.com

ROUND UP THE USUAL SUSPECTS..
SCHULZ

I WAS BORN FIRST SO I GET THE GOLD MEDAL..
I WAS BORN SECOND SO I GET THE SILVER..
I'M LUCKY WE NEVER HAD A DOG..
SCHULZ
4-27
© 1998 United Feature Syndicate, Inc.

4-28
ʻ\|\|\|?
© 1998 United Feature Syndicate, Inc.

YES, THAT'S BETTER..NOW YOU LOOK VERY WEALTHY..
SCHULZ

A World Without Cats

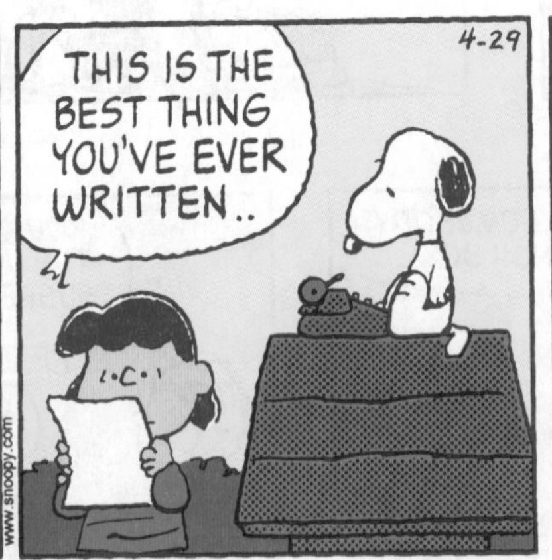
4-29
THIS IS THE BEST THING YOU'VE EVER WRITTEN..
www.snoopy.com

IF IT GETS ACCEPTED, YOU MAY HAVE TO GO ON A BOOK TOUR..
© 1998 United Feature Syndicate, Inc.

I DON'T DO PAW PRINTS..
SCHULZ

HERE'S THE WORLD FAMOUS AUTHOR ON HIS WAY TO MAIL HIS LATEST NOVEL TO THE PUBLISHER..
www.snoopy.com

!
4-30
© 1998 United Feature Syndicate, Inc.

I DIDN'T KNOW MAILBOXES COULD RUN..
SCHULZ

SOMEDAY I'M GOING TO BE SIX FEET TALL, AND EVERYONE WILL RESPECT ME
www.snoopy.com

GOOD FOR YOU..
© 1998 United Feature Syndicate, Inc.

SCHULZ
IS SIX FEET VERY HIGH?
5-1

WHAT'S THIS?
www.snoopy.com

I SUPPOSE YOU THINK IT'S SUPPERTIME..
© 1998 United Feature Syndicate, Inc.

NO, I ALWAYS WALK AROUND WITH A DISH IN MY MOUTH..
SCHULZ
5-2

PEANUTS®

by Schulz

DO YOU THINK IT'S A BROTHER'S DUTY TO HELP HIS SISTER WITH HER HOMEWORK IF SHE'S HAVING TROUBLE?
YES, I SHOULD THINK SO..
www.snoopy.com

GOOD

5-4
© 1998 United Feature Syndicate, Inc.

DUTY CALLS!
SCHULZ

I TOLD MY TEACHER HOW YOU HELPED ME WITH MY HOMEWORK LAST NIGHT..
www.snoopy.com

SHE SAID YOU GOT ALL THE ANSWERS WRONG..

SHE ASKED ME WHAT WE SHOULD DO ABOUT YOU...
5-5
© 1998 United Feature Syndicate, Inc.

I SUGGESTED LIFE IMPRISONMENT WITHOUT POSSIBILITY OF PAROLE..
SCHULZ

YES, MA'AM, I HELPED MY SISTER WITH HER HOMEWORK

WE GOT ALL THE ANSWERS WRONG? HOW COULD THAT BE?
5-6
www.snoopy.com

ANYWAY, I DID MY BEST.. I TRIED TO HELP HER...

ISN'T THERE MORE TO LIFE THAN GETTING THE ANSWERS RIGHT?
© 1998 United Feature Syndicate, Inc.
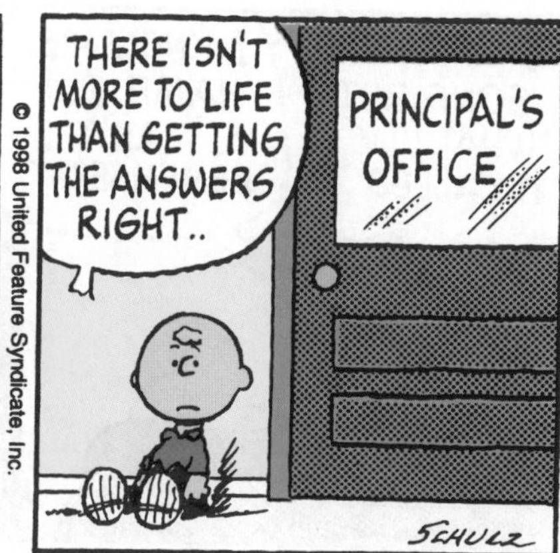
THERE ISN'T MORE TO LIFE THAN GETTING THE ANSWERS RIGHT..
PRINCIPAL'S OFFICE
SCHULZ

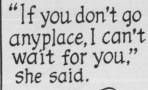

"I will always wait for you," she said. "I'm not going anyplace," he said.

5-7

THAT'S THE DUMBEST THING I'VE EVER READ!

MY OTHER SHOES WERE ALWAYS A LITTLE TIGHT.. I LIKE THE COLOR, AND THE SOLES FEEL BOUNCY, AND THE LACES ARE EASY TO TIE..

I'M SORRY...I'VE NEVER HAD A COMPLIMENT BEFORE

SCHULZ

I KNOW THE SONG, BUT WHAT WAS IT CALLED?
I KNOW HIS NAME, BUT I CAN'T REMEMBER IT..

5-9
I SHOULD BE ON THAT PROGRAM BECAUSE I KNOW ALL THE ANSWERS..
SCHULZ

PEANUTS
by SCHULZ
THIS IS MY FAVORITE TIME OF YEAR... I THINK..

"TRICK OR TREAT!"
"TRICK OR TREAT"? THIS ISN'T HALLOWEEN!

DON'T YOU KNOW WHAT MONTH THIS IS? DON'T YOU HAVE A CALENDAR?

I'M JUST A LITTLE KID.. I DON'T KNOW HOW TO READ A CALENDAR! I DON'T EVEN KNOW WHAT DAY THIS IS! NOBODY TELLS ME ANYTHING!

5-10

ALL RIGHT..HERE'S A CANDY BAR..HAPPY HALLOWEEN..
© 1998 United Feature Syndicate, Inc.

THANK YOU

BY THE WAY, JUST SO YOU KNOW, TODAY IS MOTHER'S DAY..

IT IS?
www.snoopy.com

HOW MANY DAYS 'TIL CHRISTMAS?

HEY, CHUCK.. YOU WANNA GO WITH ME?
5-11

GO WHERE?

DON'T YOU KNOW ANYTHING, CHUCK?

YOU'D BETTER BE THERE! AND DON'T FORGET, I ASKED YOU BEFORE WHAT'S-HER-NAME DID!

WHO WAS THAT?
I'VE BEEN INVITED TO SOMETHING SOMEPLACE BEFORE WHAT'S-HER-NAME INVITES ME SOMETIME..
SCHULZ

IT'S THE SPRING DANCE, CHARLIE BROWN.. JUST THINK..YOU'LL BE ABLE TO DANCE WITH THE LITTLE RED-HAIRED GIRL..

YOU'LL TAKE HER SOFT, COOL, LITTLE HAND IN YOURS, AND...

5-12
KLUNK!

FELL RIGHT OUT OF THE DESK, MA'AM..

IT'S THE SPRING DANCE, CHARLES.. WOULD YOU LIKE TO GO WITH ME?

WHO IS THIS?

SHE'S MARCIE, CHUCK, YOU BLOCKHEAD! YOU CAN'T GO WITH HER! YOU SAID YOU'D GO WITH ME!
5-13

I'M A BETTER DANCER, CHARLES..

DON'T PUSH THE ENVELOPE, CHUCK..
TANGO TANGO, CHARLES!
SCHULZ

AND WHEN YOU'RE DANCING WITH THE LITTLE RED-HAIRED GIRL, CHARLIE BROWN, SHE'LL LOOK INTO YOUR EYES...
www.snoopy.com

AND SHE'LL SEE HOW YOU LOVE HER, AND HOW YOU WILL ALWAYS LOVE HER, AND...

5-14
KLUNK!
© 1998 United Feature Syndicate, Inc.

EVER GO TO DANCES, MA'AM?
SCHULZ

© 1998 United Feature Syndicate, Inc.

5-15
SCHULZ

HEY, CHUCK, WHEN WE GO TO THE DANCE, ARE YOU GONNA PICK ME UP IN A LIMO?
OR MAYBE WE SHOULD JUST MEET THERE, HUH, CHARLES?
5-16

MEET WHERE? WHO IS THIS?
www.snoopy.com

IT'S US, CHUCK, YOU BLOCKHEAD!
© 1998 United Feature Syndicate, Inc.

I THINK YOU'VE GOT THOSE GIRLS ALL CONFUSED, BIG BROTHER..
I FORGOT TO TELL THEM TO SAVE ME THE WALTZ..
SCHULZ

PEANUTS
by SCHULZ
C'MON, ROY! YOU CAN DO IT!

WHAT ARE YOU WATCHING?
"THE NATURAL".. I'M WAITING FOR MY FAVORITE SCENE..

THIS IS WHERE ROY HOBBS HITS A HOME RUN IN THE NINTH INNING..THE BALL SMASHES INTO THE LIGHTS, AND SPARKS FLY ALL OVER THE FIELD!

MAYBE THIS TIME HE'LL STRIKE OUT..
NO, HE ALWAYS HITS A HOME RUN..I'VE WATCHED IT TWENTY TIMES..IT'S MY FAVORITE SCENE..

HELLO? YES, HE'S HERE..
www.snoopy.com

IT'S FOR YOU..
© 1998 United Feature Syndicate, Inc.

WATCHING TV.. ROY HOBBS IS UP..IT'S MY FAVORITE SCENE...SURE..UH HUH... YES..SURE..UH HUH...

YOU MISSED IT..YOU WERE RIGHT, THOUGH..HE HIT A HOME RUN UP INTO THE LIGHTS..SPARKS FLEW ALL OVER THE FIELD..
SCHULZ
5-17

I'M FEEDING YOU EARLY BECAUSE I'M GOING TO A DANCE TONIGHT..
www.snoopy.com

I'M HOPING I GET TO DANCE WITH THE LITTLE RED-HAIRED GIRL, AND...
5-18
© 1998 United Feature Syndicate, Inc.

..AND I DIDN'T KNOW YOU WERE GOING ALONG..
SCHULZ

HOLD IT RIGHT THERE, DUDE! THIS IS A DANCE! THE DOG CAN'T COME IN!
www.snoopy.com

THERE WAS A MISUNDERSTANDING.. THIS LITTLE KID THOUGHT IT WAS GOING TO BE A COSTUME BALL SO HE WORE A DOG SUIT..

OKAY, GO ON IN... HAVE A GREAT TIME..
5/19
© 1998 United Feature Syndicate, Inc.

PRETTY GOOD DOG SUIT..
SCHULZ

5-20
© 1998 United Feature Syndicate, Inc.
HI, CHARLIE BROWN! WELCOME TO THE DANCE! EVERYONE IS HERE..
I HOPE WE'RE NOT LATE..
THIS ISN'T A COSTUME BALL, IS IT?
NO
THEN WHO'S THE LITTLE KID IN THE DOG SUIT?
SCHULZ

SEE? THERE SHE IS, CHARLIE BROWN..
www.snoopy.com

THERE'S THE LITTLE RED-HAIRED GIRL JUST WAITING FOR YOU TO ASK HER TO DANCE...

I WISH I WERE SOPHISTICATED LIKE GUYS YOU READ ABOUT IN STORIES..
5-21

HERE'S THE SCOTT FITZGERALD HERO STANDING BY THE PUNCH BOWL "TRYING TO LOOK CASUAL AND UNINTERESTED IN THE DANCERS"
© 1998 United Feature Syndicate, Inc.

"DON'T GIVE IT ANOTHER THOUGHT, OLD SPORT"
SCHULZ

I CAN'T BELIEVE I'M DOING THIS..
5-22

I'M WALKING TOWARD THE LITTLE RED-HAIRED GIRL..
www.snoopy.com

I'M GOING TO ASK HER TO DANCE..I'M GETTING CLOSER.. I'M ALMOST THERE.. I'M...
© 1998 United Feature Syndicate, Inc.

CHUCK! WE'VE BEEN LOOKING FOR YOU!
COME ON, CHARLES, THEY'RE PLAYING THE "HOKEY-POKEY"
OH, GOOD GRIEF!
SCHULZ

HERE'S GATSBY STANDING BY THE PUNCH BOWL WATCHING COUPLES DANCE BY...
5-23
www.snoopy.com

"IT WAS IN NINETEEN-NINETEEN.. I ONLY STAYED FIVE MONTHS.. THAT'S WHY I CAN'T REALLY CALL MYSELF AN OXFORD MAN"
© 1998 United Feature Syndicate, Inc.

"BOTH OF US LOVED EACH OTHER ALL THAT TIME, OLD SPORT"
SCHULZ

PEANUTS
by SCHULZ
I HATE BEING CALLED A "TINY TOT"
"TINY TOT" CONCERT Today

WHAT ARE THEY FORCING US TO LISTEN TO TODAY, MARCIE?
A PIANO TRIO BY HAYDN..

SEE? THERE'S A PIANIST, A VIOLINIST AND A CELLIST..

WHO'S THE LADY SITTING ON THE BENCH WITH THE PIANO PLAYER? THEY'RE SITTING AWFULLY CLOSE..

SHE TURNS THE PAGES FOR HIM..
5-24
© 1998 United Feature Syndicate, Inc.

I SUPPOSE HE HAS A SECRETARY WHO OPENS HIS MAIL FOR HIM, TOO..

HAHAHAHAHA!
www.snoopy.com

IT'S GOING TO BE A LONG WALK HOME..
SCHULZ

CHARLIE BROWN! WHERE HAVE YOU BEEN?
I'VE BEEN DOING THE HOKEY-POKEY WITH PATTY AND MARCIE..

LISTEN..THEY'RE PLAYING A FOX TROT..
www.snoopy.com

NOW I CAN ASK THE LITTLE RED HAIRED GIRL TO DANCE..
I THINK SOMEONE IS AHEAD OF YOU..
5-25
© 1998 United Feature Syndicate, Inc.
SCHULZ

"DAISY AND GATSBY DANCED.. I REMEMBER HIS GRACEFUL CONSERVATIVE FOX TROT"

HEY, KID! AREN'T YOU THE ONE WHOSE FRIEND IS WEARING THE DOG SUIT?

ANYWAY, HE'S SICK.. I THINK HE DRANK TOO MUCH PUNCH..
www.snoopy.com

THE NURSE IS WITH HIM...
© 1998 United Feature Syndicate, Inc.

SHE'S HAVING TROUBLE GETTING THE DOG SUIT OFF..
SCHULZ
5-26

SURE, THERE I WAS HAVING A GOOD TIME AT THE DANCE, AND THEN YOU HAD TO GET SICK..
www.snoopy.com

SOMEONE SAID YOU PROBABLY DRANK TOO MUCH PUNCH..
5-27

I ATE TOO MUCH.. I DRANK TOO MUCH.. AND I DANCED TOO MUCH...
© 1998 United Feature Syndicate, Inc.

LET'S DO IT AGAIN TOMORROW NIGHT..
SCHULZ

THE HOKEY-POKEY WASN'T VERY ROMANTIC, CHUCK
I SAVED YOU THE WALTZ, CHARLES, BUT I NEVER SAW YOU..
www.snoopy.com

HOW ABOUT THE LIMO, CHUCK? WE NEVER SAW A LIMO, EITHER..
HOW COME YOU FELL DOWN DOING THE HOKEY-POKEY?
5-28
© 1998 United Feature Syndicate, Inc.

DON'T INVITE US TO ANYMORE DANCES, CHUCK
"MANY A HEART IS BROKEN AFTER THE BALL"
SCHULZ

GUESS WHAT I LEARNED IN SCHOOL TODAY..
www.snoopy.com

WE WERE HAVING LUNCH, AND I LEARNED HOW TO OPEN A BAG OF POTATO CHIPS..
© 1998 United Feature Syndicate, Inc.

WHAT'S THE CAPITAL OF NORWAY?
WHO KNOWS?
SCHULZ
5-29

DID YOU KNOW THAT GRAMMA AND GRAMPA HAVE MOVED?
MOVED?
www.snoopy.com

GRAMMA SAYS SHE TAKES FOUR PILLS A DAY, THEIR DOGS TAKE EIGHT PILLS A DAY, AND GRAMPA TAKES FIVE PILLS A DAY...
© 1998 United Feature Syndicate, Inc.

5-30
GRAMMA SAYS THEY'RE LIVING IN PILL CITY..

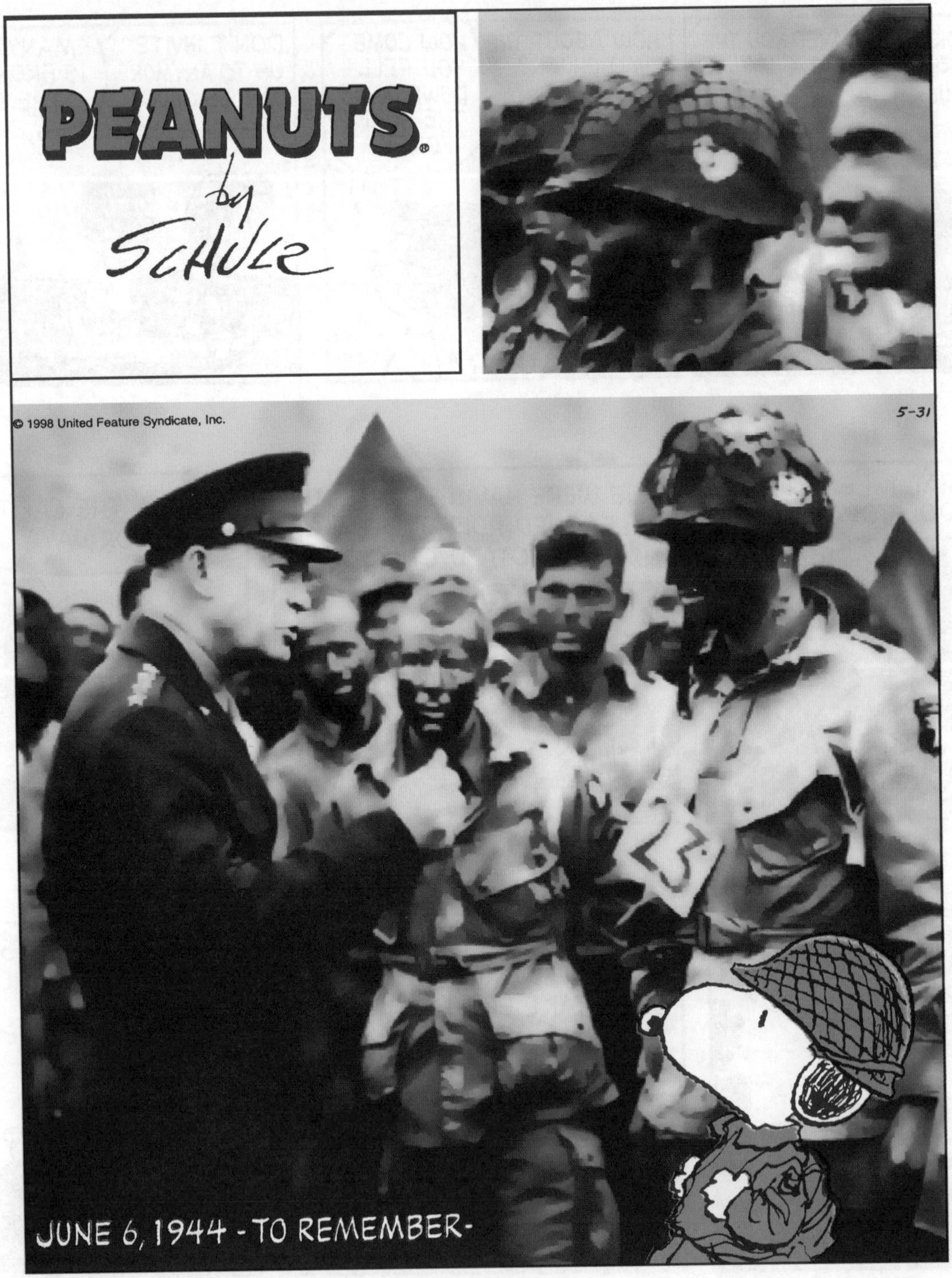

PEANUTS®

by SCHULZ

5-31

JUNE 6, 1944 -TO REMEMBER-

© 1998 United Feature Syndicate, Inc.
SCHULZ
6-1

YOU KNOW WHAT I AM, CHARLES? I'M A "REMINDER"
www.snoopy.com

WE HAVE A BOOK REPORT DUE TOMORROW..
I KNOW! I KNOW! STOP BUGGING ME!
© 1998 United Feature Syndicate, Inc.

6-2
NOBODY LIKES A "REMINDER"
SCHULZ

I'M DOOMED, MARCIE.. I'M GOING TO GET A BAD GRADE IN EVERY SUBJECT..
www.snoopy.com

YOU HAD GOOD ATTENDANCE THOUGH, SIR...

AND YOU DIDN'T SPILL ANYTHING! THAT'S WHAT IT'LL SAY ON YOUR REPORT CARD...
© 1998 United Feature Syndicate, Inc.

"SHE CAME EVERY DAY, AND SHE DIDN'T SPILL ANYTHING!"
YOU ARE DISPROPORTIONATELY WEIRD, MARCIE..
SCHULZ
6-3

RATS! I DIDN'T MAKE THE HONOR ROLL!
www.snoopy.com

IF YOU HAVE MOUSIE-BLAH HAIR, YOU NEVER MAKE THE HONOR ROLL..

FOR EIGHT GENERATIONS NO ONE IN OUR FAMILY HAS EVER MADE THE HONOR ROLL..
© 1998 United Feature Syndicate, Inc.

THEY ALL HAD MOUSIE-BLAH HAIR..
SCHULZ
6-4

6-5
© 1998 United Feature Syndicate, Inc.

LAP LAP LAP
LAP LAP LAP

WHAT COULD I DO? I NEEDED A DRINK OF WATER..
SCHULZ

6-6
© 1998 United Feature Syndicate, Inc.
SCHULZ

PEANUTS
BY SCHULZ
HE'S GOING TO HATE US..
NO, HE'LL BE GLAD TO SEE US

REMEMBER US?
WE'VE WALKED CLEAR AROUND THE WORLD..

WE NEVER DID FIND OUR BROTHER SPIKE..
MAYBE WE SHOULD HAVE STAYED ON THE FARM..

6-7
WELL, YOU BOTH LOOK LIKE YOU NEED A GOOD REST..
www.snoopy.com

WHY DON'T YOU SLEEP IN MY HOUSE TONIGHT?

YOU ASK HIM..
NO, YOU ASK HIM..
© 1998 United Feature Syndicate, Inc.

WHO GETS THE TOP BUNK, AND WHO GETS THE BOTTOM BUNK?
SCHULZ

DO YOU THINK WE SHOULD PLAN WHAT WE'RE GOING TO DO THIS SUMMER, CHARLIE BROWN?
WELL, THEY SAY THE SECRET OF LIFE IS GOOD PLANNING..
I PLAN TO EAT MY DINNER REAL FAST TONIGHT BEFORE THE COYOTES GET IT..
© 1998 United Feature Syndicate, Inc.
6-8
SCHULZ

MOM WON'T LET ME HAVE A DOG..
www.snoopy.com

HOW COME YOUR MOM LET YOU HAVE A DOG?
I DON'T KNOW

6-9
© 1998 United Feature Syndicate, Inc.

WHERE DID YOU GET YOUR MOM?
SCHULZ

IS BEETHOVEN IN THE BOWLING HALL OF FAME?
I DOUBT IT..
6-10
www.snoopy.com

PROBABLY BECAUSE HE DIDN'T WRITE BOWLING MUSIC..

KLUNK!
© 1998 United Feature Syndicate, Inc.

I'LL BET HE'D BE IN THE HALL OF FAME IF HE HAD WRITTEN BOWLING MUSIC..
SCHULZ

I DON'T HAVE A DOG NOW, BUT I KNOW I'LL HAVE ONE SOMEDAY...

www.snoopy.com

I WAS WONDERING IF YOU COULD GIVE ME SOME TIPS ON HOW TO TRAIN A DOG...

6-11
© 1998 United Feature Syndicate, Inc.

YOU DON'T GIVE TIPS?

"RED AT NIGHT.. SAILORS' DELIGHT"
6-12
www.snoopy.com

"RED IN THE MORNING, SAILORS TAKE WARNING"
!
© 1998 United Feature Syndicate, Inc.

MAYBE IT'S JUST A LITTLE SQUALL..

TELL YOUR DOG I FOUND A NEW STICK..TELL HIM I'LL THROW IT, AND HE CAN CHASE IT...

6-13

www.snoopy.com

© 1998 United Feature Syndicate, Inc.
ARE YOU TELLING HIM?

PEANUTS
by SCHULZ
GOOD LUCK!

RERUN! WHAT ARE YOU DOING HERE?
© 1998 United Feature Syndicate, Inc.

I CAME TO PLAY RIGHT FIELD..LUCY CAN'T MAKE IT TODAY SO I'M HER REPLACEMENT..

YOU DON'T HAVE TO WORRY..SHE GAVE ME HER CAP AND GLOVE, AND TAUGHT ME ALL ABOUT THE GAME..

SHE SAID SHE TAUGHT ME EVERYTHING I NEED TO KNOW..

THROW THE BALL OVER THE PLATE, YOU BLOCKHEAD!
6-14

SCHULZ
I'M GLAD SHE TAUGHT HIM EVERYTHING..

THAT WAS GOOD..MOSES WOULD HAVE BEEN PROUD OF YOU..
© 1998 United Feature Syndicate, Inc.
SCHULZ
6-15

IF YOU'RE NOT HAPPY, CHARLIE BROWN, IT'S PROBABLY YOUR DOG'S FAULT
THE DOCTOR IS IN

YOUR DOG IS SUPPOSED TO MAKE YOU HAPPY..
www.snoopy.com

6-16
© 1998 United Feature Syndicate, Inc.

MAYBE I COULD GIVE HIM A BALLOON..
SCHULZ

SOMETIMES I WONDER IF I EVEN KNOW WHAT IT WOULD TAKE TO MAKE ME HAPPY..
www.snoopy.com

6-17
HERE..GET THE BALL!
© 1998 United Feature Syndicate, Inc.

THAT USUALLY WORKS WITH DOGS..
SCHULZ

NO, A DOG'S JOB IS TO EAT AND SLEEP, AND GUARD THE HOUSE
6-18
www.snoopy.com

THE BACK..

I DON'T KNOW WHO GUARDS THE FRONT..
© 1998 United Feature Syndicate, Inc.
SCHULZ

www.snoopy.com

© 1998 United Feature Syndicate, Inc.

I AGREE.. STUPID TREE!
SCHULZ
6-19

ALSO, DOGS CAN BARK.. BIRDS CAN'T BARK..
www.snoopy.com

© 1998 United Feature Syndicate, Inc.

ISN'T BARKING..
SCHULZ
6-20

PEANUTS.
by SCHULZ
NEWS

WHAT DO I HAVE TO DO TO BE A PAPERBOY, CHARLIE BROWN?

WELL, YOU SHOULD ALWAYS TRY TO DELIVER THE PAPER ON TIME...
6-21

AND TRY TO THROW IT SO IT LANDS ON THE STEPS.. THAT'S THE WAY..

AND WATCH OUT FOR DOGS..
SCHULZ

6-22
© 1998 United Feature Syndicate, Inc.

YOU DON'T HAVE TO BRING THEM BACK..
SCHULZ

ALL YOU EVER DO IS EAT..
www.snoopy.com

HOW ARE YOU GOING TO SCARE AWAY A BURGLAR IF YOU'RE EATING?
© 1998 United Feature Syndicate, Inc.

I'LL EAT LOUDER..
6-23
SCHULZ

© 1998 United Feature Syndicate, Inc.
6-24
SCHULZ

WHAT A FACE! I'LL NEVER BE BEAUTIFUL..
YOU WILL SOMEDAY, SIR.. ALL OF YOUR FEATURES WILL SETTLE INTO THEIR PROPER SIZES AND PLACES, AND YOU'LL BE BEAUTIFUL
www.snoopy.com

WHAT ABOUT MY HANDS?
SOMEDAY YOU'LL HAVE PRETTY HANDS, SIR..
© 1998 United Feature Syndicate, Inc.
6/25

WHAT ABOUT A CERTAIN FRIEND OF MINE?
SHE'LL BE GORGEOUS!
SCHULZ

6-26

www.snoopy.com

© 1998 United Feature Syndicate, Inc.

WHY ARE YOU SO CRABBY?
SCHULZ

DOG FOOD? WELL, IT USUALLY HAS A HEARTY FLAVOR.. A LITTLE SPICY.. MAYBE A TOUCH OF GAMINESS...
www.snoopy.com

6-27
?
© 1998 United Feature Syndicate, Inc.

NO, I DON'T WANT TO KNOW WHAT A WORM TASTES LIKE..
SCHULZ

PEANUTS®
by SCHULZ

HERE'S A GREAT CAMP WE CAN GO TO, MARCIE..
I'M NOT GOING TO CAMP THIS YEAR..I'M GOING TO STAY HOME AND TAKE VIOLIN LESSONS..

YOU'RE GOING TO WHAT?
I'VE ALWAYS WANTED TO PLAY THE VIOLIN..

YOU'D GIVE UP SWIMMING, RIDING, ARCHERY AND CANOEING FOR PLAYING THE VIOLIN?
YOU CAN'T PLAY BRAHMS ON A CANOE PADDLE, SIR..
www.snoopy.com

© 1998 United Feature Syndicate, Inc.

CHECK THIS OUT, CHUCK..GREAT LOOKING CAMP, HUH?
I'M NOT SURE I'M GOING TO CAMP THIS YEAR..
6-28

OH, SURE! CAN'T PLAY BRAHMS ON A CANOE PADDLE, HUH?

I NEVER KNOW WHAT ANYONE'S TALKING ABOUT..

6-29
AWESOME, ISN'T IT? THAT'S WHERE ZAMBONIS GO DURING THE SUMMER..
© 1998 United Feature Syndicate, Inc.
SCHULZ

I HAVE THREE QUEENS, TWO JACKS, FOUR TENS, AND ONE EIGHT..
I HAVE TWO ACES, FOUR KINGS, THREE TWOS, AND ONE NINE..

SO HERE GOES!
SO HERE GOES!
www.snoopy.com

© 1998 United Feature Syndicate, Inc.
6-30

TIE GAME!
SCHULZ

HEY, CHUCK, HOW COME YOU NEVER CALL ME?

YOU'RE RIGHT.. I'M SORRY.. I SHOULD HAVE CALLED YOU...

WHY DON'T YOU HANG UP, AND I'LL CALL YOU RIGHT BACK..
7-1

THAT'S NOT THE SAME THING, CHUCK!
© 1998 United Feature Syndicate, Inc.

I THOUGHT YOU WERE ON THE PHONE..
I'M NOT GOOD AT PHONING..
SCHULZ

HI, CHUCK..JUST THOUGHT I'D CALL AGAIN..
www.snoopy.com

WOOF
7-2

WHAT? NO, JUST CURIOUS AS TO HOW YOU'VE BEEN..

WOOF WOOF WOOF
© 1998 United Feature Syndicate, Inc.

SCHULZ
YOU'RE STARTING TO REPEAT YOURSELF, CHUCK..

CHARLES, PATTY THINKS YOU DON'T CALL HER BECAUSE SHE ISN'T CUTE..
7-3

BECAUSE SHE HAS FRECKLES AND A BIG NOSE
BECAUSE SHE HAS FRECKLES AND A BIG NOSE

SO IS THAT WHY YOU DON'T CALL HER?
SO IS THAT WHY YOU DON'T CALL HER?
© 1998 United Feature Syndicate, Inc.

THIS ISN'T WORKING, IS IT?
HE SAID HE WAS MISSING HIS FAVORITE PROGRAM..
SCHULZ

MY GRAMMA USED TO READ DOG DISHES..
7-4

AFTER WE WERE THROUGH EATING, SHE'D TAKE A DOG DISH, LOOK AT IT CAREFULLY, AND TELL US THE FUTURE..

GRAMMA SAID DOG DISHES WERE MORE ACCURATE THAN TEA LEAVES..
© 1998 United Feature Syndicate, Inc.

REALLY? I NEVER HEARD OF A GRAMMA WHO READ WORMS..
SCHULZ

PEANUTS
by SCHULZ
ZZZZZZ

© 1998 United Feature Syndicate, Inc.

7-5
www.snoopy.com

TIMEOUT..
YAWN!

THERE IS NO TIMEOUT IN SLEEPING..
SCHULZ

www.snoopy.com

7-6

© 1998 United Feature Syndicate, Inc.

I KNEW IT! YOUR EARS ARE STILL JUMPING!

He began to feel uncomfortable with others in the family.
www.snoopy.com

He knew it was important for those who share a home to have similar moral values.
© 1998 United Feature Syndicate, Inc.

So the dog left.
SCHULZ
7-7

7-8

www.snoopy.com

© 1998 United Feature Syndicate, Inc.

GOTTA SAVE THE OL' THROWIN' ARM, MANAGER..
SCHULZ

THE GAME'S BEEN CALLED, CHARLIE BROWN..
BUT IT'S CLEARING UP! I CAN SEE BLUE SKY!

THAT ISN'T BLUE SKY..THOSE ARE LIGHTS FROM THE MALL..

IT LOOKS LIKE BLUE SKY TO ME..I KNOW IT'S BLUE SKY..IT'S CLEARING UP..I CAN SEE BLUE SKY..

ANYONE GOING TO THE MALL?

I JUST SAW A FARMER BEING INTERVIEWED ON TV.. HE SAID HE WAS GLAD TO SEE A LITTLE RAIN..

WAS HIS TEAM LEADING BY TEN RUNS WHEN THE GAME WAS CALLED?
I DON'T THINK THEY SAID ANYTHING ABOUT A BASEBALL GAME..

I'LL GO BACK AND WATCH SOME MORE.. I'LL LET YOU KNOW WHAT THEY SAY..

I HOPE HIS TRACTOR GETS WET!

I'LL NEVER FORGET THE EXPRESSION ON THE OTHER ATTORNEY'S FACE...

HE SAW I HAD THIS BRAND-NEW YELLOW LEGAL PAD WITH LINES ON IT..
THERE'S A LOT OF JEALOUSY AMONG ATTORNEYS

PEANUTS
by SCHULZ
HEY, MANAGER..

ASK YOUR CATCHER IF HE WANTS TO GO OVER TO MY HOUSE AFTER THE GAME FOR SOME LEMONADE..

SHE WANTS TO KNOW IF YOU WANT TO GO OVER TO HER HOUSE AFTER THE GAME FOR SOME LEMONADE..

TELL HER I WOULDN'T GO OVER TO HER HOUSE IF THEY WERE GIVING AWAY SPORTS CARS, THOUSAND DOLLAR BILLS, AND CHOCOLATE SUNDAES!

© 1998 United Feature Syndicate, Inc.
HE SAYS...

www.snoopy.com

YOU WOULDN'T?
SCHULZ
7-12

I'VE BEEN READING THOMAS WOLFE'S "YOU CAN'T GO HOME AGAIN"

MAYBE YOU SHOULD WRITE SOMETHING LIKE THAT..
7-13
© 1998 United Feature Syndicate, Inc.
www.snoopy.com

You Can Go Home Again If You Want To
SCHULZ

I DON'T SUPPOSE YOUR DOG WANTS TO COME OUT AND PLAY..
NO, I DON'T SUPPOSE HE DOES

I SUPPOSE IT WAS A WASTE OF TIME TO ASK..
I SUPPOSE IT WAS
www.snoopy.com

DO YOU SUPPOSE I MIGHT ASK AGAIN TOMORROW?
I SUPPOSE YOU MIGHT
7/14
© 1998 United Feature Syndicate, Inc.

I SUPPOSE YOU COULD GUESS WHO THAT WAS..
I SUPPOSE I COULD..
SCHULZ

HEY, MARCIE, HOW DOES THIS SOUND? "I'M SORRY I DIDN'T GET MY REPORT DONE, MA'AM"
7-15

"THERE WAS A JACKKNIFED BIG-RIG BLOCKING THE FREEWAY"

I'M GETTING MY EXCUSES READY FOR WHEN SCHOOL STARTS..

OUR SCHOOL ISN'T NEAR THE FREEWAY, SIR..

DETAILS AREN'T IMPORTANT, MARCIE..

WOULDN'T IT BE EASIER JUST TO DO THE REPORT?
© 1998 United Feature Syndicate, Inc.

YOU ARE SO WEIRD, MARCIE..
SCHULZ

7-16
www.snoopy.com
© 1998 United Feature Syndicate, Inc.

SCHULZ

MY ARM HURTS..
www.snoopy.com

WHY DON'T YOU LET ME PITCH? I HAVE A CUTE ARM!

PITCHERS DON'T HAVE CUTE ARMS!
© 1998 United Feature Syndicate, Inc.

I'LL BET TY COBB HAD A CUTE ARM, DIDN'T SHE?
SCHULZ
7-17

DO DOGS EVER LOOK AT CLOUDS?
7-18
www.snoopy.com

IF I COULD TALK, I'D TELL YOU HOW WE LOOK AT CLOUDS, AND BIRDS, AND THE MOON AND EVERYTHING, BUT DOGS CAN'T TALK..
© 1998 United Feature Syndicate, Inc.

I GUESS DOGS NEVER LOOK AT CLOUDS..
STUPID KID!
SCHULZ

PEANUTS
DOWN HERE TO THIS BIG ROCK, AND BACK AGAIN..

GET READY.. GET SET..

GO!
© 1998 United Feature Syndicate, Inc.

7-19
www.snoopy.com

HOW COME YOU ALWAYS GET BACK HERE BEFORE I DO?
SCHULZ

MY EYES
KIND OF HURT..
I THINK I'VE
BEEN WATCHING
TOO MUCH
TUMBLEWEED..
© 1998 United Feature Syndicate, Inc.
SCHULZ
7-20

SEE? THAT
MEANS AN
HOUR HAS
GONE BY..
7-21

LET'S TURN
IT OVER,
AND WATCH
IT AGAIN..
www.snoopy.com

WOW! LOOK AT
THAT! OKAY, NOW
WE'LL TURN IT
OVER AND WATCH
IT AGAIN..

© 1998 United Feature Syndicate, Inc.

I LEAD A
DUMB LIFE!
SCHULZ

A GOOD MANAGER
KNOWS HOW TO
COMMUNICATE WITH
HIS PLAYERS..
7-22

A GOOD MANAGER
EVEN SHOWS CONCERN
FOR THEIR WELFARE..
www.snoopy.com

© 1998 United Feature Syndicate, Inc.
SCHULZ

HOW'VE YOU
BEEN?

© 1998 United Feature Syndicate, Inc.
SCHULZ
THIS IS HOW I HAVE IT FIGURED.. IF THERE ARE THREE KIDS IN A FAMILY, EACH KID HAS 33⅓% RIGHTS..
90%, 5%, 5%!
SO YOU'D BETTER CHECK YOUR FIGURES AGAIN..
7-23

I SHARE MY BLANKET WITH YOU..WHAT DO YOU DO FOR ME ?
7-24
www.snoopy.com

IF YOU GIVE ME A CALL, I CAN ALWAYS COME OVER AND GUARD YOUR HOUSE..
© 1998 United Feature Syndicate, Inc.

I'M USUALLY FREE IN THE AFTERNOON DURING THE MIDDLE OF THE WEEK..
SCHULZ

© 1998 United Feature Syndicate, Inc.
I TOLD YOU..THE EARLY BIRD CATCHES THE BUS..
7-25
SCHULZ

PEANUTS
by SCHULZ
IT'S TERRIBLE TO BE LITTLE..

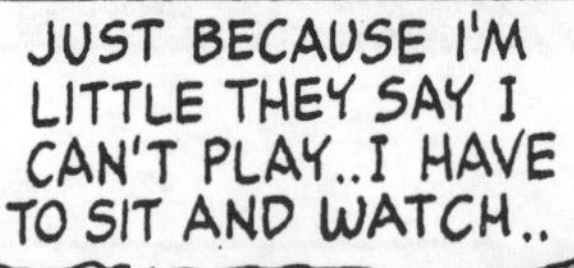
JUST BECAUSE I'M LITTLE THEY SAY I CAN'T PLAY..I HAVE TO SIT AND WATCH..

SOUVENIR!

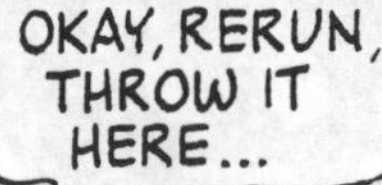
OKAY, RERUN, THROW IT HERE...

IT'S MY BALL NOW! IT'S A SOUVENIR!

STOP HIM! IT'S THE ONLY BALL WE'VE GOT! CATCH HIM! SOMEBODY CATCH HIM! CATCH HIM!
7-26

FIRST AMENDMENT!
SCHULZ

HERE'S THE WORLD WAR I FLYING ACE CROSSING NO MAN'S LAND TO VISIT HIS BROTHER SPIKE..
7-27
www.snoopy.com

HI, SPIKE..HOW ARE THINGS IN THE TRENCHES?
NOT QUITE WHAT I EXPECTED..
© 1998 United Feature Syndicate, Inc.

THE FIRST THING I NOTICED WHEN I GOT HERE IS THERE AREN'T ANY DRINKING FOUNTAINS..
SCHULZ

ANOTHER ROOT BEER FOR MY BROTHER SPIKE, S'IL VOUS PLAÎT..
www.snoopy.com

I HAD A GIRL FRIEND BACK HOME, BUT SHE'S STOPPED WRITING TO ME..

HERE'S TO ALL THE GIRL FRIENDS WHO DON'T WRITE TO US ANYMORE..
© 1998 United Feature Syndicate, Inc.

7-28
RATS!
SCHULZ

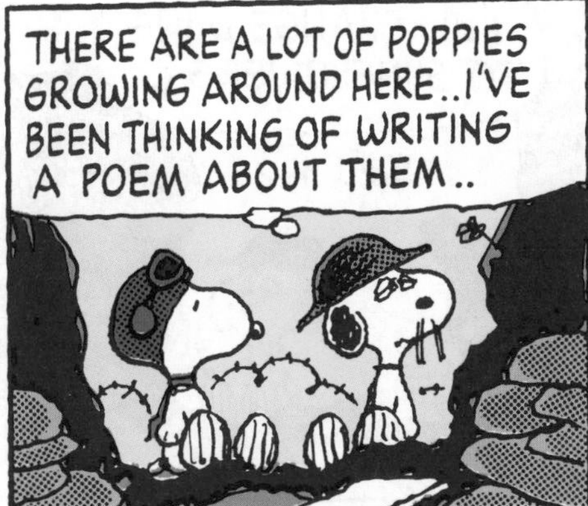
THERE ARE A LOT OF POPPIES GROWING AROUND HERE..I'VE BEEN THINKING OF WRITING A POEM ABOUT THEM..
www.snoopy.com

"IN SUCH AND SUCH FIELDS THE POPPIES BLOW.."
© 1998 United Feature Syndicate, Inc.

I CAN'T FINISH IT BECAUSE I DON'T KNOW WHERE WE ARE..
7-29
SCHULZ

HOW DOES THIS SOUND? "IN FARMERS' FIELDS THE POPPIES BLOW"
www.snoopy.com

DID YOU SAY "FARMERS" OR "FLANDERS"?
© 1998 United Feature Syndicate, Inc.

I SAID "FARMERS".. WHY WOULD I SAY "FLANDERS"?
I DON'T KNOW..IT WAS JUST A THOUGHT..
SCHULZ
7-30

7-31
THIS IS MY LATEST POEM.. SEE WHAT YOU THINK..
www.snoopy.com

© 1998 United Feature Syndicate, Inc.

DIDN'T LIKE IT, HUH?
SCHULZ

I HATE TO TELL YOU THIS, BUT SOMEONE IN ANOTHER OUTFIT HAS WRITTEN A POEM SOMETHING LIKE YOURS..
www.snoopy.com

" IN FLANDERS FIELDS THE POPPIES BLOW.."
© 1998 United Feature Syndicate, Inc.

8-1
I'LL CHANGE MINE TO SUNFLOWERS..
SCHULZ

PEANUTS
SCHULZ
OH, NO!

LOST AGAIN!

I CAN'T STAND IT!

IF WE LOSE ONE MORE GAME, I'LL GO CRAZY!
© 1998 United Feature Syndicate, Inc.

RATS!
8-2
www.snoopy.com

I'M NOT A POOR LOSER..I'M A GOOD LOSER! I'M SO GOOD AT IT I LOSE ALL THE TIME!

I JUST CAN'T STAND IT!

SCHULZ

I WONDER WHY THAT OTHER PLAYER HITS THE BALL FARTHER THAN YOU..
HE'S FIFTY YARDS YOUNGER..
© 1998 United Feature Syndicate, Inc.
8-3
SCHULZ

faithfully yours, your pen pal, Charles Brown
www.snoopy.com

P.S. Please forgive the smudge.

© 1998 United Feature Syndicate, Inc.
8/4

And the other smudge.
SCHULZ

AND THIS LITTLE KID WITH THE DOG JUMPED OVER THE FENCE, AND...
DO YOU HAVE TO TALK ALL THE TIME?
www.snoopy.com

DO YOU ALWAYS HAVE TO BE SO NOISY?
8-5

© 1998 United Feature Syndicate, Inc.

AM I BUTTERING TOO LOUD FOR YOU?
HAPPY BIRTHDAY, AMY–
SCHULZ

RATS! MY TEAM LOST AGAIN..
www.snoopy.com

THAT WASN'T A REAL GAME.. THAT WAS A MOVIE..
HOW COULD IT BE A MOVIE? THOSE WERE REAL PEOPLE..
8-6
© 1998 United Feature Syndicate, Inc.

WHEN IT WAS OVER, DID IT SAY, "THE END"?
WE'RE STILL HERE, AREN'T WE?
SCHULZ

IT'S A NEW BALL, SEE? I'LL THROW IT, AND YOU'LL CHASE IT...
www.snoopy.com

WE'LL HAVE MORE FUN THAN YOU'VE EVER HAD IN YOUR WHOLE LIFE!

8-7
© 1998 United Feature Syndicate, Inc.

ALL RIGHT, I LIED.. IT'S NOT A NEW BALL!
SCHULZ

8-8
SCHULZ
MY PUTTER WAS RIGHT HERE.. WHAT HAPPENED TO IT?
I THINK IT CRAWLED AWAY..
© 1998 United Feature Syndicate, Inc.

PEANUTS
by SCHULZ

MOM SHOULD LET US HAVE A DOG..

8-9
CLOMP!
© 1998 United Feature Syndicate, Inc.

www.snoopy.com

HAVING A DOG COULD BE FUN, DON'T YOU THINK?
SCHULZ

I DECIDED TO WRITE A LETTER..
GOOD FOR YOU..
www.snoopy.com

HOW DO YOU SPELL "BY THE WAY"?
JUST THE WAY IT SOUNDS.. "BY THE WAY"
8-10
© 1998 United Feature Syndicate, Inc.

Dear Grandma,
How have you been?
By the way, thanks for the Christmas present.
SCHULZ

YOU DID IT AGAIN! YOU TOOK MY COMIC BOOKS WITHOUT ASKING ME!

THESE ARE **MY** COMIC BOOKS, AND I DON'T WANT YOU TOUCHING THEM!
8-11
www.snoopy.com

IF YOU DO IT AGAIN, I'M GOING TO HIT YOU RIGHT OVER THE HEAD!
© 1998 United Feature Syndicate, Inc.

I'M GLAD WE HAD THIS DISCUSSION..
SCHULZ

THE FIRST THING YOU DO IS RAISE YOUR GLASS..

THEN YOU SAY, "I'LL DRINK TO THAT!"

8-12
© 1998 United Feature Syndicate, Inc.

IT TAKES A LITTLE PRACTICE..
SCHULZ

Dear Pen Pal,
8-13
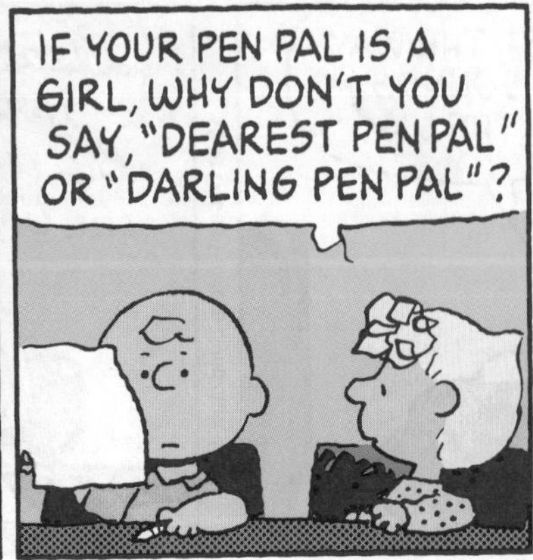
IF YOUR PEN PAL IS A GIRL, WHY DON'T YOU SAY, "DEAREST PEN PAL" OR "DARLING PEN PAL"?

AND THEN SIGN IT "AFFECTIONATELY YOURS"
© 1998 United Feature Syndicate, Inc.

ANY OTHER ADVICE?
DON'T SEND A PICTURE
SCHULZ

Dear Pen Pal,
YOU SHOULD TRY TO WRITE MORE NEATLY..
www.snoopy.com
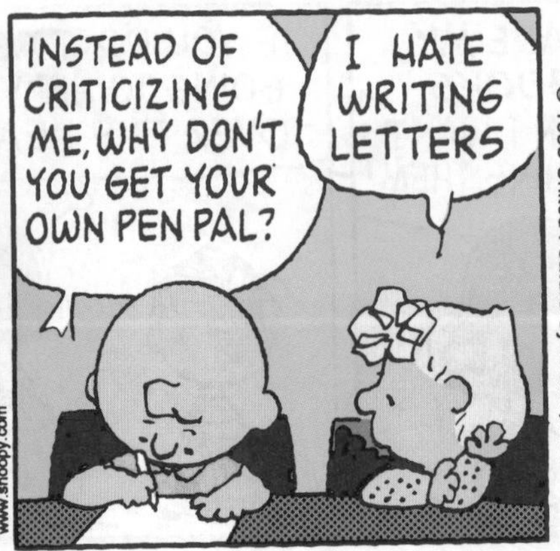
INSTEAD OF CRITICIZING ME, WHY DON'T YOU GET YOUR OWN PEN PAL?
I HATE WRITING LETTERS
© 1998 United Feature Syndicate, Inc.
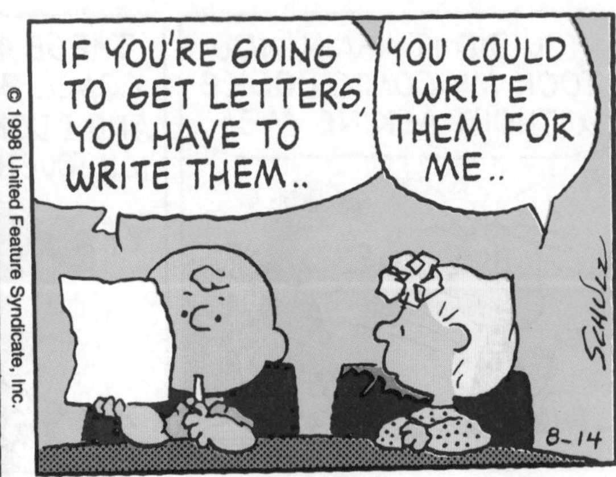
IF YOU'RE GOING TO GET LETTERS, YOU HAVE TO WRITE THEM..
YOU COULD WRITE THEM FOR ME..
SCHULZ
8-14

8-15
WELL, SPIKE, HOW ARE THINGS IN THE TRENCHES?
www.snoopy.com

IT'S GETTING WORSE..
© 1998 United Feature Syndicate, Inc.

THEY'RE STARTING TO CALL FOOT FAULTS..
SCHULZ

PEANUTS
by SCHULZ

I HAVE A GREAT IDEA..
WHAT'S THAT?

WHY DON'T YOU GO GET US A COUPLE OF ICE CREAM CONES?
ALL RIGHT, I'LL DO IT..
© 1998 United Feature Syndicate, Inc.

www.snoopy.com

8-16

THANK YOU..WHAT TOOK YOU SO LONG?

THERE WERE A FEW OTHERS AHEAD OF ME..
SCHULZ

© 1998 United Feature Syndicate, Inc.
8-17
SO WHAT I'M GOING TO DO IS TRY TO BE A BETTER PERSON..
THEY SAY IF YOU BECOME A BETTER PERSON, YOU'LL HAVE A BETTER LIFE..
IF YOU TRY TO BE A BETTER DOG, SOMETIMES YOU GET AN EXTRA COOKIE..
SCHULZ

HAS SCHOOL STARTED YET?
NO, NOT YET..
www.snoopy.com

THEN I SUPPOSE WE MIGHT AS WELL COME OUT..
WE ?
© 1998 United Feature Syndicate, Inc.

8-18
SCHULZ

WHAT ARE YOU DOING AT THE FRONT DOOR? SUPPER DISHES BELONG AT THE BACKDOOR..
www.snoopy.com

8-19
© 1998 United Feature Syndicate, Inc.

SCHULZ

© 1998 United Feature Syndicate, Inc.
SCHULZ
8-20

WAS I CUTE WHEN I WAS A BABY?
NOT AT ALL
www.snoopy.com

ACTUALLY, YOU WERE UN-CUTE..

8-21
© 1998 United Feature Syndicate, Inc.

HOW UN-CUTE?
SCHULZ

I SUPPOSE YOU REALIZE THAT SCHOOL STARTS AGAIN NEXT MONTH..
I'M READY, KID..
8-22
www.snoopy.com

I COME FROM A FAMILY OF DEDICATED SCHOOL BUILDINGS..

WE'RE A PROUD FAMILY...
© 1998 United Feature Syndicate, Inc.

OUR OLDER SISTER HAS A NEW CAFETERIA..
SCHULZ

PEANUTS
by SCHULZ
PLAY BALL!

I MAY BE TOO YOUNG TO PLAY, BUT AT LEAST I CAN WATCH THE GAME

SOMEONE SAID IF YOU CATCH A FOUL BALL, YOU CAN TAKE IT TO THE SNACK BAR AND GET A FREE DRINK..

© 1998 United Feature Syndicate, Inc.

FOUL BALL! FOUL BALL! I'LL GET IT! I'LL GET IT!

8-23

HERE IT IS! HERE IT IS!
www.snoopy.com

WELCOME TO THE SNACK BAR..
SCHULZ

HELLO, CHUCK?

MY BROTHER ISN'T HERE.. HE JUST LEFT FOR CAMP..
8-24
www.snoopy.com

CAMP? I THOUGHT HE WASN'T GOING THIS YEAR..

I DON'T KNOW.. MAYBE HE CHANGED HIS MIND..
© 1998 United Feature Syndicate, Inc.

ANYWAY, I CAN'T TALK NOW.. I'M MOVING MY THINGS INTO HIS ROOM..
SCHULZ

WHAT'S GOING ON HERE?
www.snoopy.com

BIG BROTHER! I THOUGHT YOU WENT TO CAMP..

I ONLY WENT OVER TO THE MALL.. I'M GONE FOR THIRTY MINUTES, AND YOU START MOVING YOUR STUFF INTO MY ROOM?!
© 1998 United Feature Syndicate, Inc.

THAT'S MY NEW PHILOSOPHY.. "IF YOU SEE A ROOM YOU LIKE, MOVE INTO IT.."
SCHULZ
8-25

I'M GOING INTO THE KITCHEN TO HAVE BREAKFAST.. I'LL ONLY BE IN THERE FOR MAYBE FIFTEEN MINUTES...
www.snoopy.com

WHILE I'M GONE, PLEASE DON'T START MOVING YOUR THINGS INTO MY ROOM..
8-26
© 1998 United Feature Syndicate, Inc.

I'LL PUT THESE SWEATERS BACK..
SCHULZ

SOMETIME WE SHOULD HAVE A LITTLE TALK ABOUT SISTERS..
ANY TIME YOU SAY... I'M AN EXPERT..
YOU GUYS BETTER BE CAREFUL.. IF SHE HEARS YOU, SHE'LL GET YOU SHIPPED OFF TO SOMEPLACE YOU NEVER HEARD OF..
HOW DO YOU SPELL "ADDIS ABABA"?
8/27
SCHULZ
© 1998 United Feature Syndicate, Inc.

TELL YOUR CATCHER I THINK HE'S CUTE!
8-28

SHE SAYS TO TELL YOU SHE THINKS YOU'RE CUTE!
www.snoopy.com

HE DIDN'T ANSWER..
© 1998 United Feature Syndicate, Inc.

TRY "EXCESSIVELY" CUTE..
SCHULZ

SOMETIMES I LIE AWAKE AT NIGHT, AND I ASK, "WHY ISN'T THE WORLD PERFECT?"
8-29
© 1998 United Feature Syndicate, Inc.

THEN A VOICE COMES TO ME THAT SAYS, "WE ADMIT IT..THERE ARE STILL A FEW KINKS THAT NEED WORKING OUT"
SCHULZ

PEANUTS
by SCHULZ
PSYCHIATRIC HELP 5¢
THE DOCTOR IS IN OUT AND ABOUT

WHAT WE'RE TALKING ABOUT HERE, CHARLIE BROWN, IS COMMUNICATION
THE DOCTOR IS IN

I DON'T NECESSARILY MEAN WORDS..SOMETIMES BODY LANGUAGE TELLS US EVEN MORE..

BODY LANGUAGE?
© 1998 United Feature Syndicate, Inc.

THAT'S INTERESTING..BODY LANGUAGE..COMMUNICATION..
THE DOCTOR IS IN
www.snoopy.com

MY RIGHT FIELDER IS REALLY STUPID..I TRY TO EXPLAIN THINGS TO HER, BUT I DON'T GET ANYPLACE..

MAYBE IT'S COMMUNICATION.. WHAT DO YOU THINK?

HELP 5¢
8-30
THE DOCTOR IS IN

PSYCHIATRISTS ARE BIG ON BODY LANGUAGE..
SCHULZ

© 1998 United Feature Syndicate, Inc.
SCHULZ
8-31

9-1
www.snoopy.com

© 1998 United Feature Syndicate, Inc.
SCHULZ

HEY, MARCIE..HOW SOON BEFORE SCHOOL STARTS AGAIN?
9-2

I MAY HAVE TO BORROW SOME NOTEBOOK PAPER AND THINGS..
www.snoopy.com

SO HOW SOON BEFORE SCHOOL STARTS?

DO YOU HAVE A CALENDAR?
© 1998 United Feature Syndicate, Inc.

A WHAT?
SCHULZ

THIS IS WHAT WE CAME FOR, TROOPS.. LOOK AT THAT VIEW!
♠K1086
♥A10
♦KJ53
♣K98
N
W E
S
♠32
♥75432
♦4
♣QJ1063
♠J7
♥KQJ96
♦Q9872
♣7
♠AQ954
♥8
♦A106
♣A542
© 1998 United Feature Syndicate, Inc.
9-3
SCHULZ

HEY, MANAGER.. NEXT YEAR I THINK I'LL PLAY FOR A DIFFERENT TEAM..
9-4

I'M TIRED OF LOSING ALL THE TIME..

I SUPPOSE YOU'RE GOING TO PLAY FOR SOMEONE ELSE, TOO..
© 1998 United Feature Syndicate, Inc.

I PLAY FOR WHOEVER OWNS THE SUPPER DISH
SCHULZ

HOW SHOULD I CHEER FOR YOUR TEAM TODAY, CHARLES?
9-5

SHOULD I YELL, "GO, REDS!" OR "GO, BLUES!" OR "GO, GREENS!" OR WHAT?

I DON'T KNOW, RERUN.. YELL ANYTHING YOU WANT..
© 1998 United Feature Syndicate, Inc.

GO, T-SHIRTS!
SCHULZ

PEANUTS
by
SCHULZ

9-6
© 1998 United Feature Syndicate, Inc.

www.snoopy.com

THAT LOOKS LIKE A GOOD GAME..

WHAT DO YOU CALL IT?

SLOBBER BALL..
SCHULZ

YOU HAVE TO GO TO SCHOOL TOMORROW.. YOU CAN'T HIDE UNDER YOUR BED..
www.snoopy.com

SCHOOL ISN'T SO BAD... THINK OF ALL THE THINGS YOU'RE GOING TO LEARN..
9-7
© 1998 United Feature Syndicate, Inc.

WHO ARE YOU TALKING TO?
SCHULZ

YES, MA'AM.. I'M FINISHED.. I ANSWERED ALL THE QUESTIONS..
www.snoopy.com

CAN YOU SEE THE LITTLE NOTE I ADDED AT THE BOTTOM?
SCHULZ
© 1998 United Feature Syndicate, Inc.

"DRY CLEAN ONLY"
9-8

I SEE YOUR LITTLE BROTHER HAS DECIDED TO GO TO SCHOOL..
WELL, HE'S NOT HIDING UNDER THE BED ANYMORE..
MAYBE HE'S HAD A CHANGE OF ATTITUDE..
TELL ME WHAT I'M DOING HERE! THAT'S ALL I ASK! TELL ME WHAT I'M DOING HERE!
BUS STOP
9-9
SCHULZ
© 1998 United Feature Syndicate, Inc.

HAS THE SCHOOL BUS COME YET?
IF IT HAD, DO YOU THINK I'D STILL BE STANDING HERE?
© 1998 United Feature Syndicate, Inc.

9-10
www.snoopy.com

BOO!
SCHULZ

WHAT ARE THOSE ROUND THINGS?
PEOPLE FACES..
9-11
www.snoopy.com

I'M DRAWING A FOOTBALL STADIUM FILLED WITH SIXTY-THOUSAND FANS..
© 1998 United Feature Syndicate, Inc.

I ONLY SEE TEN..
PARKING WAS A PROBLEM..
SCHULZ

9-12
WHEN I WAS LITTLE, THE SCHOOL BUS CAME BY WHERE WE LIVED..
www.snoopy.com

I USED TO JUMP UP AND DOWN AND BARK, AND ALL THE KIDS WOULD YELL AND WAVE..
© 1998 United Feature Syndicate, Inc.

DID YOU USED TO WAVE WHEN THE CACTUS BUS WENT BY?
SCHULZ

PEANUTS
by SCHULZ

IT'S IMPOLITE TO BLOW ON YOUR SOUP..
BUT IT'S HOT..

IT'S STILL IMPOLITE..

AAUGH!

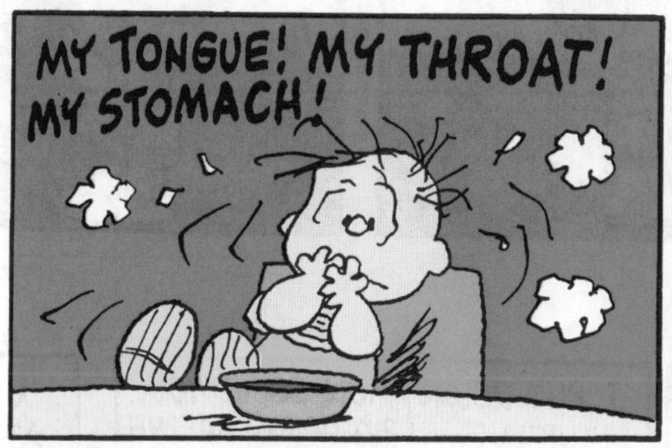
MY TONGUE! MY THROAT! MY STOMACH!

© 1998 United Feature Syndicate, Inc.
www.snoopy.com
WATER! WATER! WATER!

AAUGHH!!!

9-13
THAT'S ALSO IMPOLITE..
SCHULZ

YES, MA'AM, I BROUGHT MY DOG TO SCHOOL BECAUSE HE WAS FEELING LONELY..
9-14
www.snoopy.com

YES, MA'AM..HE'S KIND OF SMART..
© 1998 United Feature Syndicate, Inc.

TELL HER I CAN SPELL "ZAMBONI"
SCHULZ

9-15
www.snoopy.com

KICK THE BALL, MARCIE! WHAT ARE YOU WAITING FOR? WHAT ARE YOU LOOKING AT?
© 1998 United Feature Syndicate, Inc.

IT DOESN'T SAY, "LOW FAT"
SCHULZ

PSST, FRANKLIN.. WHAT'D YOU PUT DOWN FOR NUMBER SIX?
I PUT DOWN "EIGHT"

"EIGHT"? EIGHT WHAT?
"EIGHT" NOTHING.. JUST "EIGHT"

I PUT DOWN "TWELVE ELEPHANTS"
HOW COULD YOU PUT DOWN "TWELVE ELEPHANTS" IN A SPELLING TEST?
9-16
© 1998 United Feature Syndicate, Inc.

WHAT ROOM ARE WE IN?
SCHULZ

YES, MA'AM..I'M SURE SHE'S ASLEEP..
www.snoopy.com

SHOULD I WAKE HER UP?
9-17

© 1998 United Feature Syndicate, Inc.
I THINK IT'S TIME FOR HER TEN O'CLOCK FEEDING..
SCHULZ

9-18
© 1998 United Feature Syndicate, Inc.
Z

I'M AWAKE!
www.snoopy.com

PRINCIPAL'S OFFICE
Z
SCHULZ

YES, YOUR HONOR, MY CLIENT WAS STANDING ALONE IN THE FIELD MINDING HIS OWN BUSINESS..
www.snoopy.com

SUDDENLY, WITHOUT WARNING, HE WAS ATTACKED BY THREE OF THE FARMER'S CROWS!
© 1998 United Feature Syndicate, Inc.

SCHULZ
9-19
HE SAYS TO STOP SCATTERING STRAW ON THE FLOOR..

PEANUTS
by SCHULZ

YES, MA'AM.. I'M READY

I HAVE MY REPORT RIGHT HERE...
WELL, NOT EXACTLY RIGHT HERE..

ACTUALLY, MY SECRETARY STILL HAS IT.. SHE TYPED IT FOR ME LAST NIGHT..
www.snoopy.com

9-20
© 1998 United Feature Syndicate, Inc.

WAS THAT YOU SIGHING, MA'AM?
SCHULZ

HEY, CHUCK, YOU READY FOR SOME BACK YARD FOOTBALL?
9-21
www.snoopy.com

ME AN' MARCIE CAN GET OVER THERE ANYTIME YOU'RE READY..
© 1998 United Feature Syndicate, Inc.

I THINK WE'VE MOVED AWAY, AND I DON'T KNOW WHAT OUR NEW ADDRESS IS..
SCHULZ

OKAY, MARCIE, GO STRAIGHT OUT AND CUT RIGHT..
I CUT LEFT BETTER, SIR..
9-22
www.snoopy.com

IF YOU CUT LEFT, THE BALL WON'T BE THERE..
© 1998 United Feature Syndicate, Inc.

SCHULZ
THAT'S NOT A BAD IDEA..

THAT WAS A GOOD PRACTICE, HUH, MARCIE?

NO! I THINK I BROKE ALL MY ARMS AND THIRTY FINGERS..
www.snoopy.com

WELL, WE'RE GETTING YOU TOUGHENED UP FOR THE NEW SEASON, HUH?
© 1998 United Feature Syndicate, Inc.

I'M NOT INTERESTED IN GETTING TOUGHENED UP..
I'LL NEVER UNDERSTAND YOU, MARCIE..
SCHULZ
9-23

9-24
IT'S THE KICKOFF, CHUCK! HERE I COME!
I LIKE THAT GAME WHERE SOMEONE THROWS A STICK, AND I CHASE IT..
© 1998 United Feature Syndicate, Inc.
SCHULZ

© 1998 United Feature Syndicate, Inc.
SCHULZ
NICE GOING, MARCIE.. YOU KICKED THE BALL UP INTO THE TREE!
SOMEBODY CALL A CAT..
9-25

HI, CHUCK..DID YOU EVER GET MY FOOTBALL OUT OF THE TREE?
9-26

I THINK YOU OWE ME A NEW BALL, CHUCK.. AFTER ALL, THE TREE'S IN YOUR BACK YARD..
www.snoopy.com

WELL, WHAT I THINK I'LL DO IS GET A LADDER, CLIMB UP INTO THE TREE, RESCUE THE BALL, AND THEN FALL OUT OF THE TREE AND LAND ON MY HEAD..
© 1998 United Feature Syndicate, Inc.

YOU'RE A REAL HERO, CHUCK..
SCHULZ

PEANUTS
by SCHULZ

COME ON.. YOU'VE GOT TO SEE THIS..

THE MOON IS BRIGHT, AND THERE'S A CHILL IN THE AIR..
© 1998 United Feature Syndicate, Inc.

THIS WAY.. STAY CLOSE BEHIND ME..
www.snoopy.com

KIND OF SPOOKY, ISN'T IT?

SEE? THIS IS THE TIME OF NIGHT THE ZAMBONIS COME OUT..
9-27
SCHULZ

WHAT I THINK I'LL DO IS GO INTO TOWN, AND STAND SOMEPLACE, LIKE MAYBE ON A CORNER..

9-28

I'LL HAVE TO MAKE SURE I LOOK SOPHISTICATED..

WHAT'S HE STANDING HERE FOR? ISN'T HE FUNNY LOOKING?
9-29

DID YOU SEE THE FUNNY HAT HE WAS WEARING AND THE FUNNY LOOKING SHOES?

MICKEY MOUSE SHOES ARE NOT FUNNY LOOKING!
SCHULZ

SOMETIMES IF YOU STAND NEAR THE CORNER, A BEAUTIFUL HOLLYWOOD-TYPE GIRL WILL COME BY IN A CONVERTIBLE, AND TAKE YOU HOME..

"ANIMAL CLINIC"?

WHY AM I STANDING IN FRONT OF AN "ANIMAL CLINIC"?
9-30

THE DOCTOR WILL SEE YOU NOW!
SCHULZ

SPIKE, ARE YOU AWAKE? IT'S ME, NAOMI..

I SAW YOUR NAME INSIDE YOUR COLLAR.. MY MOM IS THE VET HERE..
www.snoopy.com

HE'S STILL ASLEEP, MOM..
© 1998 United Feature Syndicate, Inc.

LOOK.. HE WAS WEARING MICKEY MOUSE SHOES!
SCHULZ
10-1

ARE YOU ASLEEP, SPIKE? I GUESS YOU ARE..

MY MOM IS THE VET HERE...

SHE SAID THEY TOOK SOME TESTS, AND THEY FOUND OUT WHAT'S WRONG WITH YOU...
© 1998 United Feature Syndicate, Inc.

EVERYTHING!
SCHULZ
10-2

WHERE AM I? IS THIS A HOSPITAL? I THOUGHT I HEARD DOGS BARKING..
www.snoopy.com

IF I OPEN MY EYES, WILL I SEE A BEAUTIFUL HOLLYWOOD-TYPE GIRL WAITING TO TAKE ME HOME?
© 1998 United Feature Syndicate, Inc.

10-3
SCHULZ

PEANUTS
by SCHULZ
ARE YOU READY?
READY FOR WHAT?

© 1998 United Feature Syndicate, Inc.
ALL RIGHT, LET'S RUN THROUGH THIS ONE MORE TIME.. I'LL THROW THE BALL, AND YOU'LL CHASE IT..

YOU CAN RUN THROUGH IT A THOUSAND TIMES, AND I'M STILL NOT GOING TO DO IT!

MAYBE I CAN PUT IT ANOTHER WAY..
YOU CAN PUT IT A THOUSAND DIFFERENT WAYS, AND I'M STILL NOT GOING TO DO IT!

SOMETIMES IT'S JUST A MATTER OF EXPLAINING..
10-4

YOU CAN EXPLAIN IT A THOUSAND TIMES BUT I'M STILL NOT GOING TO DO IT..
www.snoopy.com

I THINK MAYBE YOU HAVE A FAULTY DOG..
SCHULZ

WE SAW YOU STANDING IN FRONT OF OUR "ANIMAL CLINIC"... MOM IS THE VET HERE..SHE SAID, "THAT DOG DOESN'T LOOK WELL.. BRING HIM IN HERE.."

IT'S TOO BAD DOGS CAN'T TALK..IF YOU COULD TALK, YOU COULD TELL ME HOW YOU FEEL, AND WHAT YOU'RE THINKING..

DID ANYBODY TAKE MY MICKEY MOUSE SHOES?

10-6
MOM SAYS YOU NEED EXERCISE..

SHE SAID I SHOULD WALK WITH YOU UP AND DOWN THE HALL AT LEAST TWICE A DAY..

I CAN'T STEER THIS THING!

HERE, SPIKE.. I BROUGHT YOU SOME TAPIOCA..

MOM SAYS YOU HAD DISTEMPER, BUT YOU'RE GETTING BETTER..

MAYBE YOU'LL BE ABLE TO GO HOME SOON..
10-7

DON'T CURE ME.. THIS IS A GOOD LIFE..

GUESS WHAT, SPIKE.. MOM SAYS YOU CAN GO HOME TODAY..

I HAVE TO CARRY YOU BECAUSE SHE SAID YOU'RE TOO WEAK TO WALK

THIS IS WHERE YOU LIVE ?
LIVE ?

MY PLAN WAS TO GET ADOPTED BY SOME BEAUTIFUL GIRL, BUT INSTEAD I ENDED UP IN THE HOSPITAL..

ANYWAY, HERE I AM BACK HOME AGAIN.. I GUESS I'M REALLY PRETTY LUCKY..

I STILL HAVE MY MICKEY MOUSE SHOES AND A FAITHFUL FRIEND TO LEAN ON..

OUCH!

MOM, A COUPLE OF DOGS JUST WALKED BY.. THEY ALMOST LOOKED LIKE THEY COULD BE SPIKE'S BROTHERS..

NO, THEY SEEMED TO BE GOING SOMEPLACE

I WONDER WHY THAT GIRL WAS LOOKING AT US..
PROBABLY ADMIRING US..

PEANUTS
by SCHULZ
HURRY UP!

COME ON, GET IN THE CAR.. WE'RE GOING TO GRANDMA'S HOUSE..

I'M SORRY..I HAVE TO LEAVE..
© 1998 United Feature Syndicate, Inc.

DON'T LOOK SO SAD..
www.snoopy.com

10-11
I HATE GOING OFF LIKE THIS..THEY SEEM SO LOST WITHOUT ME..

THEY JUST DON'T KNOW WHAT TO DO WITH THEMSELVES WHEN I'M GONE..

♠KQ86
♥Q104
♦AKQ5
♣83
N
W
E
S
♠A7
♥KJ876
♦87
♣KQ52
♠10942
♥53
♦1063
♣J1074
♠J53
♥A92
♦J942
♣A93
SCHULZ

THIS IS A PICTURE OF A MAN WHO WAS RAISED IN THE JUNGLE BY APES..
LIKE TARZAN

LIKE WHO?
IT'S BEEN DONE
www.snoopy.com

I'LL CHANGE IT TO A MALL..
© 1998 United Feature Syndicate, Inc.

THIS IS A PICTURE OF A MAN WHO WAS RAISED IN A MALL BY APES..
I THINK YOU'RE ON TO SOMETHING..
SCHULZ
10-12

I DREW A PICTURE OF YOUR DOG..WOULD YOU LIKE TO BUY IT?
www.snoopy.com

ARE YOU A STARVING ARTIST? IF YOU WERE A STARVING ARTIST, I'D BUY IT..
10-13
© 1998 United Feature Syndicate, Inc.

ALL I HAD FOR BREAKFAST WAS A WAFFLE..
SCHULZ

I DREW ANOTHER PICTURE OF YOUR DOG..DO YOU WANT TO BUY IT?
10-14
www.snoopy.com

THIS TIME IT'S IN COLOR..
MY DOG IS BLACK AND WHITE..
© 1998 United Feature Syndicate, Inc.

DON'T YOU LIKE PURPLE DOGS?
SCHULZ

LET'S SAY WE'RE MARRIED, AND MY DAD HAS OFFERED YOU A MILLION DOLLAR A YEAR JOB WITH HIS COMPANY..
10-15
www.snoopy.com

BUT LET'S SAY YOU INSIST ON PLAYING YOUR STUPID PIANO IN SOME SLEAZY JOINT, AND...

KLUNK!
© 1998 United Feature Syndicate, Inc.

I NEVER GET TO THE PART ABOUT THE LIMO AND THE FREE LUNCHES..
SCHULZ

WHEN YOU'RE ALONE IN THE DESERT, YOU SING SONGS ABOUT LONELINESS..
10-16
www.snoopy.com

YOU SING ABOUT LOVE, AND THE MOON, AND THE STARS AND THE ALAMO..
© 1998 United Feature Syndicate, Inc.

MAYBE YOU COULD LIP-SYNC..
SCHULZ

SEE? SHE SAYS YOU TAKE THE BOWL OUT OF THE CUPBOARD, POUR THE CEREAL INTO THE BOWL, AND THEN ADD THE MILK..
© 1998 United Feature Syndicate, Inc.

SCHULZ
10-17
THIS IS YOUR "BASIC COOKING" PROGRAM..

PEANUTS
by SCHULZ

THIS IS MY REPORT ON THE FOOTBALL CAREER OF MOSES..

YES, MA'AM.. THAT MOSES... YOU DIDN'T ?
© 1998 United Feature Syndicate, Inc.

ANYWAY, WHEN MOSES WAS YOUNG, HE SHOWED GREAT PROMISE..ALL THE PROFESSIONAL TEAMS WANTED HIM..

YES, MA'AM.. FOOTBALL TEAMS..

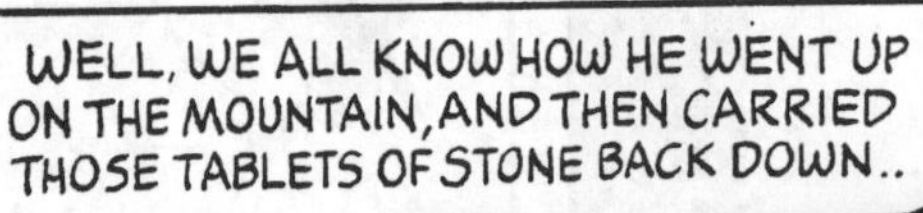
WELL, WE ALL KNOW HOW HE WENT UP ON THE MOUNTAIN, AND THEN CARRIED THOSE TABLETS OF STONE BACK DOWN..

THIS PROBABLY WAS HOW HE HURT HIS THROWING ARM..AFTER THAT, HE COULD NEVER THROW THE LONG BALL..

www.snoopy.com

HE COULD ONLY THROW A FEW SHORT SIDELINE PATTERNS..
10-18

PRETTY SOON HE GOT INVOLVED IN OTHER THINGS AND QUIT FOOTBALL..

RESEARCH? NO, MA'AM..MY GRAMPA..WELL, I FIGURE HE MUST HAVE KNOWN HIM..

I GUESS GRAMPA ISN'T AS OLD AS I THOUGHT HE WAS..
SCHULZ

LET'S COMPARE NOTES, SIR, AND SEE IF WE'VE GOT THE SAME ANSWERS..
www.snoopy.com

"TRUE, FALSE, MAYBE, WHO KNOWS? WHY NOT? SURE, WHEN? THEY DID? SOMETIME, I DID NOT, WHO, ME? IT WAS DARK, AND EVERYONE WAS GETTING HUNGRY"
10-19
© 1998 United Feature Syndicate, Inc.

I DON'T KNOW HOW YOU DO IT, SIR..
NEVER LET 'EM KNOW WHERE YOU'RE COMING FROM, MARCIE..
SCHULZ

GOOD MORNING..I'M HERE TO ASK IF YOU'D CARE TO SUBSCRIBE TO THE "GREAT PUMPKIN" NEWSLETTER
www.snoopy.com

GET OFF OUR PORCH OR I'LL SIC OUR DOG ON YOU!

10-20
© 1998 United Feature Syndicate, Inc.

I'M SORRY.. I DIDN'T MEAN TO BOTHER YOU..
THAT'S ALL RIGHT.. WE DON'T HAVE A DOG..
SCHULZ

HERE, WE'RE GIVING AWAY A DOUGHNUT WITH EVERY SUBSCRIPTION TO THE "GREAT PUMPKIN" NEWSLETTER
www.snoopy.com

I'LL TAKE A DOUGHNUT, BUT I WOULDN'T READ YOUR NEWSLETTER IF IT WERE THE LAST NEWSLETTER ON EARTH..
10-21
© 1998 United Feature Syndicate, Inc.

TAKE ONE WITH COCONUT ON IT..
SCHULZ

GOOD MORNING..WOULD YOU BE INTERESTED IN SUBSCRIBING TO OUR "GREAT PUMPKIN" NEWSLETTER?

DOES IT HAVE CARTOONS IN IT?
10-22
www.snoopy.com

YOU SHOULD GET SOMEONE TO DRAW CARTOONS IN IT..
© 1998 United Feature Syndicate, Inc.

WHAT'S THE NAME OF THE GUY WHO DRAWS "DILBERT"?
SCHULZ

GOOD MORNING..I'M HERE TO TELL YOU ABOUT THE "GREAT PUMPKIN"..

www.snoopy.com

HEY, MA! THERE'S A FALSE PROPHET AT THE DOOR..WHAT SHOULD I TELL HIM?

REALLY?
10-23
© 1998 United Feature Syndicate, Inc.

HE'S GONE.. I THINK HE HEARD YOU, MA..
SCHULZ

WE'LL RUN THIS PICTURE IN THE NEXT "GREAT PUMPKIN" NEWSLETTER..
www.snoopy.com

READERS WILL SEE DEDICATED BELIEVERS SITTING IN A PUMPKIN PATCH WAITING FOR THE "GREAT PUMPKIN"
10-24
© 1998 United Feature Syndicate, Inc.

IF WE'RE LUCKY, NO ONE WILL RECOGNIZE US..
IF ANYBODY ASKS, MY NAME IS "REX"
SCHULZ

PEANUTS®
by SCHULZ

THE WORLD FAMOUS WATCHDOG IS EVER ALERT..

WOOF!

THAT'S ALL RIGHT..EVERYTHING IS FINE..THANK YOU..

WOOF!

THAT'S OKAY..EVERYTHING IS ALL RIGHT..YOU'RE A GOOD WATCHDOG..GO BACK TO SLEEP

SIGH
10-25
© 1998 United Feature Syndicate, Inc.
www.snoopy.com

YOU TRY TO WARN THEM THAT THE WORLD HAS GONE MAD, BUT THEY WON'T LISTEN..
SCHULZ

SNOOPY, IT MAKES ME FEEL GOOD TO KNOW THAT I CAN ALWAYS TALK TO YOU ABOUT THE "GREAT PUMPKIN."
© 1998 United Feature Syndicate, Inc.

10-26
OF COURSE, IT JUST MIGHT BE THAT IT'S BECAUSE DOGS BELIEVE EVERYTHING YOU TELL THEM..
MOST DOGS..
SCHULZ

AND MY BROTHER TALKS ALL THE TIME ABOUT THIS "GREAT PUMPKIN" THING, SEE..
www.snoopy.com

SO SOMETIMES I THINK HE'S REALLY CRAZY, AND..

10-27
© 1998 United Feature Syndicate, Inc.

AND THEN I WONDER ABOUT THE REST OF OUR FAMILY, AND...
SCHULZ

SO WE'LL GO FROM HOUSE TO HOUSE "TRICK OR TREATING," AND PEOPLE WILL GIVE US THINGS..
LIKE MAYBE A BICYCLE?
www.snoopy.com

NO, NOT A BICYCLE.. MAYBE AN ORANGE OR A COOKIE..
A BICYCLE WOULD BE NICE..
© 1998 United Feature Syndicate, Inc.

YOU HAVE TO TAKE WHATEVER THEY GIVE YOU..
HOW DID I GET INVOLVED IN SOMETHING LIKE THIS?
SCHULZ
10/28

HERE'S THE BAG YOU'LL USE TO CARRY ALL THE THINGS PEOPLE WILL GIVE YOU WHEN WE GO "TRICK OR TREATING" ON HALLOWEEN NIGHT
www.snoopy.com

WHAT IF SOMEBODY GIVES ME A BICYCLE?
NOBODY'S GOING TO GIVE YOU A BICYCLE..
10-29
© 1998 United Feature Syndicate, Inc.

I'LL JUST SAY, "THANK YOU..DON'T PUT IT IN THE BAG..I'LL RIDE IT HOME!"
SCHULZ

HEY! AREN'T YOU GOING TO SIT IN THE PUMPKIN PATCH, AND WAIT FOR THE "GREAT PUMPKIN"?
WE'RE NOT AS STUPID AS YOU..WE'RE GOING "TRICK OR TREATING"
MAYBE I'LL JUST SAY, SORT OF JOKINGLY, "THANK YOU, JUST PUT THE BICYCLE IN THIS BAG"
© 1998 United Feature Syndicate, Inc.
10-30
SCHULZ

I CAN'T STAND IT..
© 1998 United Feature Syndicate, Inc.
10-31
SCHULZ

www.snoopy.com

FOR "TRICK OR TREATS" I GOT TWELVE CANDY BARS, FOURTEEN COOKIES, AND THREE TUBES OF TOOTHPASTE

www.snoopy.com

11-2

I DIDN'T GET A BICYCLE..
SCHULZ

I LOVE THE FEEL OF NEW BOOKS, MARCIE.. THE PRETTY COVERS, THE PRINT, EVEN THE SMELL..
www.snoopy.com

DO YOU EVER READ ANY OF THEM?
11-3

DO I EVER WHAT?
SCHULZ

www.snoopy.com

11-4

I DON'T KNOW..HOW CAN YOU GET YOUR FOOT CAUGHT IN A NEST?
SCHULZ

THE ONE IN BACK DIDN'T THINK THAT WAS VERY FUNNY..
© 1998 United Feature Syndicate, Inc.
11-5
SCHULZ

ALL YOU DOGS EVER THINK ABOUT IS EATING..
www.snoopy.com

YOU NEVER HAVE ANY DEEP THOUGHTS..

I HAVE DEEP THOUGHTS ALL THE TIME...
© 1998 United Feature Syndicate, Inc.
11-6

I KNEW RIGHT FROM THE START THAT "ROSEBUD" WAS HIS SLED..
SCHULZ

HE SAYS HE'S NEVER BEEN MUCH OF A JOINER..
© 1998 United Feature Syndicate, Inc.
11-7
SCHULZ

PEANUTS
by SCHULZ

HERE, READ THIS BOOK TO ME, PLEASE, BIG BROTHER..
WHY DON'T YOU READ IT YOURSELF?

I HATE READING..
© 1998 United Feature Syndicate, Inc.
11-8

JUST READ THE EXCITING PARTS..SKIP THE BORING PARTS AND DESCRIPTIONS..

"HIS NAME WAS DOUGLAS, AND ONE DAY HE..."
www.snoopy.com

WHAT DO YOU MEAN, "HE"? READ SOMETHING ABOUT A "SHE."

THEY SAY THE FAMILY THAT READS TOGETHER STAYS TOGETHER
WHERE DID YOU HEAR THAT?

I READ IT..

MAYBE SOMEBODY READ IT TO ME..
SCHULZ

THE TEACHER SAYS WE'RE SUPPOSED TO BE PAINTING FLOWERS..
I HATE PAINTING FLOWERS

I LIKE TO PAINT SUPER HEROES! SEE? MY SUPER HERO FLIES ALL OVER THE UNIVERSE!
www.snoopy.com

© 1998 United Feature Syndicate, Inc.
THE TEACHER WON'T LIKE IT..
I CALL HIM "SUNFLOWER"
11/9
SCHULZ

© 1998 United Feature Syndicate, Inc.
HALT! THAT'S FAR ENOUGH!
SCHULZ
11-10

SCHULZ and my hero, Bill Mauldin–
I THINK THE NEW REPLACEMENTS ARE GETTING SMALLER ALL THE TIME..
WILLIE AND JOE.. MY HEROES! HAPPY VETERANS DAY, MEN!
11-11 © 1998 United Feature Syndicate, Inc.

YES, MA'AM..REQUEST PERMISSION TO GO SEE THE SCHOOL NURSE..
www.snoopy.com

I FEEL AN ANXIETY ATTACK COMING ON..
11/12
© 1998 United Feature Syndicate, Inc.

HURRY, SIR! SHE'S GOING TO GET THERE BEFORE YOU DO!
SCHULZ

SO YOU'RE GOING TO FLY SOUTH FOR THE WINTER..
11-13
www.snoopy.com

I SUPPOSE YOU REALIZE IT'S A LONG WAY..
© 1998 United Feature Syndicate, Inc.

?
NO, I DON'T WANT TO CARRY YOU..
SCHULZ

IF YOU'RE GOING TO FLY SOUTH, I SUGGEST YOU'D BETTER GET STARTED..
?
www.snoopy.com

YES, TODAY IS SATURDAY..WHAT'S WRONG WITH TRAVELING ON SATURDAY?
11-14
© 1998 United Feature Syndicate, Inc.

SCHULZ
WORMS ARE CLOSED ON THE WEEKEND?

PEANUTS
by SCHULZ

I'LL HOLD THE BALL, CHARLIE BROWN, AND YOU COME RUNNING UP AND KICK IT..
I CAN DO THAT..

YOU CAN?
ABSOLUTELY! I HAVE A NEW POSITIVE ATTITUDE!

I CAN'T BELIEVE IT.. YOU ARE TRULY AMAZING! YOU TALK THE TALK AND YOU WALK THE WALK!

© 1998 United Feature Syndicate, Inc.

AAUGH!
www.snoopy.com

11-15
BUT YOU DON'T KICK THE KICK..
SCHULZ

© 1998 United Feature Syndicate, Inc.
NO, I DON'T THINK ANYONE EVER COMES AROUND HERE ANYMORE..
SCHULZ
11-16

YES, MA'AM, I PUT DOWN "TRUE" FOR ALL OF THE QUESTIONS..
www.snoopy.com

WELL, MA'AM, I REALIZE, AS I'M SURE YOU MUST ALSO REALIZE, THAT WE DO NOT LIVE IN A PERFECT WORLD..SO...
11-17
© 1998 United Feature Syndicate, Inc.

A GOOD START FOR A GOOD EXPLANATION, SIR..
WHAT I NEEDED WAS A GOOD FINISH..
SCHULZ

ASK YOUR DOG IF HE WANTS TO COME OUT AND PLAY IN THE SNOW..
www.snoopy.com

11-18
© 1998 United Feature Syndicate, Inc.

SCHULZ
SHOVELING ISN'T PLAYING..

11-19

WHEN YOU GET MARRIED, MARCIE, I'M NOT GOING TO YOUR BRIDAL SHOWER..

IF YOU'LL HELP ME WITH MY HOMEWORK, I'LL SEE TO IT THAT SOMEDAY THEY PUT A STATUE OF YOU IN THE PARK..

OKAY, WE'LL BEGIN HERE ON PAGE FOUR..
DO YOU WANT TO BE ON A HORSE OR A SKATEBOARD?
11-20

11-21
I'M WORRIED ABOUT YOUR BROTHER..LATELY HE SEEMS TO BE HANGING OUT WITH THE WRONG CROWD..

PEANUTS®

by SCHULZ

HERE'S THE WORLD FAMOUS PATRIOT SOLDIER AT VALLEY FORGE

ALL RIGHT, I SAID I'D TELL HIM, AND I WILL..
11-22

I STILL DON'T THINK HE'LL LISTEN TO ME..

YES, SIR..I'D LIKE PERMISSION TO SEE GENERAL WASHINGTON..

WELL, YES, I'D SAY IT CAUSES SUFFERING..
© 1998 United Feature Syndicate, Inc.

YES, GENERAL... I UNDERSTAND..
www.snoopy.com

I KNEW HE HAD OTHER THINGS ON HIS MIND..

WHAT I SAID WAS, "SIR, WE KEEP LOSING THESE WHITE PING PONG BALLS IN THE SNOW"
SCHULZ

I'M STARTING MY OWN POLLING FIRM.. SEE? I WROTE DOWN WHAT I THINK ABOUT EVERYTHING..
www.snoopy.com

ARE YOU GOING TO GO FROM HOUSE TO HOUSE, AND ASK OTHER PEOPLE WHAT THEY THINK ?
11-23
© 1998 United Feature Syndicate, Inc.

WHO CARES WHAT OTHER PEOPLE THINK ?
SCHULZ

"DETAILS AT ELEVEN!" THAT'S MY NEW PHILOSOPHY..
www.snoopy.com

ASK ME WHAT I DID TODAY..
WHAT DID YOU DO TODAY ?
© 1998 United Feature Syndicate, Inc.

DETAILS AT ELEVEN!
SCHULZ
11 24

"...IN HOPES THAT ST. NICHOLAS SOON WOULD BE THERE"
www.snoopy.com

THAT'S MY FAVORITE POEM.. YOU SHOULD WRITE SOMETHING LIKE THAT..
© 1998 United Feature Syndicate, Inc.

"Twas the month before Christmas"
SCHULZ
11-25

© 1998 United Feature Syndicate, Inc.
SCHULZ
MAYBE YOU SHOULDN'T TRY TO GET DRESSED AND FEED YOUR DOG AT THE SAME TIME..
11-26

WHAT'S SANTA CLAUS DOING HERE SO EARLY?
THAT ISN'T REALLY SANTA CLAUS..IT'S A DOG DRESSED UP LIKE SANTA CLAUS..
www.snoopy.com

HE SHOULDN'T EVEN BE HERE..HE SHOULD BE OUT CHASING RABBITS..
I'LL GO TELL HIM..

HEY, YOU! YOU SHOULD BE OUT CHASING RABBITS!
© 1998 United Feature Syndicate, Inc.

NEXT TIME YOU TELL HIM..
SCHULZ
11-27

SCHULZ
© 1998 United Feature Syndicate, Inc.
11-28

PEANUTS®

by SCHULZ

TOUCHDOWN!

WHAP!
GREAT CATCH, MARCIE!

FABULOUS CATCH, MARCIE!
WHAP!

UNBELIEVABLE, MARCIE!
WHAP!

11-29

PLEASE, SIR..NO MORE COMPLIMENTS

I'M LEANING INTO THE WIND BECAUSE THERE'S A BLIZZARD COMING..

IF YOU'RE LEANING INTO THE WIND, YOUR EARS SHOULD BE BLOWING BACK..

THAT'S BETTER..

CLOSE ALL THE SCHOOLS! CLOSE ALL THE SCHOOLS!

YES, MA'AM? WELL, I THOUGHT MAYBE A BLIZZARD MIGHT BE HEADED THIS WAY..

YES, MA'AM..GET OUT YOUR BOOTS..CHANGE THE ANTIFREEZE IN YOUR CAR.. CHECK STORED VEGETABLES, AND REMOVE ANY THAT SHOW SIGNS OF ROTTING..

ANYTHING ELSE? YES, MA'AM..

BRING THE DOG IN..

GO BACK TO SLEEP..THERE'S A BLIZZARD OUTSIDE, AND ALL THE SCHOOLS ARE CLOSED..
www.snoopy.com

© 1998 United Feature Syndicate, Inc.

POETRY!
12-3

I WAS WONDERING IF I COULD BORROW YOUR SLED DOG..
I DON'T HAVE A SLED DOG..
www.snoopy.com

WHAT ABOUT HIM? HE COULD PULL A SLED, COULDN'T HE?
I DON'T THINK SO..
© 1998 United Feature Syndicate, Inc.

12-4
HE TIRES EASILY..
Z
SCHULZ

RATS! I KNEW THIS WAS GOING TO HAPPEN..
12-5
www.snoopy.com

WHAT'S WRONG?
© 1998 United Feature Syndicate, Inc.

WE JUST RAN OUT OF SNOWFLAKES..
SCHULZ

PEANUTS
by SCHULZ
NOON?

I HATE TO TELL YOU THIS, BUT YOU'VE JUST SLEPT YOUR LIFE AWAY..

SLEPT MY LIFE AWAY?!

I CAN'T BELIEVE IT!

ALL THE THINGS I'D PLANNED TO DO! THE PLACES I HAD PLANNED TO GO...
www.snoopy.com

© 1998 United Feature Syndicate, Inc.
I'M SO ASHAMED! MY LIFE.. GONE! WASTED! I CAN'T BELIEVE IT..
12-6

IT'S JUST AN EXPRESSION..

Z
SCHULZ

12-7
www.snoopy.com

© 1998 United Feature Syndicate, Inc.

SCHULZ
"OBJECTS IN THE WATER DISH ARE CLOSER THAN THEY APPEAR"

I THOUGHT I'D PUT BOTH OF OUR NAMES ON OUR CHRISTMAS CARDS THIS YEAR..
12-8
www.snoopy.com

IS THAT ALL RIGHT WITH YOU? GOOD..
© 1998 United Feature Syndicate, Inc.

Merry Christmas from Spike and Joe Cactus
SCHULZ

WHEN? WHEN DO I EVER GET MY WAY?!
12-9
www.snoopy.com

YOU CAN NEVER KNOW IF YOU'RE GOING TO GET YOUR WAY..SOMETIMES YOU DO, AND SOMETIMES YOU DON'T..
© 1998 United Feature Syndicate, Inc.

SCHULZ
I LIKE TO KNOW AHEAD OF TIME..

YES, MA'AM..
ABOUT THIS
BOOK..

DO WE HAVE
TO READ THE
WHOLE BOOK?
www.snoopy.com

I MEAN, DO WE HAVE
TO READ THE PREFACE,
THE DEDICATION, THE
INTRODUCTION AND THE
SELECTED BIBLIOGRAPHY?
12-10

NO, WE DON'T
MIND READING
THE PAGE
NUMBERS..
© 1998 United Feature Syndicate, Inc.

A LITTLE
SARCASM
THERE, HUH,
MA'AM?
SCHULZ

"SO WADDYA THINK?"
THAT'S MY NEW
PHILOSOPHY.."SO
WADDYA THINK?"
ABOUT
WHAT?
www.snoopy.com

WHO CARES? SO
WADDYA THINK?
12-11
© 1998 United Feature Syndicate, Inc.

IT'S A DOG'S LIFE,
ISN'T IT? SO WADDYA THINK?
SCHULZ

© 1998 United Feature Syndicate, Inc.
I'M NOT SURE..LET'S
TRY IT AGAIN WITHOUT
THE RED NOSE..
SCHULZ
12-12

PEANUTS
by SCHULZ
FIRECAKE AGAIN..

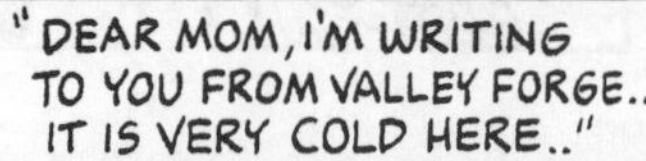
"DEAR MOM, I'M WRITING TO YOU FROM VALLEY FORGE.. IT IS VERY COLD HERE.."

"IN A FEW MINUTES I HAVE TO GO ON GUARD DUTY..I WILL WRITE MORE LATER"

www.snoopy.com

I USED TO WONDER WHAT I'D SAY IF SOMEONE ASKED ME WHAT I WAS DOING HERE..
12-13

I THINK I'VE FIGURED IT OUT...

GUARDING SNOW..
© 1998 United Feature Syndicate, Inc.
SCHULZ

YES, MA'AM..IT'S REALLY A TWO-EDGED SWORD, ISN'T IT?
www.snoopy.com

IS THE GLASS HALF FULL OR HALF EMPTY? IS IT SIX OF ONE OR HALF A DOZEN OF ANOTHER? IS THIS REALLY FOR THE GREATER PUBLIC GOOD?
© 1998 United Feature Syndicate, Inc.

12-14
I LIVE FOR YOUR ANSWERS, SIR..
SCHULZ

GOOD MORNING..WOULD YOU LIKE TO BUY A HAND-DRAWN PICTURE OF SANTA CLAUS?
12-15
www.snoopy.com

SLAM!
© 1998 United Feature Syndicate, Inc.

I ASSUME FROM YOUR RESPONSE THAT YOU'RE NOT INTERESTED..
SCHULZ

HOW WOULD YOU LIKE TO BUY A HAND-DRAWN PICTURE OF SANTA CLAUS?
www.snoopy.com

THIS DOESN'T LOOK LIKE SANTA CLAUS.. IT LOOKS MORE LIKE "DAFFY DUCK"

12-16
© 1998 United Feature Syndicate, Inc.

I'LL BET YOU DIDN'T KNOW I CAN DRAW "DAFFY DUCK"!
SCHULZ

I'M WRITING TO SANTA CLAUS..WHICH SHOULD I ASK FOR, A BICYCLE OR A DOG?
12-17

I THINK MAYBE A DOG..

YOU CAN'T FALL OFF A DOG..
SCHULZ

SO WHEN SANTA CLAUS BRINGS ME A DOG, I WON'T HAVE TO BORROW YOU ANYMORE..

I'LL THROW THE BALL, AND MY NEW DOG, THAT SANTA CLAUS IS GOING TO BRING ME, WILL CHASE IT..

ANYWAY, I JUST WANT TO THANK YOU FOR ALL THE GOOD TIMES WE'VE HAD...

I'LL PROBABLY CALL MY NEW DOG "ROVER"... I'LL SAY, "HERE, ROVER! GET THE BALL"
LOOK OUT, ROVER
SCHULZ
12-18

WHEN SANTA CLAUS BRINGS ME THE DOG, WILL HE LEAVE IT ON THE FRONT PORCH OR IN THE BACK YARD? HE WOULDN'T DROP IT DOWN THE CHIMNEY, WOULD HE?

THERE'S SOMETHING I SORT OF FEEL I SHOULD TELL YOU..
MAYBE HE'LL JUST LEAVE A GIFT CERTIFICATE..
SCHULZ
12/19

PEANUTS
by SCHULZ

HELP ME, LINUS.. I WANT TO MAKE A SPECIAL CHRISTMAS CARD FOR THE LITTLE RED-HAIRED GIRL..

DRAW A TREE, CHARLIE BROWN, WITH SOME TINY RED HEARTS HANGING ON IT..

THEN WRITE SOMETHING SORT OF PERSONAL AT THE BOTTOM...
www.snoopy.com

WHAT'S GOING ON? IS MY SWEET BABBOO HELPING MY BIG BROTHER DRAW A CHRISTMAS CARD?

© 1998 United Feature Syndicate, Inc.
12-20
I'M NOT YOUR SWEET BABBOO!!

THAT IS SO STUPID! THAT IS SO HUMONGOUSLY STUPID!
THERE! HOW DOES THAT LOOK? I DREW A TREE WITH LITTLE HEARTS ON IT..

"MERRY CHRISTMAS FROM YOUR SWEET BABBOO"?!

IT'S A FAMILY EXPRESSION..
SCHULZ

YES, SIR..MY NAME IS RERUN..DID YOU KNOW THAT SANTA CLAUS IS GOING TO BRING ME A DOG?

SO WHAT I NEED IS A LEASH, AND A COLLAR, AND A SUPPER DISH...
12-21
www.snoopy.com

AND YOU CAN JUST PUT IT ON MY TAB..
© 1998 United Feature Syndicate, Inc.

SCHULZ

I NEED YOUR ADVICE, CHARLIE BROWN...

WHEN SANTA CLAUS BRINGS ME MY DOG, I'LL HAVE TO LEARN HOW TO TAKE CARE OF HIM..
12-22
www.snoopy.com

IF YOU SHOW ME WHAT YOU FEED YOUR DOG AND WHERE HE SLEEPS, MAYBE I'LL LEARN SOMETHING..
© 1998 United Feature Syndicate, Inc.

WHAT'S THAT KID DOING ON THE RUNWAY?
SCHULZ

LISTEN TO ME..MOM DOESN'T WANT YOU TO HAVE A DOG, DOES SHE?
NO..
© 1998 United Feature Syndicate, Inc.

DO YOU REALLY THINK SANTA CLAUS IS GOING TO BRING YOU SOMETHING MOM DOESN'T WANT YOU TO HAVE?
OOO!! SUPREME COURT STUFF!
SCHULZ
12-23

SNOOPY, WHO AM I KIDDING?
12-24

LUCY IS RIGHT..SANTA CLAUS IS NEVER GOING TO BRING A DOG TO SOMEONE WHOSE MOM DOESN'T WANT HIM TO HAVE A DOG..

IF I'M LUCKY, I'LL GET A PAIR OF SOCKS AND AN ORANGE..
IF I GET A RUBBER BONE, I'LL SHARE IT..
SCHULZ

MERRY CHRISTMAS
SCHULZ
12-25

12-26
YOU HAVE TO UNDERSTAND.. I'M NOT COMPLAINING..
I UNDERSTAND..

I SIMPLY LEARNED THAT WE SHOULDN'T ALWAYS EXPECT TO GET EVERYTHING WE ASK FOR..
THAT'S CALLED "PREACHING TO THE CONVERTED"
SCHULZ

PEANUTS
by SCHULZ

12-27

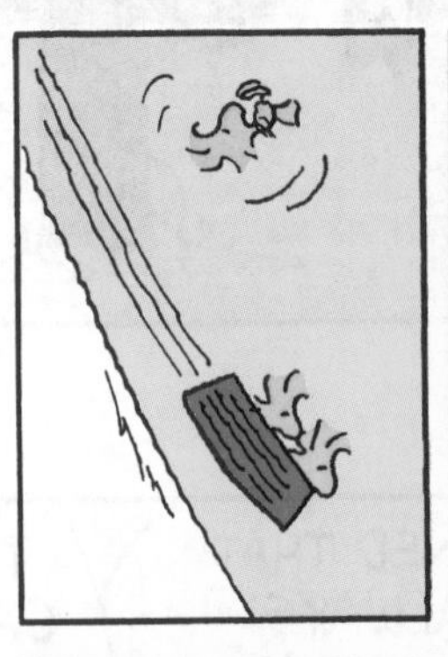

DO IT AGAIN?!
SCHULZ

Dear Grandma,
Thank you for the money you sent me for Christmas.

I plan to save it for my college education
www.snoopy.com

YOU SPENT IT ALL YESTERDAY..
© 1998 United Feature Syndicate, Inc.
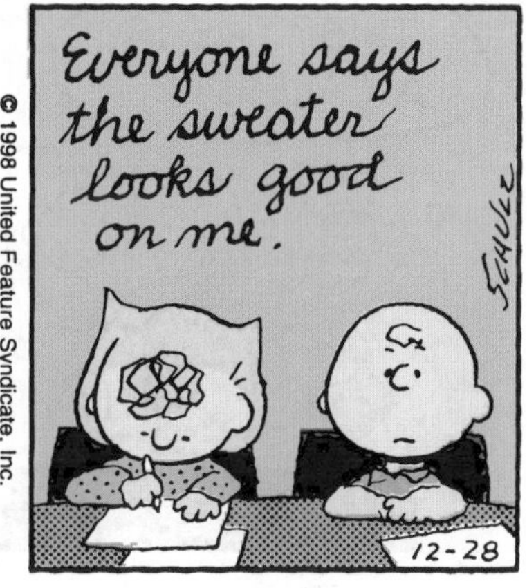
Everyone says the sweater looks good on me.
SCHULZ
12-28

Dear Other Grandma,
"OTHER GRANDMA"?
www.snoopy.com
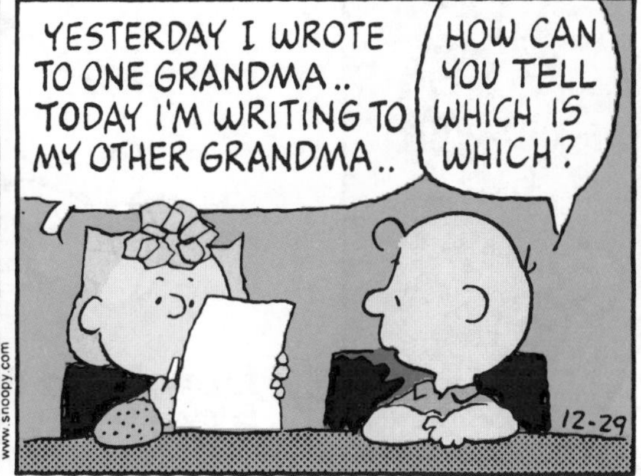
YESTERDAY I WROTE TO ONE GRANDMA.. TODAY I'M WRITING TO MY OTHER GRANDMA..
HOW CAN YOU TELL WHICH IS WHICH?
12-29
© 1998 United Feature Syndicate, Inc.

IT DOESN'T MATTER..ALL GRANDMAS LOOK ALIKE FROM A DISTANCE..
SCHULZ

HEY, MARCIE..YOU KNOW THE BOOK WE WERE SUPPOSED TO READ? I READ THE WHOLE THING!

WHAT YOU MEAN IS, YOU SAW THE MOVIE ON TV..
12-30

BUT I WROTE A GOOD REPORT..

WHAT YOU MEAN IS, YOU COPIED IT OUT OF THE TV GUIDE..
© 1998 United Feature Syndicate, Inc.

DON'T ASK ME TO BE A BRIDESMAID AT YOUR WEDDING, MARCIE..I'M BUSY THAT DAY..
SCHULZ

THIS? THIS IS A CALENDAR..
www.snoopy.com

IT TELLS YOU WHAT DAY IT IS, WHAT MONTH IT IS, AND WHAT YEAR IT IS..
© 1998 United Feature Syndicate, Inc.

?
NO, IT DOESN'T TELL YOU WHERE YOUR MOM IS..
SCHULZ
12-31

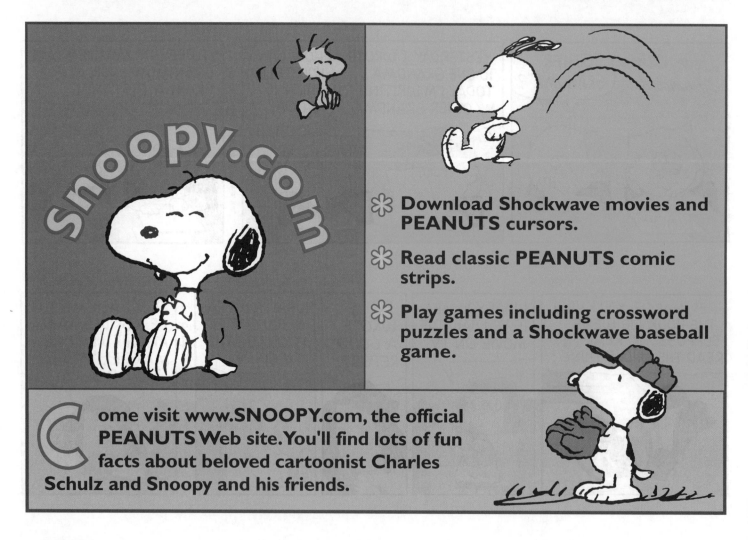

IT'S A BIG WORLD,
CHARLIE
BROWN
BY CHARLES M. SCHULZ

It's a Big World, Charlie Brown

YES, SIR.. IS THIS WHERE YOU'RE SELLING ATHLETE'S AUTOGRAPHS?
www.unitedmedia.com

I'D LIKE A BASEBALL WITH JOE SHLABOTNIK'S AUTOGRAPH.. WHO IS HE? HE'S MY HERO!

IS HE HERE? WELL, JUST ASK HIM TO SIGN A BALL, AND I'LL PAY FOR IT..
© 1996 United Feature Syndicate, Inc.

I USED TO HAVE A LASSIE DOG DISH, BUT SHE NEVER SIGNED IT..
SCHULZ
12-30

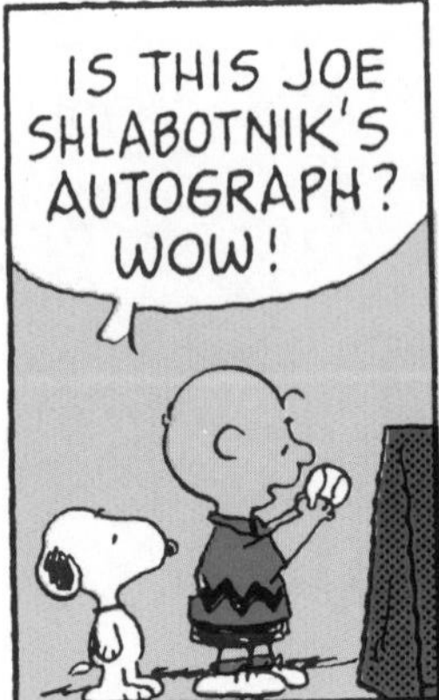
IS THIS JOE SHLABOTNIK'S AUTOGRAPH? WOW!
www.unitedmedia.com

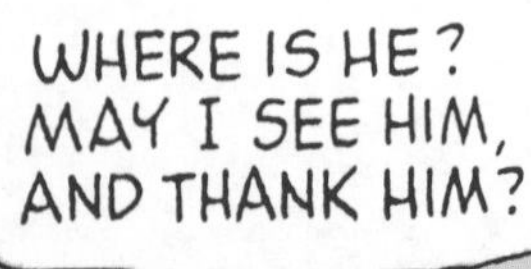
WHERE IS HE? MAY I SEE HIM, AND THANK HIM?

WELL, TELL HIM I APPRECIATE THE AUTOGRAPH..

..EVEN THOUGH IT TOOK ALL THE MONEY I'VE GOT..
12-31
© 1996 United Feature Syndicate, Inc.

WOW! I'LL BE THE ENVY OF EVERY JOE SHLABOTNIK FAN IN THE WORLD!
ALL ONE OF YOU!
SCHULZ

SEE? IT'S AN AUTOGRAPHED JOE SHLABOTNIK BASEBALL..

I DON'T THINK SO, CHARLIE BROWN.. THIS ISN'T JOE'S SIGNATURE..
1-1-97

IT'S A FORGERY!
GOOD GRIEF!
www.unitedmedia.com

THEY CHEATED A LITTLE KID! AN INNOCENT, TRUSTING, HERO WORSHIPPING LITTLE KID..
© 1996 United Feature Syndicate, Inc.
ME!
SCHULZ

YES, SIR.. I THINK YOU SOLD ME A FORGERY.. THIS IS NOT JOE SHLABOTNIK'S SIGNATURE
www.unitedmedia.com

GET LOST?! YOU SELL ME A FAKE AUTOGRAPH, AND THEN TELL ME TO GET LOST?!!

WHAT AM I GOING TO DO ABOUT IT?
1-2-97
© 1996 United Feature Syndicate, Inc.

LET ME INTRODUCE YOU TO MY WORLD FAMOUS ATTACK DOG..
SCHULZ

HEY, KID.. DO YOU WANT A JOB?
A WHAT?
www.unitedmedia.com

C'MON, I'LL SHOW YOU.. MY HAND IS KILLING ME FROM ALL THAT AUTOGRAPHING
YOU MEAN..

SURE! I HAVE TO AUTOGRAPH ALL THIS STUFF, SEE? ARE YOU A GOOD SPELLER?
© 1996 United Feature Syndicate, Inc.

1-3-97
YESTERDAY, SOMEBODY WANTED A "JOE SHLABOTNIK" OR SOMETHING.. GIVE ME A BREAK!
I CAN SPELL SHLABOTNIK
SCHULZ

© 1996 United Feature Syndicate, Inc.
..AND YOUR JOB WOULD BE TO HELP ME FORGE THE AUTOGRAPHS ON ALL THESE BATS, AND BALLS, AND PICTURES AND EVERYTHING..
WILL YOU COME TO SEE ME ON VISITOR'S DAY?
SCHULZ
1-4-97

PEANUTS
SCHULZ
© 1996 United Feature Syndicate, Inc.
IT'S STILL SNOWING..
www.unitedmedia.com
WHERE'S YOUR DOG?
OUTSIDE
OUTSIDE ?!
POOR DOG.. STANDING OUT THERE IN THE SNOW ALL ALONE..
I WONDER WHAT HE'S THINKING..
HERE'S THE REVOLUTIONARY WAR PATRIOT STANDING GUARD AT VALLEY FORGE..
1-5-97
SCHULZ

1-6-97
HERE'S A LIST OF THE ATHLETES' NAMES..ALL YOU HAVE TO DO IS FORGE THEIR SIGNATURES..YOU CAN START WITH THE BASKETBALLS..
SCHULZ
© 1996 United Feature Syndicate, Inc.

WHAT'S THIS? THIS ISN'T A BASKETBALL PLAYER'S AUTOGRAPH!

I DON'T DO FAKE AUTOGRAPHS..THAT'S MY DAD'S NAME... HE'S A BARBER..
www.unitedmedia.com

A FAMOUS BARBER?
© 1996 United Feature Syndicate, Inc.

TELL HIM TO AUTOGRAPH A BARBER POLE! WE COULD SELL IT!
SCHULZ
1-7-97

WE HAVE TO TALK..
www.unitedmedia.com

BUT HOW CAN WE TALK IF YOU'RE A DOG, AND DOGS CAN'T TALK?
WOOF!
© 1996 United Feature Syndicate, Inc.

1-8-97
WOOFING ISN'T TALKING..
SCHULZ

1-9-97
MAYBE IT'S A GOOD THING YOU CAN'T TALK..

YOU'RE JUST THE KIND WHO WOULD TALK WITHOUT THINKING, TALK OUT OF TURN, ALWAYS SAY THE WRONG THING, AND TALK WITHOUT LISTENING..
www.unitedmedia.com
© 1996 United Feature Syndicate, Inc.

OR AM I DESCRIBING MYSELF ?
SCHULZ

WHERE WILL IT ALL END?
WHERE WILL WHAT ALL END?

THAT'S MY NEW PHILOSOPHY.."WHERE WILL IT ALL END?"
1-10-97

I'M PROUD OF YOU.. IT SOUNDS LIKE YOU'VE BEEN DOING SOME REAL THINKING..
www.unitedmedia.com
© 1996 United Feature Syndicate, Inc.

WHERE WILL IT ALL END?
SCHULZ

1-11-97

www.unitedmedia.com

© 1996 United Feature Syndicate, Inc.

YOU JUST DON'T UNDERSTAND, DO YOU?
SCHULZ

PEANUTS
by Schulz
"DEAR MOM, I'VE NEVER BEEN SO COLD IN MY LIFE"

HERE'S THE WORLD FAMOUS REVOLUTIONARY WAR PATRIOT STANDING GUARD AT VALLEY FORGE..

TELL GENERAL WASHINGTON ONE OF HIS MEN WANTS TO SEE HIM..

YES, SIR..I HAVE A LITTLE SUGGESTION..

YOU MAY OR MAY NOT HAVE NOTICED THAT THERE'S A LOT OF SNOW HERE..
© 1997 United Feature Syndicate, Inc.
1-12

MY IDEA IS WE BUILD A SKATING RINK OUT THERE..WE COULD ORGANIZE A HOCKEY TEAM..

MAYBE EVEN START SOME KIND OF A FIGURE SKATING CLUB..

WE COULD EVEN INVITE SOME OF THE CHICKS FROM TOWN FOR A SKATING PARTY..

www.unitedmedia.com

I DIDN'T GET A CHANCE TO TELL HIM HE COULD DRIVE THE ZAMBONI..
SCHULZ

I'M TIRED OF ALL THIS KINDERGARTEN STUFF..
WHY DON'T WE RUN AWAY TO PARIS?
1-13
www.unitedmedia.com

IF WE GOT ON A PLANE AT MIDNIGHT, WE COULD BE IN PARIS TOMORROW..
© 1997 United Feature Syndicate, Inc.

DO YOU HAVE ANY MONEY?
I HAVE FIFTY CENTS..MAYBE WE COULD GET UPGRADED TO BUSINESS CLASS
SCHULZ

THERE'S THIS CUTE LITTLE GIRL WHO SITS NEXT TO ME IN KINDERGARTEN..
1-14
www.unitedmedia.com

I TOLD HER MAYBE SHE AND I COULD GO TO PARIS SOMEDAY..
© 1997 United Feature Syndicate, Inc.

I DON'T EVEN KNOW WHERE PARIS IS..
SCHULZ

THE TEACHER SAYS THE PRINCIPAL WANTS TO SEE YOU
ME?
www.unitedmedia.com

1-15

YES, MA'AM..I WAS TOLD THE PRINCIPAL WANTS TO SEE ME

WHY ME? I'M NOBODY..
© 1997 United Feature Syndicate, Inc.

I DON'T EVEN HAVE A DOG..
SCHULZ

YES, SIR, MR. PRINCIPAL... WHO? THE LITTLE GIRL WITH THE BRAIDS? SURE, WE'RE IN THE SAME KINDERGARTEN CLASS..
1-16

DID I ASK HER TO GO TO PARIS?

WELL, SURE, BUT THAT WAS JUST A JOKE..
www.unitedmedia.com

I MEAN, HOW...
© 1997 United Feature Syndicate, Inc.

HARASSMENT?!!
SCHULZ

1-17

www.unitedmedia.com

IT'S ONLY ME! I'M HOME EARLY..
© 1997 United Feature Syndicate, Inc.

I'VE BEEN FIRED!
SCHULZ

THIS LITTLE GIRL IN MY CLASS WAS SORT OF DEPRESSED, SEE, SO I SAID, "WHY DON'T WE RUN AWAY TO PARIS?" IT WAS A JOKE

SHE THOUGHT IT WAS FUNNY SO SHE TOLD HER MOTHER, WHO TOLD OUR TEACHER, WHO TOLD THE PRINCIPAL, AND I GOT FIRED!
1-18
www.unitedmedia.com

SUSPENDED
I GUESS SO..
© 1997 United Feature Syndicate, Inc.

HARASSMENT?
STUPIDITY!
SCHULZ

PEANUTS
© 1997 United Feature Syndicate, Inc.
1-19
WHAP!
www.unitedmedia.com
WUMP
NOT FAIR! TEN AGAINST ONE!

SO I GOT SUSPENDED FROM SCHOOL FOR A DAY..
1-20
www.unitedmedia.com

ALL BECAUSE I ASKED A LITTLE GIRL TO GO TO PARIS.. IT WAS JUST A JOKE!

DO YOU THINK I DID WRONG?

SORRY..I KEEP FORGETTING THAT DOGS CAN'T TALK..
© 1997 United Feature Syndicate, Inc.

IT'S JUST AS WELL..I HAVE SOME PRETTY STRONG OPINIONS..
SCHULZ

AND THEY HAVE A SECRETARY OF DEFENSE AND A SECRETARY OF AGRICULTURE...
1-21
www.unitedmedia.com

BUT THEY DON'T HAVE A SECRETARY OF BIRDS SO YOU CAN NEVER BE THE SECRETARY OF BIRDS..
© 1997 United Feature Syndicate, Inc.

YOU'RE RIGHT..WHO CARES?
SCHULZ

1-22
SCHULZ
© 1997 United Feature Syndicate, Inc.

GOOD NIGHT, SIR..
GOOD NIGHT, MARCIE
www.unitedmedia.com

IF YOU DREAM TONIGHT ABOUT ANYONE I KNOW, GREET THEM FOR ME..

TELL THEM I REMEMBER ALL THE GOOD TIMES, AND TO KEEP IN TOUCH..
© 1997 United Feature Syndicate, Inc.

MARGINALLY WEIRD..
1-23
SCHULZ

MY BACK HURTS..I THINK I HAVE KINDERGARTEN STRESS..
www.unitedmedia.com

"KINDERGARTEN STRESS"?
THEY DEMAND TOO MUCH FROM US..
1-24
© 1997 United Feature Syndicate, Inc.

WE HAVE TO REMEMBER OUR NAMES AND EVERYTHING..
SCHOOL BUS
SCHULZ

YOU ARE OF NO IMPORTANCE, DID YOU KNOW THAT?
1-25
www.unitedmedia.com

YOU ARE ONLY THE TINIEST SPECK IN AN ENORMOUS UNIVERSE!

© 1997 United Feature Syndicate, Inc.

THEN I MIGHT AS WELL GO BACK TO SLEEP..
SCHULZ

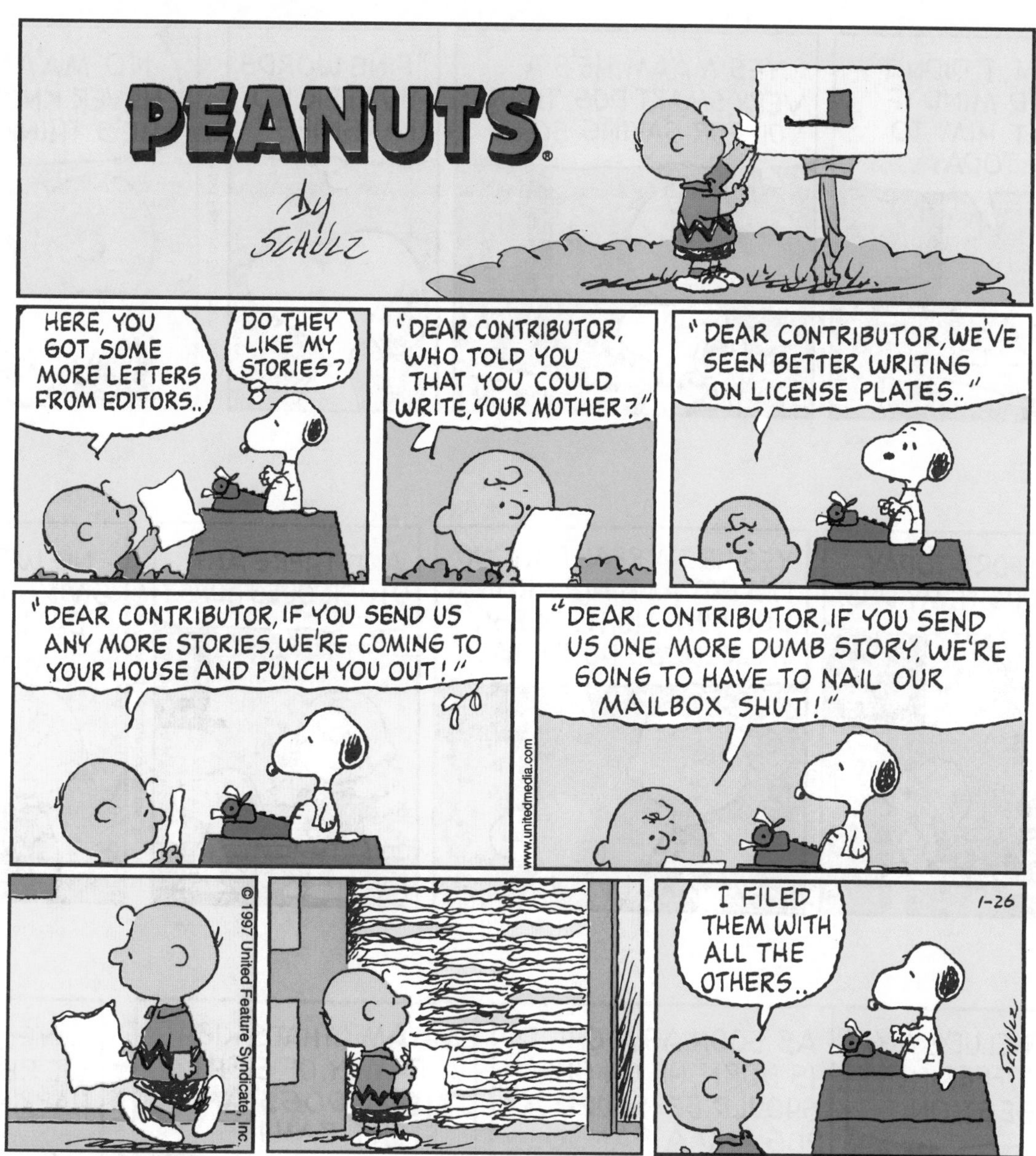
PEANUTS
By SCHULZ
HERE, YOU GOT SOME MORE LETTERS FROM EDITORS..
DO THEY LIKE MY STORIES?
"DEAR CONTRIBUTOR, WHO TOLD YOU THAT YOU COULD WRITE, YOUR MOTHER?"
"DEAR CONTRIBUTOR, WE'VE SEEN BETTER WRITING ON LICENSE PLATES.."
"DEAR CONTRIBUTOR, IF YOU SEND US ANY MORE STORIES, WE'RE COMING TO YOUR HOUSE AND PUNCH YOU OUT!"
www.unitedmedia.com
"DEAR CONTRIBUTOR, IF YOU SEND US ONE MORE DUMB STORY, WE'RE GOING TO HAVE TO NAIL OUR MAILBOX SHUT!"
© 1997 United Feature Syndicate, Inc.
1-26
I FILED THEM WITH ALL THE OTHERS..
SCHULZ

YES, MA'AM, I DIDN'T THINK YOU'D MIND IF I BROUGHT HIM TO SCHOOL TODAY..
1-27

YES, MA'AM, HE'S A VERY SMART DOG..THANK YOU FOR SAYING SO..
www.unitedmedia.com

"FINE WORDS BUTTER NO PARSNIPS"
© 1997 United Feature Syndicate, Inc.

NO, MA'AM, I NEVER KNOW WHAT HE'S THINKING..
SCHULZ

FOR MY REPORT TODAY I HAVE BROUGHT MY DOG..
www.unitedmedia.com

YES, HE'S A REAL DOG..NO, IT'S NOT A LITTLE KID IN A DOG SUIT..NO, HE DOESN'T TALK..DOGS DON'T TALK
1-28

ARE THERE ANY OTHER QUESTIONS?
© 1997 United Feature Syndicate, Inc.

NO, WE'RE NOT GIVING OUT FREE BALLOONS!
SCHULZ

AND I CONCLUDE MY REPORT BY OFFERING THIS SUGGESTION...

AS SOON AS A CHILD IS BORN, HE OR SHE SHOULD BE ISSUED A DOG AND A BANJO..
www.unitedmedia.com

MA'AM? THAT'S RIGHT.. A FAMILY OF EIGHT.. EIGHT DOGS AND EIGHT BANJOS..
1-29
© 1997 United Feature Syndicate, Inc.

YES, MA'AM.. WE'RE TALKING HAPPINESS HERE!
SCHULZ

SOME KID AT SCHOOL TODAY SAID AS SOON AS WE'RE BORN WE SHOULD BE ISSUED A DOG AND A BANJO..
THAT WAS ME..
www.unitedmedia.com

ALL MY FRIENDS THINK YOU'RE CRAZY..
YOU DON'T HAVE ANY FRIENDS..
1-30
© 1997 United Feature Syndicate, Inc.

IF I HAD ANY FRIENDS, THEY'D ALL THINK YOU WERE CRAZY..
SCHULZ

© 1997 United Feature Syndicate, Inc.
LET'S HEAR THIS AGAIN, CHARLIE BROWN..
YES, TELL US YOUR IDEA AGAIN
AS SOON AS A CHILD IS BORN, HE OR SHE IS ISSUED A DOG AND A BANJO..
WHAT GOOD WOULD THAT DO?
THE DOG COULD LEARN TO PLAY THE BANJO..
SCHULZ
1-31

THERE I WAS, SOUND ASLEEP.. SUDDENLY, I WAS PLAGUED BY A SELF DOUBT!
2-1
www.unitedmedia.com

YOU?
© 1997 United Feature Syndicate, Inc.

YOU'RE PROBABLY RIGHT..
SCHULZ

PEANUTS
by SCHULZ
© 1997 United Feature Syndicate, Inc.
www.unitedmedia.com
BEST GAME WE'VE EVER HAD!
2-2
SCHULZ

WE WERE BEHIND FORTY TO NOTHING! DID WE QUIT? NO!
www.unitedmedia.com

WE DIDN'T KNOW THE MEANING OF THE WORD "QUIT"!
2-3

"QUIT.. TO STOP OR DISCONTINUE"
© 1997 United Feature Syndicate, Inc.

WE LOST THE GAME, AND LEARNED THE MEANING OF THE WORD "QUIT"!
SCHULZ

HERE, MARCIE..SHARPEN THIS PENCIL..
www.unitedmedia.com

SHARPEN IT YOURSELF! WHO ARE YOU, THE FAIRY PRINCESS?
BOY, YOU SURE ARE CRABBY..

WELL, YOU DIDN'T SAY "PLEASE"
2-4
© 1997 United Feature Syndicate, Inc.

HERE, CRABBY.. PLEASE SHARPEN THIS PENCIL..
SCHULZ

SIR, DO YOU REALLY THINK I'VE BEEN CRABBY LATELY?

I DON'T KNOW, MARCIE.. IT SEEMS TO ME YOU'RE CRABBY ALL THE TIME..
www.unitedmedia.com
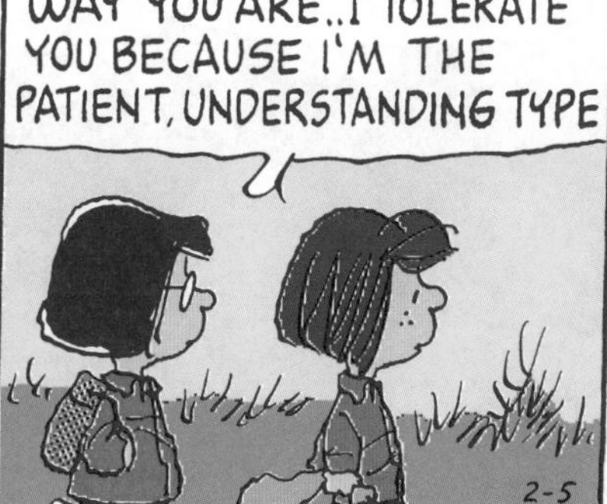
I THINK THAT'S JUST THE WAY YOU ARE..I TOLERATE YOU BECAUSE I'M THE PATIENT, UNDERSTANDING TYPE
2-5
© 1997 United Feature Syndicate, Inc.

I APPRECIATE YOUR DUMB ATTITUDE, SIR..
SCHULZ

DO YOU THINK I'M CRABBY, CHARLES?
DO I THINK YOU'RE WHAT?

CRABBY.. YOU KNOW.. ILL TEMPERED
NO, YOU'RE NOT CRABBY AT ALL..
2-6
www.unitedmedia.com

SEE?
© 1997 United Feature Syndicate, Inc.

WHAT DO YOU KNOW, CHUCK?!
SCHULZ

GOOD MORNING, CRABBY..

YOU WANT CRABBY? HERE'S CRABBY!

AAUGH!!
2-7

SCHULZ
© 1997 United Feature Syndicate, Inc.

THAT WAS FUN
YOU'RE CRABBILY WEIRD, MARCIE..

© 1997 United Feature Syndicate, Inc.
I WONDER WHAT IT WOULD BE LIKE TO GO ON A LONG TRIP..
LIKE MAYBE TO THE MOUNTAINS..
HOW COULD YOU BE SURE YOU'D HAVE A GOOD TIME?
TAKE YOUR DOG ALONG..
2-8
SCHULZ

PEANUTS
by SCHULZ
YES, MA'AM..
MY REPORT TODAY ASKS THE QUESTION, "WHERE WILL IT ALL END?"
WE ALL NEED A PHILOSOPHY.. MY OLD PHILOSOPHY WAS, "WHATEVER, WHO CARES? AND HOW SHOULD I KNOW?"
CAN A PHILOSOPHY CARRY US THROUGH TROUBLED TIMES?
© 1997 United Feature Syndicate, Inc.
www.unitedmedia.com
WHAT HAPPENS WHEN OUR PHILOSOPHY FAILS?
2-9
WE TURN TO THAT MOST ANCIENT OF DESPERATE CRIES..
"MOM!"
SCHULZ
HAVE YOU EVER HAD TWENTY-EIGHT STUDENTS AND A TEACHER LOOK AT YOU LIKE YOU'VE LOST YOUR MIND?

MY PITCHER'S MOUND MAY BE COVERED WITH SNOW, BUT THE MEMORIES ARE STILL HERE..
2-10

FORTY TO NOTHING, TWENTY TO NOTHING, FIFTY-THREE TO NOTHING, SIXTY TO NOTHING..

AND THAT GREAT GAME WHEN YOU GOT HIT ON THE HEAD BY A FLY BALL..
I DON'T REMEMBER THAT..
SCHULZ

ARE WE GONNA HAVE A BASEBALL TEAM AGAIN THIS YEAR?
2-11

YES, BUT WE WEREN'T GOING TO TELL YOU..

WE WERE ALL HOPING YOU WOULDN'T FIND OUT BECAUSE WE ALL KNOW YOU'RE THE WORST PLAYER IN THE HISTORY OF THE GAME..

PUT ME DOWN FOR RIGHT FIELD
SIGH
SCHULZ

I THINK OUR TEAM IS IN TROUBLE THIS YEAR, CHARLIE BROWN..WE'RE WEAK AT EVERY POSITION..

EXCEPT RIGHT FIELD.. SHE'S EXCEPTIONALLY CUTE..
2-12

OUR RIGHT FIELDER IS COMPLETELY HOPELESS..
BUT CUTE..
SCHULZ

HERE, I MADE YOU A VALENTINE..
www.unitedmedia.com

SEE? I WROTE A LITTLE POEM, AND THEN I DREW SOME HEARTS AROUND IT..
© 1997 United Feature Syndicate, Inc.

2-13
IT'S IN BLACK AND WHITE..
SCHULZ

IF I HOLD MY HANDS OUT LIKE THIS, YOU CAN PUT A VALENTINE RIGHT IN THEM..

OR YOU CAN STAND LIKE THAT FOR THE REST OF YOUR LIFE, AND NEVER GET ANYTHING..
© 1997 United Feature Syndicate, Inc.

IT FEELS LIKE IT MIGHT RAIN..
SCHULZ
2-14

SOMETIMES I LIE AWAKE AT NIGHT, AND A VOICE ASKS, "DID YOU TAKE YOUR PILLS?"
2-15
www.unitedmedia.com

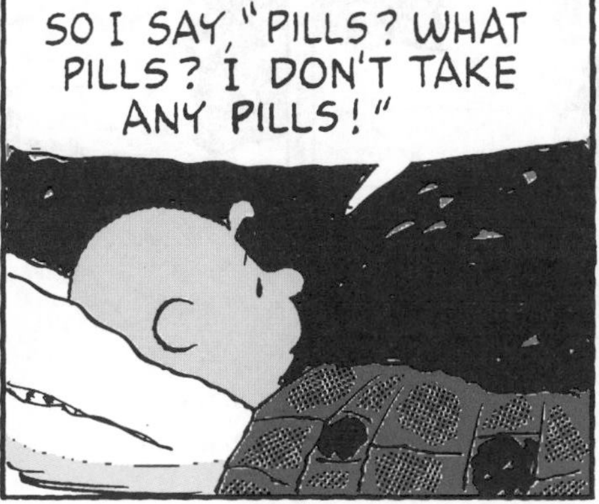
SO I SAY, "PILLS? WHAT PILLS? I DON'T TAKE ANY PILLS!"
© 1997 United Feature Syndicate, Inc.

THEN THE VOICE SAYS, "SORRY, WE CAN'T KEEP TRACK OF EVERYTHING.."
SCHULZ

PEANUTS
by SCHULZ
HERE'S THE WORLD FAMOUS PATRIOT SOLDIER AT VALLEY FORGE..
I MUST SEE GENERAL WASHINGTON!
I HAVE TO KNOW!
© 1997 United Feature Syndicate, Inc.
2-16
TELL ME, SIR! I HAVE TO KNOW! DID THE MAIL ARRIVE?
www.unitedmedia.com
DID I GET ANY VALENTINES?
SCHULZ

2-17
WELL, I'M OFF TO SCHOOL.. I'LL SEE YOU THIS AFTERNOON
© 1997 United Feature Syndicate, Inc.

IF YOU DECIDE TO GO TO THE MALL, THE KEYS ARE IN THE STATION WAGON..
www.unitedmedia.com

HE KNOWS I CAN'T SEE OVER THE STEERING WHEEL..
SCHULZ

I THINK I'VE DISCOVERED THE SECRET TO LIFE..
© 1997 United Feature Syndicate, Inc.

2-18
YOU JUST HANG AROUND UNTIL YOU GET USED TO IT..
SCHULZ

I KNOW WHEN I'M NOT WANTED!

I DON'T HAVE TO STAY HERE
2-19
www.unitedmedia.com

I CAN LEAVE, YOU KNOW!

DON'T FORGET, I'LL BE TWENTY-ONE IN ANOTHER...

..FOURTEEN YEARS!
© 1997 United Feature Syndicate, Inc.
SCHULZ

2-20
SEE? AFTER THAT, THINGS IN THE PALACE WERE NEVER THE SAME..
WHAT DO YOU THINK WENT WRONG?
THEY PROBABLY FORGOT TO FEED THE DOG..
SCHULZ
© 1997 United Feature Syndicate, Inc.

YES, SIR.. I'D LIKE TO SEE A NEW BASEBALL GLOVE..
www.unitedmedia.com

COULD I TRY THAT ONE THERE?

2-21
© 1997 United Feature Syndicate, Inc.

I'LL TAKE IT..
SCHULZ

I JUST BOUGHT A NEW BASEBALL GLOVE..
2-22
www.unitedmedia.com

I REALLY NEEDED IT.. A GOOD PLAYER NEEDS GOOD EQUIPMENT..
© 1997 United Feature Syndicate, Inc.

MAYBE IT'LL EVEN IMPROVE YOUR "WON-LOST AGAIN" AVERAGE..
SCHULZ

PEANUTS
by
SCHULZ

I'VE COME TO SEE MY SWEET BABBOO..
I'M NOT HER SWEET BABBOO!

I JUST WANT TO THANK HIM FOR THE VALENTINE..

I NEVER SENT HER A VALENTINE!

DON'T YOU KNOW SARCASM WHEN YOU HEAR IT?
© 1997 United Feature Syndicate, Inc.

TELL HER I...

TELL HER YOURSELF!

THANKS FOR THE VALENTINE..

I NEVER SENT YOU A VALENTINE..
DON'T YOU KNOW SARCASM WHEN YOU HEAR IT?
SCHULZ
2-23

DO YOU LIKE ME, CHARLES?
DO I WHAT?

"DO I WHAT?" I WALK ALL THE WAY OVER HERE TO ASK YOU A QUESTION, AND ALL YOU CAN SAY IS, "DO I WHAT?"
2-24

FORGET IT, CHARLES!
FORGET WHAT?
SCHULZ

HI, CHARLES..REMEMBER YESTERDAY WHEN I WENT TO YOUR HOUSE?
2-25

I WALKED ALL THE WAY OVER THERE TO ASK YOU IF YOU LIKE ME..

TO DO WHAT?

I CAN'T STAND IT!
SCHULZ

I WENT OVER TO SEE CHARLES YESTERDAY..
YOU DID WHAT?

"YOU DID WHAT?" I JUST TOLD YOU! WHY DO YOU ASK ME AGAIN?!
2-26

DOESN'T ANYONE TALK ANYMORE? "COOL!" "NO PROBLEM!" "WHATEVER!" "HOW Y'DOIN'?"

I'M SO DEPRESSED
YOU'RE WHAT?
SCHULZ

IT'S TOO BAD YOU CAN'T TALK, SNOOPY.. IF YOU COULD, I'LL BET YOU WOULDN'T SAY "COOL," OR "WHATEVER" OR "NO PROBLEM"
© 1997 United Feature Syndicate, Inc.

SCHULZ 2-27
I'LL BET YOU'D SAY SOMETHING REALLY WORTHWHILE..
"SOCCER MOM"

SO I'LL ASK YOU AGAIN, CHARLES..DO YOU LIKE ME?
OF COURSE, I LIKE YOU..
www.unitedmedia.com

WOW!
WELL, THERE'S THIS TV PROGRAM I'M WATCHING, SO...
© 1997 United Feature Syndicate, Inc.

SCHULZ
SO I END UP SITTING ON THE PORCH WITH A DOG..
NO PROBLEM, SWEETIE
2-28

SCHULZ
IN THE BACK ROW THERE.. LET'S TAKE THE CAP OFF, OKAY?
3-1
© 1997 United Feature Syndicate, Inc.

PEANUTS®

by SCHULZ

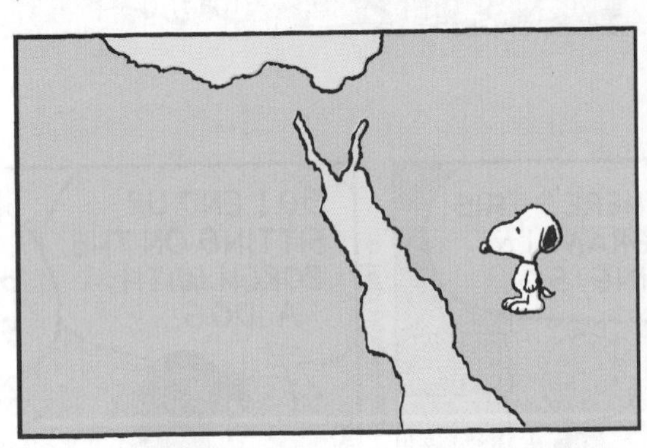

LET'S CHECK THE BOARD, AND SEE WHO YOU PLAY IN THE FIRST ROUND..

OH, NO! YOU PLAY "CRYBABY" BOOBIE! SHE'S THE BIGGEST COMPLAINER AROUND
www.unitedmedia.com

3-3
IT'S TOO COLD TO PLAY TODAY! YESTERDAY IT WAS TOO HOT! THE NET IS TOO HIGH! MY LEG HURTS! MY ELBOW HURTS!
I PROBABLY SHOULD KICK HER.. DOGS ARE ALLOWED TO KICK PEOPLE..
© 1997 United Feature Syndicate, Inc.
SCHULZ

WHAT'S GOING ON?
THIS IS THE FIRST MATCH..SNOOPY'S PLAYING "CRYBABY" BOOBIE..
© 1997 United Feature Syndicate, Inc.

3-4
WHOSE SERVE IS IT? I CAN'T SERVE IN THE SUN! I'LL RECEIVE! THE NET LOOKS TOO HIGH! MY KNEE HURTS! MY EARS HURT!
I THINK I'LL KICK HER..DOGS ARE ALLOWED TO KICK PEOPLE..
SCHULZ

WHO'S AHEAD NOW?
I'M NOT SURE..
www.unitedmedia.com

OUT! THAT BALL WAS OUT!

I CALLED IT OUT BECAUSE I SAW IT OUT SO I CALLED IT OUT! IT WAS WAY OUT!
© 1997 United Feature Syndicate, Inc.

SHOULD I JUMP OVER THE NET AND KICK HER, OR RUN AROUND THE NET AND KICK HER?

SCHULZ

3-5

OUT! THAT BALL WAS OUT! WAY OUT!
3-6

LONG! WAY LONG! WIDE AND LONG! WAY OUT!
www.unitedmedia.com

LONG! OUT! WAY OUT! OUT! OUT!
© 1997 United Feature Syndicate, Inc.

LET ME KNOW IF I EVER GET ONE IN..
SCHULZ

OUT! OUT!
3-7

THAT WAS OUT, WASN'T IT, MOM?
www.unitedmedia.com

MOM SAID IT WAS OUT!
© 1997 United Feature Syndicate, Inc.

MY MOM WOULD HAVE CALLED IT "IN".
SCHULZ

ANOTHER LOB!
3-8
www.unitedmedia.com

I HATE PLAYING SOMEONE WHO LOBS ALL THE TIME!
© 1997 United Feature Syndicate, Inc.

THAT WASN'T A LOB.. THAT WAS MY OVERHEAD SMASH!
SCHULZ

PEANUTS
by SCHULZ

WOW! I'M SO TANGLED UP I CAN'T MOVE! COULD YOU GO FOR HELP?
3-9

WAIT A MINUTE..WHAT I NEED MORE THAN ANYTHING IS A DRINK OF WATER..
www.unitedmedia.com

I HATE TO SAY THIS, BUT I DON'T THINK I CAN DRINK OUT OF A DOG DISH..

© 1997 United Feature Syndicate, Inc.

SCHULZ

I WON! I WON! I'M THE CHAMPION! I WON!!
www.unitedmedia.com

HEY, MOM! I WON!!

3-10
© 1997 United Feature Syndicate, Inc.

MOM! I THINK THAT DOG KICKED ME!
SCHULZ

I LIKE DOING WATERCOLORS
I HATE IT.. IT'S TOO HARD..
www.unitedmedia.com

NO, MA'AM.. I HAVEN'T STARTED YET.. I DON'T HAVE ANY WATER..
SCHULZ
© 1997 United Feature Syndicate, Inc.

3-11
I DRANK IT..

DO YOU HAVE A PENCIL I CAN BORROW, MARCIE?
www.unitedmedia.com

AND MAYBE SOME PAPER, AND AN ERASER, AND A RULER, AND YOUR MATH BOOK, AND...
© 1997 United Feature Syndicate, Inc.
SCHULZ

MARCIE!
3-12

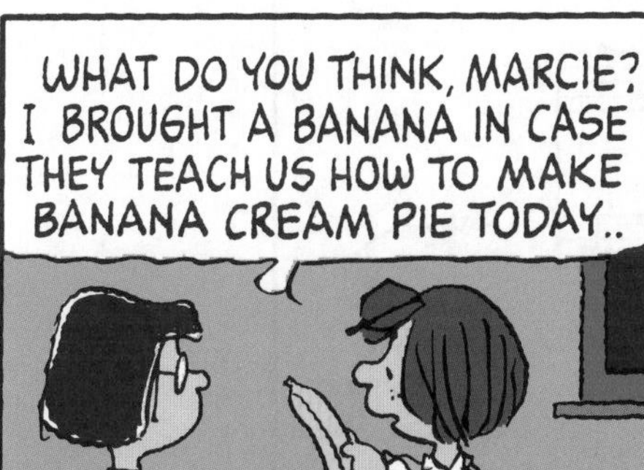
WHAT DO YOU THINK, MARCIE? I BROUGHT A BANANA IN CASE THEY TEACH US HOW TO MAKE BANANA CREAM PIE TODAY..
3-13

WE DON'T HAVE COOKING CLASSES, SIR..
WE DON'T?
www.unitedmedia.com

SUGGESTION TIME, MA'AM..LET'S FORGET THE MATH, AND CONCENTRATE ON BANANA CREAM PIE..
© 1997 United Feature Syndicate, Inc.

YOU'RE BECOMING INCREASINGLY WEIRD, SIR..
SCHULZ

I'M NOT GOING TO SCHOOL ANYMORE.. THE TEACHER HATES ME, THE PRINCIPAL HATES ME, THE CUSTODIAN HATES ME, THE SCHOOL BOARD HATES ME...

3-14
www.unitedmedia.com

YOU'D BETTER GET DRESSED..YOU'LL MISS THE SCHOOL BUS..
© 1997 United Feature Syndicate, Inc.

SCHULZ
THE BUS DRIVER HATES ME!

www.unitedmedia.com

3-15

© 1997 United Feature Syndicate, Inc.

SCHULZ

PEANUTS
by SCHULZ

WHAT IS?
IT'S CALLED "PEANUTS GALLERY"

A NEW PIECE COMPOSED BY ELLEN TAAFFE ZWILICH.. WE'RE ALL IN IT!
WHAT DO YOU MEAN, WE'RE ALL IN IT?

IT HAS A GREAT BEGINNING.. "SCHROEDER'S BEETHOVEN FANTASY.."

THEN THERE'S "LULLABY FOR LINUS," "SNOOPY DOES THE SAMBA," AND "CHARLIE BROWN'S LAMENT.."

www.unitedmedia.com

THEN THERE'S "LUCY FREAKS OUT" AND "PEPPERMINT PATTY AND MARCIE LEAD THE PARADE"!

3-16

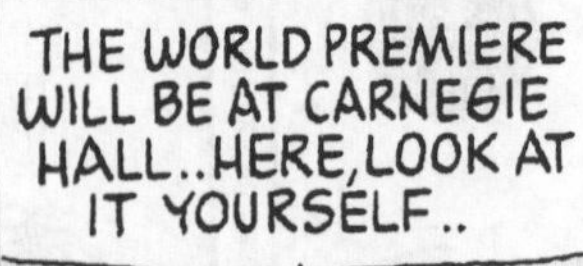
THE WORLD PREMIERE WILL BE AT CARNEGIE HALL..HERE, LOOK AT IT YOURSELF..

© 1997 United Feature Syndicate, Inc.

MY PART SHOULD BE LONGER..
SCHULZ

A NEW SEASON! THIS IS WHERE I BELONG! THIS IS MY LIFE!
www.unitedmedia.com

I STAND HERE LIKE THE CAPTAIN OF A SHIP!
3-17

NOTHING CAN SINK THIS VESSEL EXCEPT...

HI, MANAGER! I'M READY TO GO!
© 1997 United Feature Syndicate, Inc.

..AN ICEBERG!
SCHULZ

"PIGPEN," I DON'T UNDERSTAND YOU..
www.unitedmedia.com

THIS IS THE FIRST INNING OF OUR FIRST GAME, AND YOU'RE ALREADY COVERED WITH DIRT..
3-18
© 1997 United Feature Syndicate, Inc.

THIS ISN'T ALL FROM TODAY.. SOME OF IT'S LEFT OVER FROM LAST YEAR..
SCHULZ

DO ME A FAVOR..GO ASK "PIGPEN" WHY HE DOESN'T WEAR A BASEBALL CAP..
www.unitedmedia.com

THE MANAGER WANTS TO KNOW WHY YOU DON'T WEAR A CAP..
© 1997 United Feature Syndicate, Inc.

HE SAID HE DOESN'T WANT TO MUSS UP HIS HAIR..
SCHULZ
3-19

"PIGPEN," WHY CAN'T YOU LOOK NEAT LIKE THE OTHER PLAYERS?
www.unitedmedia.com

3-20
LAST YEAR I BATTED .712
© 1997 United Feature Syndicate, Inc.

NEATNESS DOESN'T BAT .712 !
SCHULZ

WAP!

www.unitedmedia.com

© 1997 United Feature Syndicate, Inc.

3-21
"PIGPEN" SLIDES INTO HOME! HE'S SAFE! HE'S GETTING UP! HE'S DUSTING HIMSELF OFF..
WHY?
SCHULZ

REMEMBER, IF A FLY BALL COMES YOUR WAY, DON'T FORGET TO ALLOW FOR THE WIND!

© 1997 United Feature Syndicate, Inc.

www.unitedmedia.com

3-22
I'M WORKING ON IT!
SCHULZ

PEANUTS®
by SCHULZ
YAWN

© 1997 United Feature Syndicate, Inc.

CLOMP!

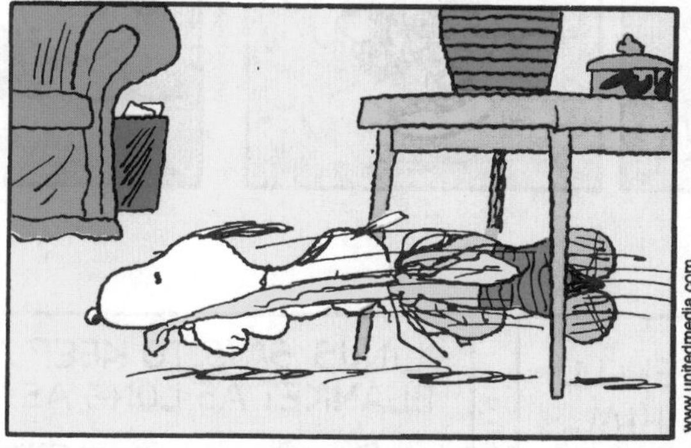
www.unitedmedia.com

3-23

STUPID DOG!
SCHULZ

WE HAVE A MATH TEST TODAY..
I'M NOT WORRIED
U.S. MAI
www.unitedmedia.com

AND THEN A HISTORY TEST AND A SPELLING TEST..
I'M NOT WORRIED
3-24
© 1997 United Feature Syndicate, Inc.

AND AFTER SCHOOL, OUR FIRST GAME..
NOW I'M WORRIED
SCHULZ

WHEN YOU LOSE THE FIRST GAME OF THE SEASON, IT'S A LONG WALK HOME..
3-25
www.unitedmedia.com

IF ANYTHING GETS IN YOUR WAY, YOU JUST WANT TO KICK IT!

© 1997 United Feature Syndicate, Inc.

THEN YOU DISCOVER YOU CAN'T EVEN KICK GOOD..
SCHULZ

YES, I HEARD YOU LOST THE FIRST GAME OF THE SEASON..

I'VE NEVER SEEN MY BIG BROTHER SO DEPRESSED..
www.unitedmedia.com

SURE, I'LL TELL HIM..
© 1997 United Feature Syndicate, Inc.

LINUS SAYS TO KEEP THE BLANKET AS LONG AS YOU WANT..
SCHULZ
3-26

I'M SORRY, CHARLIE BROWN.. I HAVE TO TAKE MY BLANKET BACK..
I DON'T KNOW WHERE IT IS..
3-27
www.unitedmedia.com

YOU DON'T KNOW WHERE IT IS?!!
© 1997 United Feature Syndicate, Inc.

I'D BETTER LEAVE... DOGS GET BLAMED FOR EVERYTHING..
SCHULZ

YOU WERE DEPRESSED SO I LENT YOU MY BLANKET..
www.unitedmedia.com

AND NOW YOU SAY YOU DON'T KNOW WHERE IT IS?!!
3-28

HOW COULD YOU DO THIS TO ME?!
© 1997 United Feature Syndicate, Inc.

POOR SWEET BABBOO..
I'M NOT YOUR SWEET BABBOO!
SCHULZ

LINUS! I FOUND YOUR BLANKET! IT WAS BEHIND THE COUCH!
www.unitedmedia.com

WOW! WHAT A RELIEF! I'LL NEVER LET GO OF IT AGAIN!
© 1997 United Feature Syndicate, Inc.

CLOMP!
GOOD THINKING!
SCHULZ
3-29

PEANUTS®

by SCHULZ

HELLO? THIS IS "RERUN.." OH, HI, GRAMMA.. HOW ARE YOU?
3-31

I'M FINE, THANK YOU.. KINDERGARTEN?
www.unitedmedia.com
© 1997 United Feature Syndicate, Inc.

YES, I'M DOING FINE KINDERGARTENWISE..
SCHULZ

YOU KNOW WHAT I'D LIKE TO DO? I'D LIKE TO TELL YOU THAT THE LITTLE RED-HAIRED GIRL IS AT THE DOOR, AND THEN, WHEN YOU RUN TO SEE HER, I'D YELL, "APRIL FOOL!"

THAT'S WHAT I'D REALLY LIKE TO DO..
4-1
www.unitedmedia.com

BY THE WAY, THERE'S A GIANT LIZARD CRAWLING UP YOUR BACK..
AAUGH!
© 1997 United Feature Syndicate, Inc.

APRIL FOOL!
SCHULZ

I HEAR YOU MADE AN IMPASSIONED SPEECH TO THE JURY YESTERDAY..
4-2
© 1997 United Feature Syndicate, Inc.

DID IT BRING TEARS TO THEIR EYES?
NO, THEY FELL ASLEEP
SCHULZ

4-3

AAUGH!!
www.unitedmedia.com
© 1997 United Feature Syndicate, Inc.

WHAT'D YOU DO THAT FOR?!
I DIDN'T MEAN TO.. IT WAS A DOG THING..
SCHULZ

4-4
www.unitedmedia.com

I HATE TO TELL YOU THIS, MA'AM, BUT THE ROOF IS LEAKING AGAIN..

NO, I CAN'T GIVE YOU MY HOMEWORK BECAUSE IT'S IN MY BINDER WHICH IS KEEPING ME FROM DROWNING..

© 1997 United Feature Syndicate, Inc.
WHEN YOU SIGH, MA'AM, IT REMINDS ME OF A BREEZE WEAVING ITS WAY THROUGH THE PINES..
SCHULZ

..AND WHEN AN ACTIVITY GETS OUT OF HAND, IT CAN BECOME A COMPULSION..
PSYCHIATRIC HELP 5¢
THE DOCTOR IS IN
ANYONE FOR "OLD MAID"? ONE MORE GAME? ANYONE? COME ON.. ANYONE?
© 1997 United Feature Syndicate, Inc.
SCHULZ
4-5

She called him "cute"
PEANUTS®
by SCHULZ

© 1997 United Feature Syndicate, Inc.
She called him "adorable,"

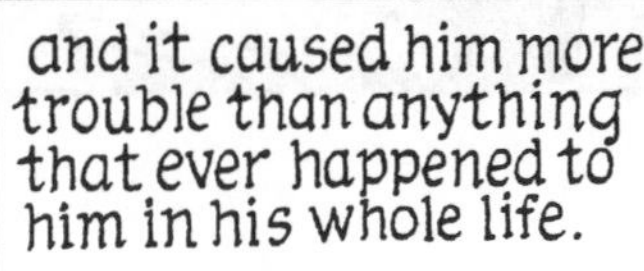
and it caused him more trouble than anything that ever happened to him in his whole life.

"adorable" HMM..

THAT'S A PRETTY GOOD BEGINNING..
4-6
www.unitedmedia.com

A GOOD BEGINNING IS VERY IMPORTANT..

I LIKE A GOOD BEGINNING..

THIS ISN'T THE BEGINNING.. THIS IS THE ENDING!
SCHULZ

YES, MA'AM, I THINK OUR ROOF IS LEAKING AGAIN..
4-7
www.unitedmedia.com

IS IT KEEPING ME AWAKE?
© 1997 United Feature Syndicate, Inc.

SARCASM DOES NOT BECOME YOU, MA'AM..
SCHULZ

SIR, THE ROOF IS LEAKING AGAIN, AND YOU'RE GETTING ALL WET..
www.unitedmedia.com

I DON'T LIKE TO COMPLAIN, MARCIE..
4-8

THEN I'LL DO IT FOR YOU!

WE WERE JUST WONDERING, MA'AM, IF PERCHANCE YOU MIGHT HAVE NOTICED...
© 1997 United Feature Syndicate, Inc.

THE ROOF IS LEAKING!
SCHULZ

THIS IS HOW IT IS, MR. PRINCIPAL..

HALF THE KIDS IN OUR CLASS CAN'T READ, AND HALF CAN'T MULTIPLY 6X8..
www.unitedmedia.com

NONE OF THEM EVER HEARD OF BOSNIA, AND COULDN'T TELL YOU WHO WROTE "HAMLET"

4-9

I TALKED TO THE PRINCIPAL, SIR..
WHAT'D HE SAY ABOUT THE ROOF LEAKING?
© 1997 United Feature Syndicate, Inc.

I FORGOT TO MENTION IT..
SCHULZ

GOOD NEWS, SIR.. THE PRINCIPAL ASKED THE CUSTODIAN TO CLIMB UP, AND FIX THE LEAK IN THE ROOF..
4-10

HOWEVER, YOU MAY HAVE TO WAIT A WHILE LONGER...

THE CUSTODIAN FELL OFF THE ROOF!
SCHULZ

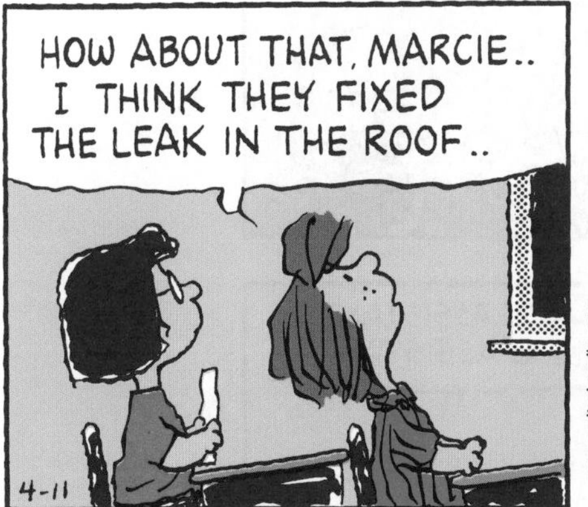
HOW ABOUT THAT, MARCIE.. I THINK THEY FIXED THE LEAK IN THE ROOF..
4-11

LET'S JUST HOPE THERE AREN'T SOME OTHER PLACES WHERE...

SCHULZ

IT'S A WATER DISH.. WHAT DID YOU THINK IT WAS?
?

SURE, GO AHEAD.. HAVE A DRINK..
4-12

NO, I DON'T HAVE ANY PAPER CUPS..
SCHULZ

PEANUTS
by SCHULZ

YOUR JOB WILL BE TO HOLD THE KITE..

DOES MY JOB HAVE A TITLE?
© 1997 United Feature Syndicate, Inc.

CALL YOURSELF ANYTHING YOU WANT.. JUST LET GO OF THE KITE AFTER I START RUNNING..

I CAN BE THE "KITE ASSISTANT."
www.unitedmedia.com

OR MAYBE "HEAD KITE ASSISTANT.." OR EVEN "CHIEF KITE ASSISTANT.."

RIP!
4-13

HOW ABOUT "EX-KITE ASSISTANT FOURTH CLASS"?
I CAN'T STAND IT! I JUST CAN'T STAND IT!
SCHULZ

IF SHE READS TO US AGAIN ABOUT DICK AND JANE, I'LL GO CRAZY..
4-14

YES, MA'AM, I THINK THE CLASS MIGHT LIKE TO HEAR THE PART WHERE ANNA KARENINA THROWS HERSELF UNDER THE TRAIN..

ALL RIGHT, LET'S HEAR HOW DICK AND JANE ARE DOING..

I HAVE ANOTHER NEW PHILOSOPHY..

"WHAT DID YOU EXPECT, A MEDAL?"
4-15

SOME PHILOSOPHIES TAKE A THOUSAND YEARS..I THINK OF THEM IN TWO MINUTES..

ALL RIGHT, WHO TOOK THE LAST COOKIE?!

IN FACT, WHO TOOK THE FIRST COOKIE?!

4-16
I TOOK THE TWELFTH ONE..

NATURE HIKES ARE IMPORTANT..

THEY'RE IMPORTANT BECAUSE WE NEED TO BE ACQUAINTED WITH OUR SURROUNDINGS
4-17
www.unitedmedia.com

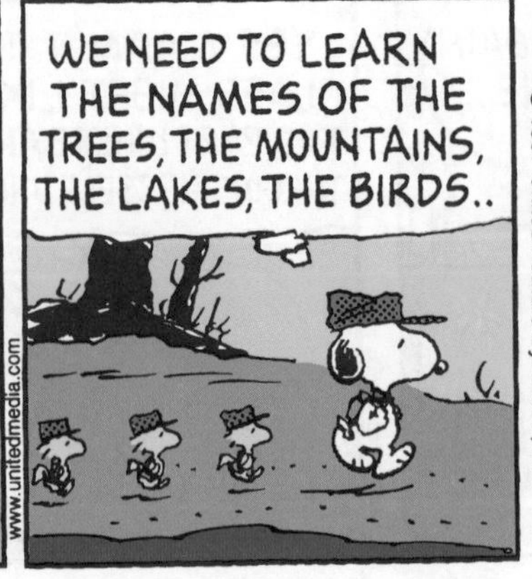
WE NEED TO LEARN THE NAMES OF THE TREES, THE MOUNTAINS, THE LAKES, THE BIRDS..
© 1997 United Feature Syndicate, Inc.

YES, I KNOW YOUR NAME IS "BILL"
SCHULZ

GUESS WHAT..IN KINDERGARTEN TODAY WE LEARNED TO TIE OUR SHOES..
www.unitedmedia.com

I THINK I'M PRETTY GOOD AT IT..I'M A FAST LEARNER
© 1997 United Feature Syndicate, Inc.

4-18
THOSE AREN'T YOUR SHOES!
SCHULZ

JUST CHECKING IN, MANAGER..
4-19
www.unitedmedia.com

JUST LETTING YOU KNOW EVERYTHING IS TAKEN CARE OF OUT IN RIGHT FIELD..
© 1997 United Feature Syndicate, Inc.

I ABSOLUTELY REFUSE TO ASK WHAT THAT'S ALL ABOUT..
SCHULZ

RING
PEANUTS
by SCHULZ
RATS!
IT'S PROBABLY THE ROUND-HEADED KID..

SALLY? I'M SPENDING THE NIGHT HERE AT LINUS' HOUSE..

WELL, I FED YOUR DOG LIKE YOU ASKED

WHEN YOU PUT HIM OUTSIDE FOR THE NIGHT, GIVE HIM A HUG, AND SAY, "SLEEP TIGHT"

AND THEN SAY, "MAY A HOST OF ANGELS DANCE AT YOUR FEET.."
4-20
www.unitedmedia.com

SLEEP TIGHT..MAY A HOST OF ANGELS DANCE AT YOUR FEET..

© 1997 United Feature Syndicate, Inc.

THIS IS GOING TO BE A LONG NIGHT..
SCHULZ

4-21
© 1997 United Feature Syndicate, Inc.
SEE? I'M DRAWING A LANDSCAPE..
IT NEEDS A WATERFALL, AND A MOUNTAIN, AND A DEER STANDING IN A MEADOW, AND A SUNSET, AND A TINY LOG CABIN, AND A STREAM WITH A TROUT JUMPING OUT OF THE WATER..
AND A BORDER COLLIE HERDING SOME SHEEP..
SCHULZ

It was a dark and stormy night.

www.unitedmedia.com

NO, NOT AGAIN..
4-22

© 1997 United Feature Syndicate, Inc.

It was one of those dark nights when you weren't sure if it was going to be stormy or not.
SCHULZ

Gentlemen,
Enclosed please find my latest short story.

4-23
www.unitedmedia.com

U.S. MAIL
© 1997 United Feature Syndicate, Inc.

SCHULZ
U.S. MAIL

NO, MA'AM, I RAISED MY LEFT HAND..

WHEN I RAISE MY LEFT HAND, IT MEANS I'M NOT SURE, BUT WHEN I RAISE MY RIGHT HAND, IT MEANS I'M SURE..
4-24
www.unitedmedia.com

SEE? THIS TIME I RAISED MY LEFT HAND..
© 1997 United Feature Syndicate, Inc.

MA'AM, WHERE ARE YOU GOING? COME BACK!
SCHULZ

HERE YOU ARE, SIR... ENJOY YOUR MEAL..
4-25

www.unitedmedia.com

SIGH
© 1997 United Feature Syndicate, Inc.

DOGS DON'T GIVE TIPS..
SCHULZ

DON'T FEEL BAD.. I'LL GET ONE FOR YOU TOMORROW..
4-26
© 1997 United Feature Syndicate, Inc.
SCHULZ

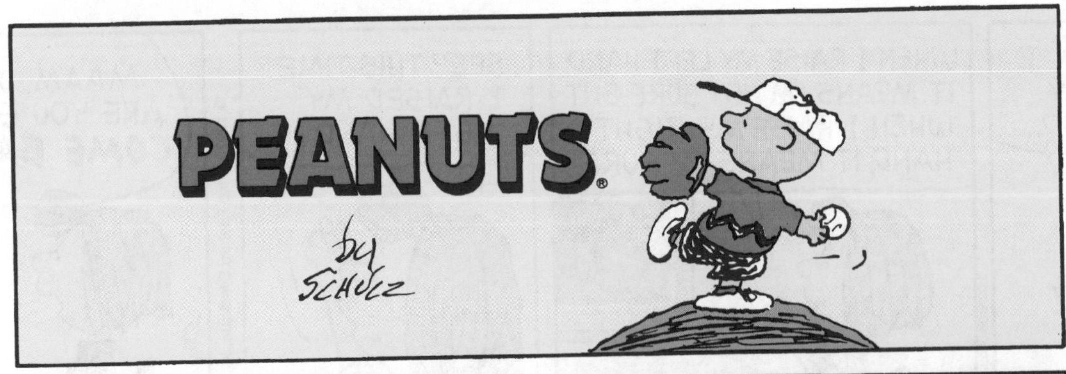
PEANUTS®
by SCHULZ

© 1997 United Feature Syndicate, Inc.

4-27
www.unitedmedia.com

WHY CAN'T I HAVE A NORMAL TEAM LIKE EVERYONE ELSE?
SCHULZ

YES, MA'AM..READ US AGAIN ABOUT THE CLUMSY KID WHO FELL DOWN THE RABBIT HOLE..

"ALICE"
AND ABOUT THE CHESAPEAKE CAT..
© 1997 United Feature Syndicate, Inc.
www.unitedmedia.com

"CHESHIRE"
AND ABOUT HOW SHE MET TIGER WOODS..
4-28

SHE NEVER MET TIGER WOODS..
READ US ANYTHING YOU WANT, MA'AM..
SCHULZ

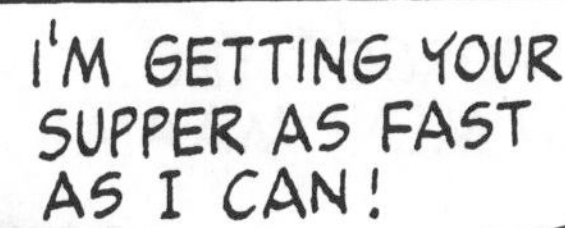
I'M GETTING YOUR SUPPER AS FAST AS I CAN!

www.unitedmedia.com

I KNOW YOU'RE HUNGRY, BUT YOU DON'T HAVE TO BREAK THE DOOR DOWN!
4-29

© 1997 United Feature Syndicate, Inc.
SCHULZ

I DON'T THINK I SHOULD GO TO SCHOOL ANYMORE..

INSTEAD OF GETTING SMARTER, I'M GETTING DUMBER EVERY DAY..
www.unitedmedia.com
© 1997 United Feature Syndicate, Inc.

4-30
I FIGURE IN ABOUT ONE MORE MONTH I'LL BOTTOM OUT..
SCHULZ

YOU GOT HERE FAST.. WHEN DID YOU LEAVE?
www.unitedmedia.com

THE BIG WING WAS ON TWO, AND THE SMALL WING WAS ON NINE?
5-1
© 1997 United Feature Syndicate, Inc.

SOMEDAY YOU SHOULD LEARN TO TELL TIME..
SCHULZ

FLOWERS FOR THE TEACHER?
www.unitedmedia.com

WHAT ARE YOU TRYING TO DO, MARCIE, GET TO BE AN OFFICER?
5-2
© 1997 United Feature Syndicate, Inc.

DON'T FORGET THE ENLISTED MEN, MA'AM..
SCHULZ

© 1997 United Feature Syndicate, Inc.
BEETHOVEN COULD HAVE GOT MORE WORK DONE IF HE HADN'T HAD TO WORRY ABOUT HIS NEPHEW..
I DIDN'T HAVE ANY COLD CEREAL THIS MORNING BECAUSE MY STUPID BROTHER USED UP ALL THE MILK!
5-3

www.unitedmedia.com
WHAT DO BALL PLAYERS TALK ABOUT WHEN THEY MEET OUT ON THE MOUND?
DON'T ASK!
SCHULZ

PEANUTS
by SCHULZ

SO THIS LADY STOPS HER CAR, LEANS OUT THE WINDOW, AND ASKS ME WHERE I GOT THESE NICE SHOES...

I WANTED TO TELL HER THAT MY WEALTHY FRIEND, MICKEY MOUSE, GAVE THEM TO ME..

HOWEVER, SHE DROVE AWAY BEFORE I COULD SAY ANYTHING, WHICH I COULDN'T ANYWAY BECAUSE DOGS CAN'T TALK..
5-4

MICKEY THINKS HE CAN TALK, BUT HE REALLY CAN'T..
© 1997 United Feature Syndicate, Inc.

HIS VOICE IS DUBBED IN..
www.unitedmedia.com
SCHULZ

MY LIFE IS LIKE A COLORING BOOK! EACH DAY I HAVE A NEW PAGE WITH NEW PICTURES TO COLOR..

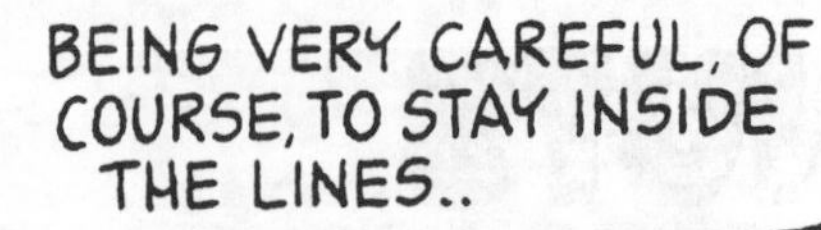

BEING VERY CAREFUL, OF COURSE, TO STAY INSIDE THE LINES..

MY LIFE IS LIKE A MESSY COLORING BOOK..
SCHULZ
5-5

IT IS DAWN..HERE'S THE WORLD WAR I FLYING ACE WALKING OUT ONTO THE AERODROME...

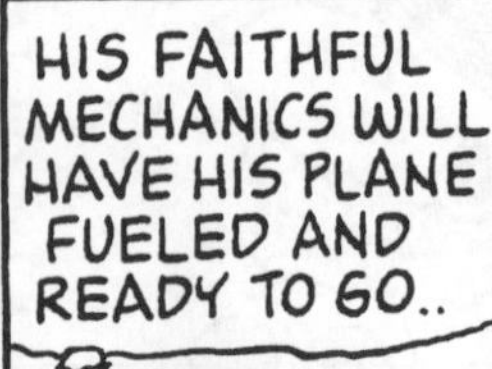

HIS FAITHFUL MECHANICS WILL HAVE HIS PLANE FUELED AND READY TO GO..

HE KNOWS THEY WILL THINK OF NOTHING ELSE UNTIL HE RETURNS

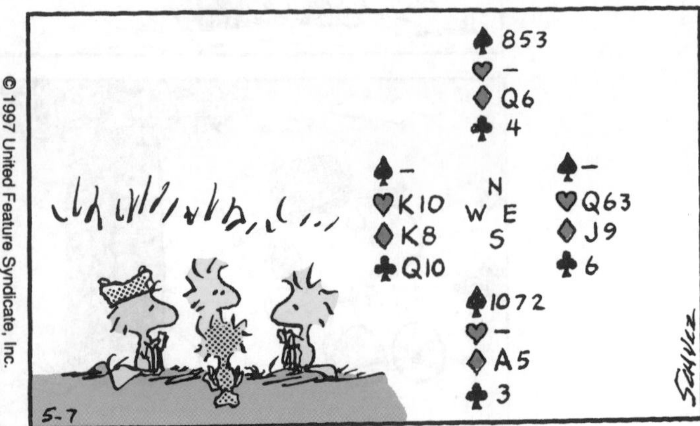

AS SOON AS THEY FINISH PLAYING THIS HAND..

HERE'S THE WORLD WAR I FLYING ACE RETURNING TO THE AERODROME...

HE KNOWS HIS FAITHFUL MECHANICS WILL JUMP UP AND DOWN AND CHEER WHEN THEY SEE HIM LAND..
© 1997 United Feature Syndicate, Inc.

5-8
♠K10 7
♥984
♦AJ108
♣Q73
♠J43
♥AQ10763
♦—
♣K1096
N
W E
S
♠82
♥J
♦Q7652
♣J8542
♠AQ965
♥K52
♦K943
♣A
SCHULZ

WHAT KIND OF FAITHFUL MECHANICS ARE YOU?!
5-9

THERE I WAS, OFF FIGHTING THE RED BARON, WHILE YOU GUYS WERE PLAYING BRIDGE!
www.unitedmedia.com

WHAT DO YOU HAVE TO SAY FOR YOURSELVES?
© 1997 United Feature Syndicate, Inc.

?
WELL, WITH THREE KINGS, I'D HAVE GONE RIGHT TO SIX SPADES..
SCHULZ

SOMETIMES I LIE AWAKE AT NIGHT, AND I ASK, "DOES ANYONE REMEMBER ME?"
5-10
© 1997 United Feature Syndicate, Inc.

THEN A VOICE COMES TO ME OUT OF THE DARK THAT SAYS, "SURE, FRANK, WE REMEMBER YOU"
SCHULZ

PEANUTS
by SCHULZ

SAY WE'VE BEEN MARRIED FOR ABOUT SIX MONTHS...

AND LET'S SAY I'VE MADE A BEAUTIFUL TUNA CASSEROLE FOR DINNER...

YOU WALK INTO THE KITCHEN, AND YOU SAY, "WHAT, TUNA CASSEROLE AGAIN?"
© 1997 United Feature Syndicate, Inc.

I'D NEVER SAY THAT..
THEN I SAY, "I WORKED HARD MAKING THIS CASSEROLE, BUT ALL YOU CARE ABOUT IS THAT STUPID PIANO!"
5-11

THEN YOU WALK OUT..
www.unitedmedia.com

SORRY I'M LATE..I GOT INVOLVED IN A MARITAL DISPUTE..

I NEVER KNOW WHAT ANYONE IS TALKING ABOUT..
SCHULZ

I NEED HELP WITH MY HOMEWORK..
www.unitedmedia.com

WE ALL NEED HELP WITH OUR HOMEWORK..WE'RE ALL PLEADING FOR SOMEONE TO LISTEN..WE'RE ALL DESPERATE
5-12
© 1997 United Feature Syndicate, Inc.

I LIVE IN THE WRONG HOUSE..
SCHULZ

NO, THAT'S NOT A STAR..IT'S A COMET..
5-13
www.unitedmedia.com

?
HOW DO I KNOW? IT SAYS SO ON THE SIDE..
© 1997 United Feature Syndicate, Inc.

HE NEVER BELIEVES ANYTHING I TELL HIM..
SCHULZ

COME ON, CHARLIE BROWN, STRIKE THIS GUY OUT! YOU CAN DO IT!
www.unitedmedia.com

5-14

© 1997 United Feature Syndicate, Inc.

WHAT CAN I SAY?
SCHULZ

YES, MA'AM.. I'M WRITING A STORY..

IT'S ABOUT THIS KID WHO'S IN KINDERGARTEN, AND HOW THE STRESS IS SLOWLY DESTROYING HIM..

EVERY MORNING HE...

MA'AM?
5-15
© 1997 United Feature Syndicate, Inc.

WELL, I HAVE ANOTHER ONE HERE ABOUT SOME PURPLE BUNNIES..
SCHULZ

SOMEWHERE IN THIS GREAT CITY THERE HAS TO BE A MAILBOX WITH A LOVE LETTER FOR ME

BUT THIS ISN'T IT..
www.unitedmedia.com

STUPID MAILBOX!
5-16
© 1997 United Feature Syndicate, Inc.

STUPID KID!
SCHULZ

OKAY, LUCY, STAND WAY BACK THERE BY THOSE BUSHES..
5-17

I'M GONNA HIT YOU A FLY BALL..
www.unitedmedia.com

TRY TO GET IT BACK AS FAST AS YOU CAN
© 1997 United Feature Syndicate, Inc.

IT'S IN HERE SOMEPLACE..
SCHULZ

PEANUTS
SCHULZ

© 1997 United Feature Syndicate, Inc.

www.unitedmedia.com

5-18

LIKE I'VE SAID BEFORE, NEVER TAKE A SHORTCUT THROUGH A MINIATURE GOLF COURSE..
SCHULZ

NO, MA'AM, BUT I CAN MAKE A WILD GUESS...
5-19

"ZEBRAS"! I'LL SAY "ZEBRAS"!

SIR, THE ANSWER IS "TWELVE."

"TWELVE ZEBRAS"!
SCHULZ

HERE'S THE WORLD FAMOUS PATRIOT SOLDIER STANDING GUARD AT VALLEY FORGE..
5-20

"THESE ARE THE TIMES THAT TRY MEN'S SOULS"

TO PUT IT ANOTHER WAY, "I HOPE I MAKE THE CUT"
SCHULZ

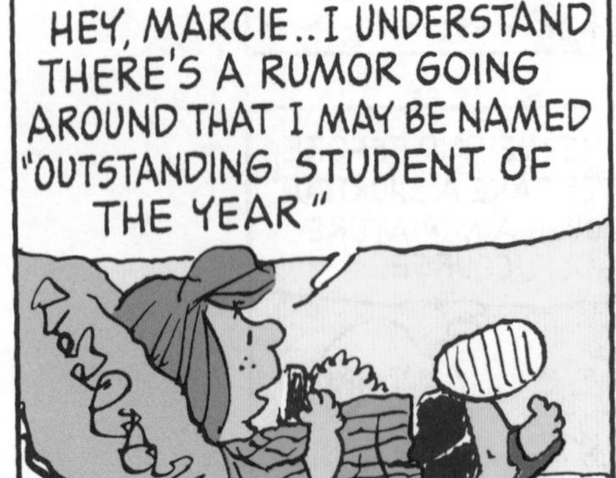
HEY, MARCIE.. I UNDERSTAND THERE'S A RUMOR GOING AROUND THAT I MAY BE NAMED "OUTSTANDING STUDENT OF THE YEAR"

THAT'S INTERESTING, SIR.. I HEARD ANOTHER RUMOR THAT THE MOON IS GOING TO FALL OUT OF THE SKY..

5-21

I'M HANGING UP, MARCIE..
SCHULZ

MORALE IS LOW AT VALLEY FORGE..
5-22

THE TROOPS ARE HUNGRY.. NOTHING TO EAT BUT FIRECAKE AND WATER..
www.unitedmedia.com

AND THIS MORNING GENERAL WASHINGTON GAVE US MORE BAD NEWS...

WE'RE ALL OUT OF GRAPE JELLY!
© 1997 United Feature Syndicate, Inc.
SCHULZ

SEE, MARCIE? HERE ARE THE NAMES OF EVERYONE WHO'S UP FOR "OUTSTANDING STUDENT OF THE YEAR"... THERE'S MY NAME, SEE?
I COUNTED THEM, SIR.. YOU'RE FOUR HUNDREDTH ON THE LIST..
www.unitedmedia.com

FOUR HUNDREDTH AND MOVING UP FAST!
© 1997 United Feature Syndicate, Inc.
SCHULZ
5-23

I NEED HELP WITH MY HOMEWORK..
AGAIN?

5-24
I HOPE YOU APPRECIATE THIS..
www.unitedmedia.com

CALL ME IF YOU EVER NEED YOUR SHOES TIED..
© 1997 United Feature Syndicate, Inc.
SCHULZ

PEANUTS
by SCHULZ

FLY? SURE, I KNOW BIRDS CAN FLY..

WHAT'S SO GREAT ABOUT THAT?

DOGS CAN DO A LOT OF THINGS BIRDS CAN'T DO..

DOGS CAN BARK!
© 1997 United Feature Syndicate, Inc.

5-25

www.unitedmedia.com

WOOF!
SCHULZ

IT'S ANOTHER COLD DAY AT VALLEY FORGE..I'VE BAKED GENERAL WASHINGTON A PIECE OF FIRECAKE..
5-26
www.unitedmedia.com

HE SAYS TO ME, "WHERE'S THE GRAPE JELLY?" I TELL HIM WE HAVEN'T HAD GRAPE JELLY FOR SIX WEEKS..

THEN HE SAYS, "CAN'T SOMEONE GO OVER TO THE MALL, AND GET SOME?"
© 1997 United Feature Syndicate, Inc.

IT WAS TOO HARD TO EXPLAIN
SCHULZ

CAN YOU BELIEVE IT, CHUCK? CAN YOU BELIEVE IT?
BELIEVE WHAT?
www.unitedmedia.com

MARCIE WAS NAMED "OUTSTANDING STUDENT OF THE YEAR"! I THOUGHT I WAS GOING TO WIN!
5-27
© 1997 United Feature Syndicate, Inc.

I'VE NEVER BEEN SO DEPRESSED IN ALL MY LIFE..
YOU SHOULD HAVE BEEN AT VALLEY FORGE..
SCHULZ

OH, SURE, MARCIE..STAND OUT IN FRONT OF MY HOUSE WITH YOUR STUPID TROPHY!
www.unitedmedia.com

I JUST THOUGHT YOU'D LIKE TO CONGRATULATE ME.. AND MAYBE SHARE IN MY GLORY...
5-28

YOU THINK I'M JEALOUS, DON'T YOU? WELL, I'M NOT JEALOUS!
© 1997 United Feature Syndicate, Inc.

I MEAN, I'M LIKE NOT TOTALLY JEALOUS!
SCHULZ

WHY WASN'T I NAMED "OUTSTANDING STUDENT OF THE YEAR," CHUCK? TELL ME WHY, CHUCK..
5-29
www.unitedmedia.com

MAYBE BECAUSE YOU FALL ASLEEP IN CLASS EVERY DAY..
YOU DON'T LIKE ME, DO YOU, CHUCK?
© 1997 United Feature Syndicate, Inc.

I'M JUST TRYING TO EXPLAIN WHY YOU PROBABLY...
Z
SCHULZ

YES, MA'AM.. I KNOW I DIDN'T MAKE "OUTSTANDING STUDENT OF THE YEAR".. I KNOW I DIDN'T WIN...

BUT WHAT I NEED TO KNOW IS, DID I COME IN SECOND OR MAYBE THIRD?

5-30
www.unitedmedia.com

FOUR HUNDREDTH?!
© 1997 United Feature Syndicate, Inc.

PROBABLY A LOT CLOSER THAN IT SOUNDS, HUH, MA'AM?
SCHULZ

I SUPPOSE HAVING A DOG HELPS TO MAKE YOU FEEL BETTER WHEN YOU'RE DEPRESSED, HUH, CHUCK?
I WOULDN'T KNOW..
SAY "GOODBYE" TO VALLEY FORGE, MEN.. WE'RE MOVING OUT!
5-31
SCHULZ
© 1997 United Feature Syndicate, Inc.

PEANUTS
by SCHULZ
SEE?

SEE THESE FINGERS? THESE ARE "MAGIC FINGERS"!

I HAVE THE "GOLDEN TOUCH"!

I CAN SPIN THE NUMBERS, AND OPEN MY SCHOOL LOCKER EVERY TIME!
6-1
www.unitedmedia.com

I CAN OPEN A BOTTLE OF BABY ASPIRIN FOR MY DAD IN A MINUTE!

© 1997 United Feature Syndicate, Inc.

I THINK YOUR MAGIC FINGERS LEFT YOUR LUNCH BOX BACK AT THE BUS STOP..

STUPID FINGERS!
SCHULZ

THIS IS MY FAVORITE PROGRAM..

WHY? ALL THEY'RE DOING IS DANCING..
www.unitedmedia.com
6-2

© 1997 United Feature Syndicate, Inc.
I LIKE TO WATCH OLD PEOPLE HAVING FUN..
SCHULZ

© 1997 United Feature Syndicate, Inc.
WHERE'S EVERYBODY GOING? COME BACK!
YOU DON'T SEE ME LEAVING, DO YOU? YOU DON'T SEE OUR SHORTSTOP LEAVING, DO YOU?
6-3
AND MISS ALL THE FUN?!
SCHULZ

A KID THREW A TANTRUM TODAY IN KINDERGARTEN..

HE KICKED AND SCREAMED AND WOULDN'T GET UP OFF THE FLOOR..

www.unitedmedia.com
I FINALLY HAD TO TALK TO HIM MYSELF...

YOU'D BETTER GET UP RIGHT NOW, KID, BEFORE THE ZAMBONI RUNS OVER YOU!
6-4

© 1997 United Feature Syndicate, Inc.
HE GOT UP!
SCHULZ

YES, MA'AM, OUR FIRST YEAR IN KINDERGARTEN HAS GONE BY FAST..
6-5
www.unitedmedia.com

I SUPPOSE YOU'LL BE AWAY ALL SUMMER, WON'T YOU?
© 1997 United Feature Syndicate, Inc.

IS THERE A NUMBER WHERE WE COULD REACH YOU?
SCHULZ

JUNE 6, 1944, "TO REMEMBER"
SCHULZ
© 1997 United Feature Syndicate, Inc.

WHAT ARE YOU DOING HERE? I THOUGHT YOU WANTED TO SEE THE COWBOY MOVIE..
www.unitedmedia.com

I DID, BUT LUCY WANTS TO SEE THIS SPACE MOVIE..
6-7

WE TOOK A VOTE...
© 1997 United Feature Syndicate, Inc.
SCHULZ

I LOST, ONE TO ONE..

PEANUTS
by SCHULZ

LOOK, MARCIE.. I READ THE BOOK, AND I WROTE THE REPORT!

I'M GONNA HAND IT IN TODAY..

SCHOOL IS OUT, SIR.. IT'S VACATION TIME
OUT?
© 1997 United Feature Syndicate, Inc.

SCHOOL IS OUT?
UNTIL SEPTEMBER..
6-8

BUT I READ THE BOOK! I WROTE THE REPORT!

THE SCHOOL IS CLOSED, SIR.. THERE'S NO ONE THERE EXCEPT THE CUSTODIAN..

www.unitedmedia.com

ANYONE WANT TO HEAR A GOOD BOOK REPORT?
CUSTODIAN
SCHULZ

THIS LOOKS LIKE A GOOD CAMP..
NO, IT DOESN'T

IT'S RIGHT BY A LAKE
WHO CARES?

AND NEAR SOME MOUNTAINS
HILLS
© 1997 United Feature Syndicate, Inc.

AND THEY HAVE HORSES
ONE HORSE

THEY SAY THE FOOD IS GOOD
COLD CEREAL

WELL, SHALL WE GO THERE?
WHY NOT?
SCHULZ
6-9

I HEAR YOU'VE DECIDED NOT TO GO TO SUMMER CAMP AFTER ALL..
WHEN YOU HAVE A DOG, YOU SHOULD STAY HOME, AND MAKE YOUR DOG HAPPY..THAT'S WHAT YOU SHOULD DO.. YOU SHOULD STAY HOME..
EXCEPT FOR THOSE OBVIOUSLY NECESSARY SHORT TRIPS IN TO BUY DOG FOOD..
© 1997 United Feature Syndicate, Inc.
6-10
SCHULZ

I THINK I HEARD SOMEONE AT THE DOOR..
www.unitedmedia.com

IT'S PROBABLY NOBODY IMPORTANT
6-11
© 1997 United Feature Syndicate, Inc.

SCHULZ
YOU'RE RIGHT..
WE'RE HARDLY IMPORTANT AT ALL..

ANDY! OLAF! WHAT ARE YOU GUYS DOING HERE?
WE LEFT THE FARM.. WE DIDN'T FIT IN..

WE'RE LOOKING FOR A NEW HOME..
WE THOUGHT YOU MIGHT BE ABLE TO TELL US WHERE OUR KIND WOULD FIT IN...

SOMETIMES I THINK ABOUT MY BROTHERS, ANDY AND OLAF... I WONDER WHAT THEY'RE DOING NOW..
6-12
SCHULZ

I'VE COME TO OFFER YOU A FREE DOG..

HE NEEDS A HOME, AND YOU NEED HIS COMFORTING COMPANIONSHIP..

HE COMES FROM A LONG LINE OF CHAMPIONS... YOU WANT A DOG? HERE IS JUST THE DOG FOR YOU!

6-13
WHERE?
SCHULZ

I'VE COME TO OFFER YOU A FREE DOG.. HIS NAME IS "OLAF"

DOES HE BITE?
ONLY IF ATTACKED BY A PIZZA..

CAN HE DO TRICKS?
HE'S DOING ONE NOW..
6-14

HE'S STANDING ON THE PORCH WITHOUT FALLING OFF..
SCHULZ

PEANUTS
by SCHULZ
THE DOCTOR IS IN
NO PROBLEM

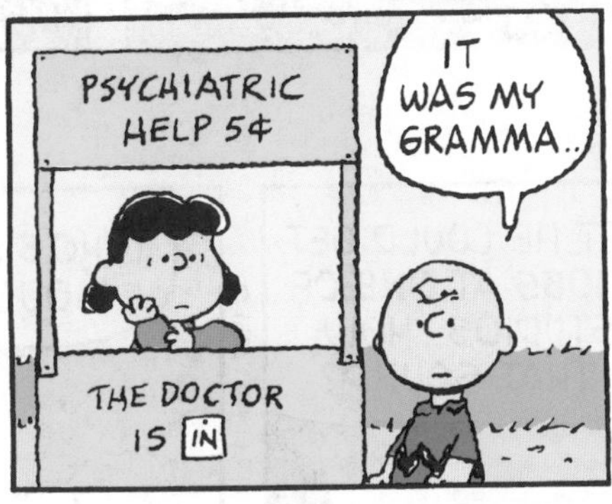
PSYCHIATRIC HELP 5¢
IT WAS MY GRAMMA..
THE DOCTOR IS IN

SHE ALWAYS USED TO SAY, "LAUGH AT THE DINNER TABLE.. CRY BEFORE BED"

I DON'T KNOW... GRAMMAS SAY SOME STRANGE THINGS..
THE DOCTOR IS IN
© 1997 United Feature Syndicate, Inc.

BUT I THINK I'VE BEGUN TO BELIEVE HER..I THINK I'M AFRAID TO BE HAPPY..
6-15
www.unitedmedia.com

HOW CAN YOU BE AFRAID TO BE HAPPY?
BECAUSE WHENEVER YOU GET TOO HAPPY, SOMETHING BAD ALWAYS HAPPENS..

ARE YOU HAPPY RIGHT NOW?
I GUESS SO..
THE DOCTOR IS IN

KLUNK!

TELL ME SOME MORE ABOUT THIS GRAMMA OF YOURS..
THE DOCTC IS IN
SCHULZ

HOW WOULD YOU LIKE TO HAVE A FREE DOG? THIS IS ANDY AND THIS IS OLAF..
www.unitedmedia.com

MOM SAYS DOGS ARE TOO MUCH TROUBLE, THEY BARK TOO MUCH, AND OUR YARD ISN'T BIG ENOUGH..

WELL, AT LEAST SHE DIDN'T SAY ANYTHING ABOUT PREFERRING CATS
© 1997 United Feature Syndicate, Inc.

MOM SAYS DO YOU HAPPEN TO HAVE A CAT?
SCHULZ
6-16

MAYBE YOU GUYS SHOULD GO VISIT OUR BROTHER SPIKE IN THE DESERT..HE KNOWS MICKEY MOUSE..

MICKEY MOUSE HAS A LOT OF FRIENDS IN HOLLYWOOD..
www.unitedmedia.com
6-17

I'LL BET HE COULD GET YOU JOBS AT ONE OF THE STUDIOS.. HOW DOES THAT SOUND?
© 1997 United Feature Syndicate, Inc.

WHO'S MICKEY MOUSE?
SCHULZ

I WROTE TO SPIKE SO HE'LL BE EXPECTING YOU

REMEMBER, THE MOON IS ALWAYS OVER HOLLYWOOD SO JUST FOLLOW THE MOON..
6-18
© 1997 United Feature Syndicate, Inc.

THE LAST TIME WE WENT SOMEPLACE, HE TOLD US THE NORTH STAR IS ALWAYS OVER MINNEAPOLIS..
SCHULZ

About a month after Andy and Olaf left, I received a note from Spike.

He said Andy and Olaf never arrived.

I remember saying goodbye to them that morning.
6-19

That's the last time we ever saw them.
SCHULZ

I THOUGHT WE WERE GOING TO BIBLE CAMP..
IT GOT CANCELED

YOU MEAN I MEMORIZED ALL THOSE BIBLE VERSES FOR NOTHING?

6-20

"JESUS WEPT"
"REMEMBER LOT'S WIFE"

I CAN DO LONGER ONES, TOO..

"THOU ART THE MAN!" "LET MY PEOPLE GO!"
SCHULZ

THAT OTHER TEAM IS TRASH-TALKING US, CHARLIE BROWN..

I GOT EVEN WITH THEM, THOUGH...
6-21

I SAID, "YOU GUYS THINK YOU'RE SO GREAT..MOZART WAS WRITING SYMPHONIES WHEN HE WAS YOUR AGE!"

THAT REALLY SHUT 'EM UP..
I'LL BET IT DID..
SCHULZ

PEANUTS
by SCHULZ

© 1997 United Feature Syndicate, Inc.

WHEW!

HERE.. ANYONE ELSE WANT A DRINK?

6-22
WHAT'S WRONG WITH DOG LIPS?
SCHULZ
www.unitedmedia.com

I HOPE THAT TENT DOESN'T GET TOO HEAVY FOR YOU, MARCIE..
THIS ISN'T A TENT, SIR.. THESE ARE MARSHMALLOWS
6-23
SCHULZ
© 1997 United Feature Syndicate, Inc.

WE SHOULD CALL CHUCK, AND TELL HIM WE WERE SITTING BY THE CAMPFIRE, AND WE WERE THINKING OF HIM..
www.unitedmedia.com

I WASN'T THINKING OF HIM, SIR..
YOU WEREN'T?
6-24
© 1997 United Feature Syndicate, Inc.
SCHULZ

HEY, CHUCK..MARCIE AND I WERE SITTING BY THE CAMPFIRE, BUT WE WEREN'T THINKING OF YOU..

I'M WRITING TO CHUCK TO TELL HIM HOW MUCH WE MISS HIM, AND HOW WE THINK OF HIM NIGHT AND DAY...
www.unitedmedia.com

I'M GOING TO FOOL HIM..I'M USING PINK STATIONERY SO HE'LL THINK IT'S A LOVE LETTER..
© 1997 United Feature Syndicate, Inc.

IT IS A LOVE LETTER..
IT IS?
6-25
SCHULZ

I DON'T THINK YOU'RE BEING FAIR TO CHARLES, SIR..
6-26

ONE DAY YOU TELL HIM WE'RE NOT THINKING OF HIM..THE NEXT DAY YOU TELL HIM WE MISS HIM..

YOU'RE PLAYING LOVERS' GAMES, SIR
LOVERS AREN'T REAL PEOPLE, MARCIE..
SCHULZ

JUNK MAIL! ALL WE EVER GET IS JUNK MAIL!
6-27

HERE, WE GOT SOME JUNK MAIL WITH YOUR NAME ON IT...

"WE MISS YOU, AND WE THINK OF YOU NIGHT AND DAY"... AND IT'S ON PINK STATIONERY..

PROBABLY A TIRE COMPANY OR SOMETHING
SCHULZ

HI, CHUCK..IS THAT YOU? I'M CALLING BECAUSE MARCIE SAYS I HAVEN'T BEEN FAIR WITH YOU...
6-28

SHE SAYS I TELL YOU WE DON'T THINK ABOUT YOU, AND THEN THAT WE ACTUALLY MISS YOU

HAVE I BEEN UNFAIR, CHUCK? WHAT DO YOU THINK? TELL ME..

WOOF!
SCHULZ

PEANUTS
by SCHULZ
IS IT THEM?

I HATE BEING LEFT HOME ALONE
6-29

MAYBE THEY'LL NEVER COME BACK..
www.unitedmedia.com

THAT ROUND-HEADED KID WOULDN'T LEAVE ME, WOULD HE? NO, HE WOULDN'T! WOULD HE?

I'M NEVER SURE THEY'RE COMING BACK UNTIL I SEE THE HEADLIGHTS COMING AROUND THE CORNER..

I SHOULDN'T KEEP LOOKING..

BUT I CAN'T HELP IT...

IS THAT THEM?
© 1997 United Feature Syndicate, Inc.

NO, IT WASN'T THEM..

WATCHED HEADLIGHTS NEVER COME..
SCHULZ

HEY, CHUCK..WE'RE BACK FROM CAMP! DID YOU LIKE MY LETTER?
www.unitedmedia.com

I POURED MY HEART INTO THAT LETTER, CHUCK..
6-30

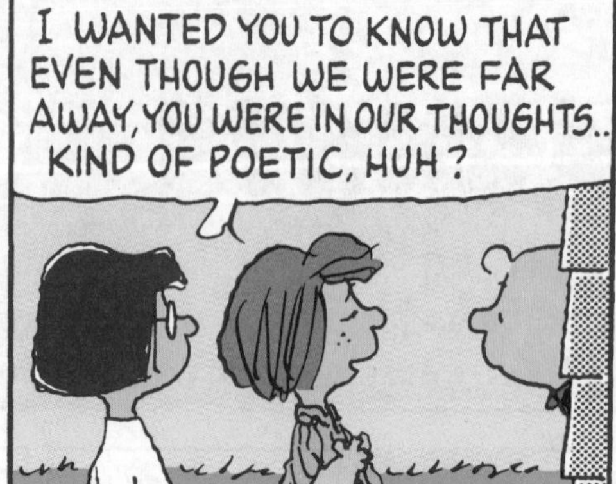
I WANTED YOU TO KNOW THAT EVEN THOUGH WE WERE FAR AWAY, YOU WERE IN OUR THOUGHTS.. KIND OF POETIC, HUH ?
© 1997 United Feature Syndicate, Inc.

ANYWAY, CHUCK..DID YOU LIKE MY LETTER?
WHAT LETTER?
SCHULZ

WHAT LETTER?! WHAT DO YOU MEAN, WHAT LETTER?!
www.unitedmedia.com

I WROTE YOU A LOVE LETTER, CHUCK! I WROTE IT ON PINK STATIONERY!!
7-1

IS THAT WHAT THAT WAS? I THOUGHT IT WAS JUNK MAIL SO I THREW IT AWAY..
© 1997 United Feature Syndicate, Inc.

AAUGH!
A JUNK MAIL LOVE LETTER! HA HA HA HA!!
SCHULZ

CHARLES THOUGHT YOUR LOVE LETTER WAS JUNK MAIL SO HE THREW IT AWAY! HA HA HA HA HA HA!!

YOU SHOULDN'T BE LAUGHING, MARCIE.. YOU SHOULD BE FEELING SORRY FOR ME
www.unitedmedia.com

HOW'S THIS, SIR? SEE? I'M FEELING SORRY FOR YOU..
7-2
© 1997 United Feature Syndicate, Inc.

JUNK MAIL! HA HA HA HA!
I CAN'T STAND IT..
SCHULZ

I GUESS I LEARNED SOMETHING, MARCIE..A BROKEN HEART STAYS WITH YOU FOREVER...
7-3

NEVER GIVE YOUR HEART TO A BLOCKHEAD..

THAT'S GOOD ADVICE, SIR.. I'LL REMEMBER THAT, SIR..
SCHULZ

BONK!

I HIT YOU ON THE HEAD SO I THINK THAT MEANS YOU GET A FREE SHOT...

7-4
BONK!
SCHULZ

I'VE OFTEN WONDERED IF YOU CAN SEE THE OCEAN FROM THERE..
7-5

NO? THEN I THINK YOU CAN TAKE THE LIFE JACKET OFF..
SCHULZ

PEANUTS
by SCHULZ
AND THANKS FOR LETTING YOUR DOG COME OUT AND PLAY WITH ME..

© 1997 United Feature Syndicate, Inc.
THIS IS THE GAME I'VE INVENTED, AND HERE ARE THE RULES..

I'LL THROW THE BALL, AND YOU'LL CATCH IT, OKAY?
7-6

IF YOU CATCH IT ON THE FIRST BOUNCE, YOU GET THREE POINTS..

www.unitedmedia.com
TWO BOUNCES, YOU GET TWO POINTS.. THREE BOUNCES, ONE POINT..IF YOU DON'T CATCH IT, I GET TEN POINTS...

THERE WAS ONE OTHER RULE, TOO, BUT I'VE FORGOTTEN WHAT IT WAS...

NOW I REMEMBER.. NO BODY CHECKING!
SCHULZ

I REMEMBER WHEN MICKEY MOUSE GAVE ME THESE NICE YELLOW SHOES...
7-7

I WANTED TO DO SOMETHING FOR HIM IN RETURN TO SHOW MY APPRECIATION...

I OFFERED HIM MY HAT, BUT IT WOULDN'T FIT OVER HIS EARS..
SCHULZ

SORRY I MISSED THAT ONE, MANAGER..YOU HAVE MY HEARTFELT APOLOGY..

I'D RATHER HAVE YOU CATCH ONE FLY BALL THAN HAVE FIFTY HEARTFELT APOLOGIES!

HOW ABOUT FIFTY APOLOGIES, BUT WE LEAVE OUT THE HEARTFELTS?
7-8
SCHULZ

THE GOVERNMENT'S "MIDNIGHT BASKETBALL" PROGRAM HAS STILL TO REACH SOME OUTLYING AREAS..
7-9
SCHULZ
© 1997 United Feature Syndicate, Inc.

7-10
© 1997 United Feature Syndicate, Inc.
HAVING AN OLDER SISTER IS LIKE HAVING A COMPASS TO GUIDE YOU THROUGH LIFE..
IS THAT TRUE?
I'M NOT HERE..
SCHULZ

© 1997 United Feature Syndicate, Inc.
SCHULZ
7-11

I'LL BET MY LIFE WOULD HAVE BEEN A LOT DIFFERENT IF MOM HAD MADE ME TAKE PIANO LESSONS..
© 1997 United Feature Syndicate, Inc.
7-12
SCHULZ

PEANUTS
by SCHULZ

C'MON, CHARLIE BROWN..STRIKE OUT THE FAT KID!

THAT'S OKAY.. LET'S GET THE SKINNY KID!

© 1997 United Feature Syndicate, Inc.

HEY, CEMENT HEAD! WHO SAID YOU COULD HIT?!

HEY, NOODLE NECK! YOU SWING LIKE MY GRANDMOTHER!

WELL, WE LOST AGAIN.. BY THE WAY, SOME OF THEIR PLAYERS WANT TO TALK TO YOU..
PLAYERS? WHAT PLAYERS?
7-13

www.unitedmedia.com

THE FAT KID, THE SKINNY KID, CEMENT HEAD, AND NOODLE NECK..
I THINK I'LL GO HOME A DIFFERENT WAY..
SCHULZ

I'M GETTING SO I DON'T TRUST ANYBODY..
YOU DON'T EVEN TRUST ME ?

I TRUST YOU ABOUT AS FAR AS YOU CAN THROW THAT BLANKET..

7-14

MY SISTER TRUSTS ME EIGHT FEET..
SCHULZ

WHAT'S LONGER THAN A LINE THAT STRETCHES AROUND THE WORLD?

A LINE FROM HERE TO THE SUN ?

7-15
NO, A SUMMER READING LIST..
SCHULZ

MARCIE, WHAT DO I DO AFTER I FINISH READING THE BOOKS ON THIS LIST ?

WRITE A REPORT ON EACH ONE..
7-16

SURE, MARCIE..

TELL THE TEACHER HOW MUCH YOU LIKED THEM..

SURE, MARCIE..
SCHULZ

DOGS ARE LUCKY.. DOGS DON'T HAVE TO WASTE THEIR SUMMER READING "SILAS MARNER"
I READ A BOOK ABOUT A CAT ONCE..
www.unitedmedia.com
7-17

I READ IT WHEN I WAS GOING TO OBEDIENCE SCHOOL..

"SILAS MARNER" IS ON OUR "REQUIRED READING" LIST..
SO WAS THE CAT BOOK..
© 1997 United Feature Syndicate, Inc.
SCHULZ

OKAY, MARCIE, I'VE FINISHED READING "SILAS MARNER"... NOW, WHAT DO I DO?
www.unitedmedia.com

NOW, YOU WRITE YOUR REPORT..

YOU'RE KIDDING.. ON THE BOOK?
WHY NOT? DID YOU ACTUALLY READ IT?
© 1997 United Feature Syndicate, Inc.

YES, BUT I DIDN'T PAY ANY ATTENTION..
SCHULZ
7-18

LOOK, I FOUND A LIST OF THE PLAYERS ON THE OTHER TEAM..

"CLAY, BLAKE, MORGAN, TRAVIS, TRENT, HUNTER.."
www.unitedmedia.com

"BAILEY, MADISON, TAYLOR AND JUSTIN"
© 1997 United Feature Syndicate, Inc.

NOBODY'S NAMED BILL ANYMORE..
SCHULZ
7-19

PEANUTS
by SCHULZ

OKAY, YOU PUT DOWN A NINE SO I'LL PUT DOWN A..

TEN!

OKAY, YOU PUT DOWN A TEN SO I'LL PUT DOWN A...

JACK!
© 1997 United Feature Syndicate, Inc.

OKAY, YOU PUT DOWN A JACK SO I'LL PUT DOWN A...

QUEEN!

OKAY, YOU PUT DOWN A QUEEN SO I'LL PUT DOWN A...

KING!
www.unitedmedia.com

WHAT KIND OF GAME ARE YOU GUYS PLAYING?

7-20
WE DON'T HAVE THE SLIGHTEST IDEA..
SCHULZ

EXCUSE ME.. CAN ANYONE TELL ME IF MY PLANE IS READY?
7-21
www.unitedmedia.com

YES, I CAN SEE THIS IS AN IMPORTANT HAND..
♠KJ7
♥AK109
♦J87
♣AJ5
♠3
♥7632
♦1094
♣Q7642
N
W E
S
♠1098542
♥Q
♦AKQ62
♣9
♠AQ6
♥J854
♦53
♣K1083

© 1997 United Feature Syndicate, Inc.
NO, I REALIZE YOU'RE NOT PLAYING "OLD MAID"
SCHULZ

I HEARD YOU! YOU DON'T HAVE TO YELL AT ME!
www.unitedmedia.com

I WASN'T YELLING... I WAS EXPRESSING MYSELF FORCEFULLY!
7-22
© 1997 United Feature Syndicate, Inc.

LET'S TRY GOING BACK TO YELLING..
SCHULZ

© 1997 United Feature Syndicate, Inc.
GO AWAY, DOG!
7-23

AAUGH!

FAKED HER OUT!
SCHULZ

WHEN I'M OUT WALKING, I ALWAYS FEEL SAFER WITH MY DOG FOLLOWING RIGHT BEHIND..
© 1997 United Feature Syndicate, Inc.
7-24

I FEEL THE SAME WAY..
SCHULZ

Dear Pen Pal,
DOES YOUR PEN PAL READ ENGLISH?
www.unitedmedia.com

How have you been? I am fine.
© 1997 United Feature Syndicate, Inc.
7-25

OF COURSE
DOES SHE READ SMUDGE?
SCHULZ

© 1997 United Feature Syndicate, Inc.
MY DENTIST TOLD ME TODAY WHAT I CAN DO TO AVOID GETTING CAVITIES..
HOW ABOUT TRIPLE BOGEYS?
SCHULZ
7-26

OKAY, LET'S TRY IT AGAIN!
PEANUTS®
by SCHULZ

© 1997 United Feature Syndicate, Inc.

ALL RIGHT, RERUN..THAT'S ENOUGH..WE'LL LET YOU PLAY AGAIN SOME OTHER TIME..

I'M BRINGING SOMEONE ELSE IN TO PLAY SHORTSTOP..
www.unitedmedia.com

A DOG?!

HOW EMBARRASSING.. I WAS REPLACED BY A DOG!

YOU THINK YOU WERE EMBARRASSED.. HOW ABOUT ME?
7-27

SCHULZ

I DON'T KNOW... I SURE DON'T SEE IT..
www.unitedmedia.com

I'LL RUN BACK TO THE PRO SHOP, AND ASK THEM..
7-28
© 1997 United Feature Syndicate, Inc.

HAS ANYONE TURNED IN A CHEESEBURGER?
SCHULZ

I'M KICKING THIS BEACH BALL CLEAR ACROSS THE OCEAN WHERE SOME OTHER LITTLE KID CAN FIND IT..
www.unitedmedia.com

THIS IS A LAKE..
7-29
© 1997 United Feature Syndicate, Inc.

SOMEBODY BETTER TELL THAT KID..
SCHULZ

WHAT ARE YOU LOOKING AT?
I'M LOOKING FOR PIRATE SHIPS..
7-30

I THINK MAYBE I SEE ONE..

WHERE? I DON'T SEE A THING..
RIGHT OUT THERE..
© 1997 United Feature Syndicate, Inc.

BUT I CAN'T TELL..IT'S EITHER A PIRATE SHIP OR A ZAMBONI..
SCHULZ

A PIRATE SHIP! I SEE A PIRATE SHIP!
7-31

HERE'S BLACKBEAGLE, THE WORLD FAMOUS PIRATE, LEADING HIS SCURVY BAND ASHORE...
www.unitedmedia.com

© 1997 United Feature Syndicate, Inc.
SOMEBODY TELL CONRAD HE'S ONLY SUPPOSED TO WEAR ONE EYE PATCH..
BONK!
SCHULZ

SOME PIRATES JUST LANDED ON THE BEACH! A REAL NASTY LOOKING BUNCH!
www.unitedmedia.com

I WONDER IF THEY'RE HERE TO LOOK FOR BURIED TREASURE..
8-1
© 1997 United Feature Syndicate, Inc.

THEY HAD CHOCOLATE, STRAWBERRY, AND MARBLE FUDGE, BUT I'M GLAD WE ALL ORDERED VANILLA..
SCHULZ

"NO!" THAT'S MY NEW PHILOSOPHY..
8-2
www.unitedmedia.com

I DON'T CARE WHAT ANYONE SAYS, THE ANSWER IS, "NO!"
THAT'S YOUR NEW PHILOSOPHY, HUH?

YES! I MEAN, "NO!"
© 1997 United Feature Syndicate, Inc.

YOU RUINED MY NEW PHILOSOPHY..
SCHULZ

HARICOT VERT
PEANUTS
by SCHULZ

I'M GOING TO PLAY A TRICK ON MY DOG..

BEFORE I FEED HIM TONIGHT, I'M GOING TO SHOW HIM THIS MENU... WHAT HE WON'T KNOW, IS THAT IT'S ALL IN FRENCH..

THIS IS GOING TO BE SO FUNNY..

8-3
GOOD EVENING, SIR.. WOULD YOU LIKE TO SEE OUR MENU?

HOW DID YOUR TRICK GO? WAS IT FUNNY?
IT WAS KIND OF FUNNY..
SCHULZ

HEY, MANAGER.. I'M FILING A COMPLAINT WITH THE LEAGUE OFFICE THAT YOU'RE TOO HARD ON YOUR PLAYERS..
www.unitedmedia.com

WE DON'T HAVE A LEAGUE OFFICE

© 1997 United Feature Syndicate, Inc.

8-4
I FILED IT WITH YOUR CATCHER..

THIS IS A PRETTY GOOD STORY..
www.unitedmedia.com

BUT HOW DOES IT FEEL TO KNOW THAT NO MATTER WHAT YOU WRITE, IT WILL NEVER BE AS GOOD AS "WAR AND PEACE"?
© 1997 United Feature Syndicate, Inc.

DON'T TELL MY MOM..
SCHULZ
HAPPY BIRTHDAY, AMY
8-5

Dear Pen Pal,
Once again I take pen in hand

YOU DROPPED IT..
RATS!
www.unitedmedia.com

NOW, YOU HAVE TO SAY, "ONCE AGAIN I TAKE PEN IN HAND, BUT I DROPPED IT.. SO ONCE MORE I TAKE PEN IN HAND.."
© 1997 United Feature Syndicate, Inc.
8/6

ISN'T THERE SOMETHING ELSE YOU COULD BE DOING?
SCHULZ

WHY DON'T YOU GET A PEN PAL OF YOUR OWN? THEN YOU WOULDN'T ALWAYS BE BOTHERING ME

I HATE WRITING LETTERS..I LIKE TO GET LETTERS, BUT I HATE WRITING THEM

MAYBE YOU COULD WRITE THEM FOR ME..
BUT WOULD YOU LET ME READ THE ONES YOU GOT BACK?

ARE YOU KIDDING?!

I DON'T LOOK SO BAD AFTER ALL!
8/8

THAT'S ALWAYS BEEN MY AMBITION...

TO NOT LOOK SO BAD AFTER ALL..

WELCOME TO THIS YEAR'S ALL-STAR GAME!
8-9

WE ARE PROUD TO ANNOUNCE THAT THIS YEAR WE HAVE TWICE AS MANY PEOPLE WATCHING OUR GAME AS WE HAD LAST YEAR!

LAST YEAR I WAS THE ONLY ONE..
SCHULZ

PEANUTS
by SCHULZ

8-10

THEY SAY, WHEN YOU FALL OFF A HORSE, YOU SHOULD GET RIGHT BACK ON..
STAY WHERE YOU ARE..I'LL GO FIND A HORSE
SCHULZ

© 1997 United Feature Syndicate, Inc.
8-11

www.unitedmedia.com

GROUND RULE DOUBLE!
SCHULZ

ASK YOUR DAD IF HE WANTS ME TO RAKE YOUR LEAVES..
www.unitedmedia.com

OUR LEAVES ARE STILL ON THE TREES..

YOU'RE RIGHT..
© 1997 United Feature Syndicate, Inc.
SCHULZ
8/12

SHOULD I COME BACK TOMORROW?

I THOUGHT YOU WERE GOING TO MAKE SOME MONEY RAKING LEAVES..
www.unitedmedia.com

THE LEAVES ARE STILL ON THE TREES..
© 1997 United Feature Syndicate, Inc.

8-13
RAKE 'EM OFF!
SCHULZ

I THINK I HAVE IT FIGURED OUT..

8-14
FIVE THOUSAND TWO HUNDRED AND EIGHTY TIMES AROUND THE LAKE IS ONE MILE..

NO, IF YOU FALL IN, YOU HAVE TO START OVER..
© 1997 United Feature Syndicate, Inc.
SCHULZ

I HAVE A PROBLEM, MARCIE..I NEED YOUR ADVICE..
www.unitedmedia.com

I WAS SUPPOSED TO BE GOING TO SUMMER SCHOOL, BUT I FORGOT ALL ABOUT IT..

I DON'T KNOW WHAT TO SAY, SIR..I'VE NEVER DONE ANYTHING THAT DUMB...
8-15

WHEN WE GO AWAY TO COLLEGE, MARCIE, LET'S NOT ROOM TOGETHER..
© 1997 United Feature Syndicate, Inc.
SCHULZ

IF I GET A BITE, YOU GRAB THE NET..
www.unitedmedia.com

8-16
NOW!
© 1997 United Feature Syndicate, Inc.

SCHULZ

PEANUTS
by
SCHULZ

8-17

CLOMP!

© 1997 United Feature Syndicate, Inc.

www.unitedmedia.com

AAUGH!

BONK!

SCHULZ
MY REGULAR DOG USUALLY LIES ON TOP OF THE DOGHOUSE

YOU HAVE SOME VISITORS OUT FRONT..
www.unitedmedia.com

DON'T TELL ME...
© 1997 United Feature Syndicate, Inc.

WE'RE BACK! I THINK WE TOOK A WRONG TURN..
SCHULZ
8-18

YOU GUYS HAVE BEEN WANDERING AROUND FOR THREE MONTHS?!
WE COULDN'T FIND THE DESERT.. WE ENDED UP IN ALASKA...
WE GOT JOBS AS SLED DOGS.. DID YOU KNOW "ROSEBUD" WAS A SLED?
8-19
SCHULZ
© 1997 United Feature Syndicate, Inc.

ASK YOUR DOG IF HE WANTS TO COME OUT AND PLAY..
www.unitedmedia.com

8-20
© 1997 United Feature Syndicate, Inc.

THERE'S A STUPID KID OUT FRONT WHO WANTS TO PLAY..
ASK HIM IF HE KNOWS "GO FISH"
SCHULZ

8-21
HERE YOU GO.. THREE DOGS, THREE SUPPERS!
www.unitedmedia.com

SUPPERTIME! IT'S SUPPERTIME! YES, IT'S SUPPERTIME!
© 1997 United Feature Syndicate, Inc.

WHAT WAS THAT ALL ABOUT?
I'M SORRY.. HE KIND OF EXPECTS IT..
EVERY NIGHT? HOW EMBARRASSING
SCHULZ

I THINK WE HAVE A PROBLEM..

MY DAD SAYS WE CAN'T AFFORD TO FEED THREE DOGS..
© 1997 United Feature Syndicate, Inc.

8-22
OF COURSE, ONE OF YOUR BROTHERS EATS MORE THAN ALL OF YOU..
WHICH ONE?
SCHULZ

WE'VE DECIDED WE SHOULD BE MOVING ON.. YOUR FAMILY CAN'T AFFORD THREE DOGS..

WE'LL TRY TO FIND OUR BROTHER SPIKE.. HE KNOWS MICKEY MOUSE, WHO IS VERY WEALTHY, AND CAN GET US JOBS IN HOLLYWOOD..
© 1997 United Feature Syndicate, Inc.

BE CAREFUL CROSSING THE STREET..
SCHULZ
8-23

ASK HIM YOURSELF..
PEANUTS
by SCHULZ

NO, RERUN! NO!
BUT WHY NOT?

YOU CAN'T BE ON THE TEAM BECAUSE YOU'RE TOO YOUNG AND TOO LITTLE!

THAT'S DISCRIMINATION!

MAYBE SO, BUT I CAN'T HELP IT..
THEN HOW ABOUT THIS?
© 1997 United Feature Syndicate, Inc.

HOW ABOUT WHAT?
I HAVE A COURT ORDER SIGNED BY MY ATTORNEY THAT SAYS YOU HAVE TO LET ME PLAY!
www.unitedmedia.com
8-24

A COURT ORDER?
I'M GOING OUT TO CENTER FIELD!

I WONDER WHERE HE GOT A COURT ORDER..

MOM ALWAYS WANTED ME TO BE AN ATTORNEY..
SCHULZ

And so my brothers Andy and Olaf left to find our brother Spike who lives in the desert.

8-25

I DON'T THINK THAT WAS A DESERT..
THAT KID LOOKED AT ME REAL FUNNY..
SCHULZ

IS THERE SOMETHING WRONG WITH US, OLAF? HAVE WE WASTED OUR LIVES?

IT'LL BE DIFFERENT WHEN WE FIND SPIKE, AND HE INTRODUCES US TO MICKEY MOUSE..

MAYBE HE CAN GET US ON SOME TALK SHOWS..

WE CAN'T TALK
MAYBE WE COULD PRETEND WE'RE LITTLE KIDS IN DOG SUITS..
SCHULZ
8-26

WE SHOULDN'T HAVE TO BE HIDING IN BARNS, OLAF.. MAYBE WE SHOULD HAVE BEEN HUNTING DOGS..
I CHASED A RABBIT ONCE.. HE JUST LAUGHED AT ME.. LATER WE BECAME QUITE GOOD FRIENDS..
SCHULZ
8-27

SO! ANOTHER DAY OF WALKING..

MA! I FOUND A DOG!!
SCHULZ

When the little girl caught Andy and took him home, Olaf was left alone.

What should he do? Should he go on by himself, or should he wait around and see what happens to Andy?

8-29

THIS WASN'T MY IDEA..
SCHULZ

PSST, ANDY! I'VE COME TO HELP YOU ESCAPE..
I CAN'T ESCAPE.. I'M TIED TO A TREE!

PEANUTS
by SCHULZ

YES, SIR.. WE'RE HERE TO BUY SCHOOL SUPPLIES..

YOU GO FIRST, MARCIE..

WELL, I'LL NEED A NEW BINDER, SOME PAPER, A SMALL NOTEBOOK, SIX PENCILS, A BALL POINT PEN...
8-31

..A SPELLING DICTIONARY, AN EIGHTEEN-INCH RULER, A PLASTIC TRIANGLE, AND A WORLD MAP..

www.unitedmedia.com
SCHULZ

LUNCH SACKS..
© 1997 United Feature Syndicate, Inc.

Days turned into weeks.. weeks into months.

We never heard anything more from Andy and Olaf.

I imagine they're still out there somewhere, walking and walking, trying to find their brother Spike in the desert.

IT SAYS, "TO CROSS STREET, PUSH BUTTON"
IT'S PROBABLY SOME KIND OF TRICK..
US MAIL
SCHULZ
9-1

I HAVE A NEW PHILOSOPHY.. "WHY ME?"
9-2

DO THIS! DO THAT! WHY ME? GO HERE! GO THERE! WHY ME?

IF YOU'D MOVE A LITTLE BIT, I COULD SEE THE TV...
WHY ME?
SCHULZ

SCHOOL STARTS AGAIN NEXT WEEK, RERUN..

I'M NOT GOING.. THE TEACHER HATES ME..

YOUR OLD TEACHER MOVED AWAY.. THIS YEAR YOU'LL HAVE A NEW TEACHER..

SHE DOESN'T EVEN KNOW ME, AND ALREADY SHE HATES ME!
9-3
SCHULZ

9-4
" HOLDER OF THIS TICKET ASSUMES ALL RISK INCIDENTAL TO THE GAME OF BASEBALL.."
BONK!
" IF REGULATION GAME IS NOT PLAYED ON THIS DATE, THIS TICKET MAY BE..."
© 1997 United Feature Syndicate, Inc.
SCHULZ

WHY ARE YOU HIDING UNDER YOUR BED?
9-5

SCHOOL STARTS NEXT WEEK..
www.unitedmedia.com

YOU HID UNDER YOUR BED LAST YEAR AND IT DIDN'T WORK...
© 1997 United Feature Syndicate, Inc.

I'M BETTER AT IT NOW..
SCHULZ

9-6
OKAY, YOU PLAYED THE KING SO I'LL PLAY THE ACE !!
SMART PLAY..
SCHULZ
© 1997 United Feature Syndicate, Inc.

PEANUTS
by SCHULZ

AN ERASER?
AND ON THE FIRST DAY OF SCHOOL..

I DECIDED WE ALL NEED TO SHOW MORE RESPECT.. TO BE MORE CONSIDERATE.. MORE POLITE...

"SO WHEN THE TEACHER CAME IN, I STOOD UP, AND GREETED HER"..

GOOD MORNING, MA'AM..

"I LOOKED AROUND, AND I WAS THE ONLY ONE STANDING SO I SAT DOWN.."

"THE TEACHER DIDN'T SAY ANYTHING.. SHE JUST STARED AT ME LIKE MAYBE SHE WAS IN SHOCK..."
© 1997 United Feature Syndicate, Inc.
9-7
www.unitedmedia.com

THAT'S WHEN I GOT HIT ON THE BACK OF MY HEAD WITH AN ERASER..
SCHULZ

YOUR HAIR LOOKS NICE TODAY, SIR..
THANKS, MARCIE.. I WANT TO LOOK MY BEST WHEN THE TEACHER ASKS ME THAT VERY..
9-8
www.unitedmedia.com

© 1997 United Feature Syndicate, Inc.

...FIRST QUESTION
SCHULZ

HOW WAS SCHOOL TODAY?
I DIDN'T GO.. I MEAN, I GOT TO THE FRONT DOOR, BUT I DIDN'T GO IN..
www.unitedmedia.com

I SAT ON THE STEPS FOR A WHILE..THEN I OPENED THE DOOR...

DOES ANYONE IN THERE NEED ME ?!
9-9
© 1997 United Feature Syndicate, Inc.

NOBODY ANSWERED SO I WENT HOME..
SCHULZ

9-10

www.unitedmedia.com

DIDN'T SCARE ME A BIT..
© 1997 United Feature Syndicate, Inc.

BIRDS CAN'T SAY, "BOO!"
SCHULZ

I STAYED UP 'TIL TEN O'CLOCK READING ABOUT COLUMBUS..
I MEMORIZED EVERY SPELLING WORD ON THIS LIST..
I READ THIS WHOLE BOOK TWICE..
I MEMORIZED EVERY CAPITAL OF EVERY STATE..
I'M WEARING A COPPER BRACELET..
9-11
© 1997 United Feature Syndicate, Inc.
SCHULZ

As she said, "Goodbye" and ran up the steps, he knew he would never see her again.

9-12

"Oh, well," he thought. "I still have my dog."
© 1997 United Feature Syndicate, Inc.

Little did he know, his dog had been planning to leave him.
SCHULZ

PEANUTS
by SCHULZ
SURE, IT'S ALWAYS ME, ISN'T IT?

ALL RIGHT, IF THAT'S THE WAY EVERYBODY FEELS, I'LL LEAVE!

I KNOW WHEN I'M NOT WANTED! I KNOW WHEN I'M NOT LOVED! I KNOW WHEN EVERYONE IS AGAINST ME!

WHEN ?

WHEN?! WHAT DO YOU MEAN, WHEN?!
www.unitedmedia.com

I MEAN, DID YOU KNOW THE EXACT MOMENT WHEN YOU WEREN'T WANTED, AND NOT LOVED, AND EVERYONE WAS AGAINST YOU?
9-14

OR DID YOU MAYBE HAVE THE FEELING COMING ON LAST WEEK OR LAST MONTH, OR MAYBE...

© 1997 United Feature Syndicate, Inc.

FOR INSTANCE, I KNEW THE EXACT MOMENT WHEN I WAS OVERDOING IT..
SCHULZ

C'MON, MARCIE.. WE NEED THE PRACTICE!
IT'S RAINING, AND I HATE FOOTBALL..

WHAT IF YOU MARRY SOMEBODY WHO LIKES TO GO TO FOOTBALL GAMES?
MY HUSBAND WILL BE VERY WEALTHY AND OWN A LUXURY BOX

DON'T COUNT ON IT, MARCIE!

I'M SORRY I WAS LATE, MA'AM..

WE HAD A LITTLE TROUBLE AT HOME..

OUR KITCHEN WAS FULL OF SQUABBLES..

YES, YOUR HONOR, THIS IS MY CLIENT, ALICE, THE INJURED PARTY, WHO FELL DOWN THE RABBIT-HOLE..

WE INTEND TO PROVE NEGLIGENCE ON THE PART OF THE PROPERTY OWNER FOR FAILING TO POST A WARNING SIGN BY THE RABBIT-HOLE..

HOW DID YOUR CASE COME OUT TODAY?
THE JUDGE TOLD ME TO TAKE MY HAT OFF IN THE COURTROOM..

QUICK, MARCIE..I NEED A PENCIL AND SOME PAPER..
www.unitedmedia.com

AND I NEED AN ERASER, A PEN AND A RULER..
© 1997 United Feature Syndicate, Inc.

9-18
NO, MA'AM..I'M HER CADDIE..
SCHULZ

YES, MA'AM, I KNOW THE ANSWER, BUT I THINK I'LL KEEP IT TO MYSELF...
www.unitedmedia.com

I DON'T WANT TO HUMILIATE EVERYONE ELSE BY MAKING THEM FEEL STUPID..I'M SORT OF HUMBLE THAT WAY..
9-19
© 1997 United Feature Syndicate, Inc.

THE ANSWER IS "TWELVE"
THAT'S WHAT I WAS GOING TO SAY..
SCHULZ

THIS IS GOING TO BE A BATTLE, CHUCK! SOME OF US MAY NOT COME OUT ALIVE!
IN THAT CASE, LET'S THINK ABOUT WHO FEEDS THE DOG..
© 1997 United Feature Syndicate, Inc.
9-20
SCHULZ

PEANUTS
by SCHULZ
CHARLIE BROWN..

SO WHAT WE'LL DO, SEE, IS I'LL HOLD THE BALL, AND YOU COME RUNNING UP AND KICK IT..

SURE, AND YOU PULL IT AWAY, AND I LAND ON MY BACK AND KILL MYSELF..

NOT NECESSARILY.. PEOPLE CHANGE.. TIMES CHANGE.. YOU CAN FEEL IT IN THE AIR..

I THINK SHE MAY BE RIGHT.. I'VE NOTICED THAT SAME FEELING.. TIMES ARE CHANGING...

9-21
THAT MEANS I'M GONNA KICK THAT BALL CLEAR OVER THE BORDER!
© 1997 United Feature Syndicate, Inc.

AAUGH!
WHERE? WHERE?!

WHUMP!
www.unitedmedia.com

SORRY, CHARLIE BROWN.. I THOUGHT I HEARD SOMEONE SAY THE MILLENNIUM IS COMING..
SCHULZ

© 1997 United Feature Syndicate, Inc.
SIR, WHY DO SOME OF YOUR CLUBS WEAR BEDROOM SLIPPERS?
JUST CARRY THE BAG, MARCIE..
9-22
SCHULZ

YES, SIR.. MY DOG NEEDS A NEW SUPPER DISH..

www.unitedmedia.com
HE WEARS THEM OUT VERY FAST..

NO, I ONLY FEED HIM ONCE A DAY..
© 1997 United Feature Syndicate, Inc.
9/23

PLEASE! JUST PAY HIM, AND LET'S GET OUT OF HERE..
SCHULZ

THE MAN AT THE STORE THOUGHT IT WAS VERY FUNNY THAT YOU WEAR OUT SO MANY SUPPER DISHES..

www.unitedmedia.com
HE SAID HIS DOG HAS HAD THE SAME DISH ALL HIS LIFE..
© 1997 United Feature Syndicate, Inc.

HE PROBABLY NEVER LICKS THE BOTTOM OF THE DISH..
SCHULZ
9-24

YES, SIR..WE NEED ANOTHER NEW SUPPER DISH..

THE OTHER ONE DIDN'T LAST LONG..SEE? HE ATE RIGHT THROUGH THE BOTTOM

WE BOUGHT IT HERE YESTERDAY, REMEMBER?
9-25

NO, I THINK HE ATE THE SALES SLIP..
SCHULZ

MY DAD SAYS WE CAN'T AFFORD TO KEEP BUYING YOU NEW SUPPER DISHES..

HE SAYS HE MAY HAVE TO REMORTGAGE OUR HOUSE AND HIS BARBER SHOP...

I DON'T KNOW.. HE MAY JUST BE JOKING..

I CAN'T LAUGH WHILE I'M EATING..
9-26
SCHULZ

MY BRAND OF FOOTBALL AGGRAVATES YOU, DOESN'T IT, SIR?
SCHULZ
9-27

PEANUTS
by SCHULZ

LET'S TRY MY SECRET PLAY, SIR..

WE HAVE A SECRET PLAY, CHARLES..THIS PLAY IS SO SECRET NO ONE HAS EVER HEARD OF IT!

I THINK THEY'D LIKE TO KNOW WHAT OUR SECRET PLAY IS, SIR..
www.unitedmedia.com

WELL, DON'T TELL THEM!
OH, I'D NEVER DO THAT..

TO ME, A SECRET IS A SECRET! A PERSON SHOULD NEVER TELL A SECRET..
9-28

© 1997 United Feature Syndicate, Inc.

IT WORKED, SIR! WE BORED THEM RIGHT OUT OF THE GAME..
SCHULZ

"I'm a border collie," he said. "I have to be gone a lot. I have to herd sheep."

9-29

"Then, go!" she said. "But don't expect me to wait for you!"

He knew he'd never see her again, and he knew there was nothing he could do about it.

THIS IS A GOOD STORY.. DOES IT HAVE A TITLE?
"Border Collies Don't Cry"
SCHULZ

IF I WERE YOU, I'D BE TOTALLY ASHAMED TO HAVE SOMEONE SEE ME SITTING AROUND HOLDING A STUPID BLANKET!

AND THAT DOG LYING IN YOUR LAP LOOKS EVEN MORE RIDICULOUS..

I'D BITE HER, BUT I'M FACING THE WRONG WAY..
9-30
SCHULZ

THE WAY I SEE IT, YOU HAVE TWO CHOICES..

YOU CAN HELP ME WITH MY SPELLING WORDS..
10-1

OR YOU CAN TAKE THE BLAME FOR THE INK I SPILLED DOWN THE COLLAR OF THE KID WHO SITS IN FRONT OF ME..

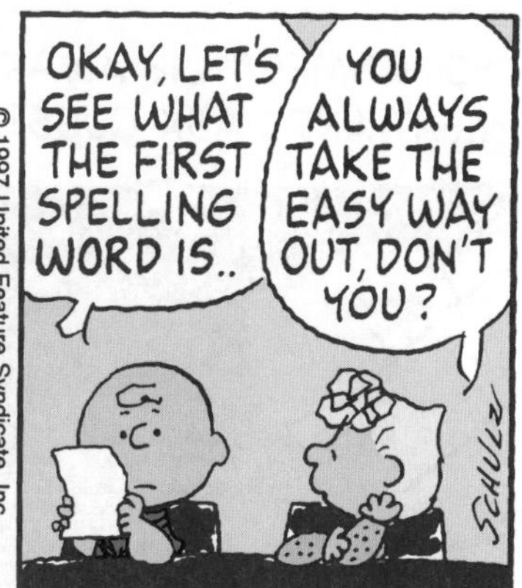

OKAY, LET'S SEE WHAT THE FIRST SPELLING WORD IS..
YOU ALWAYS TAKE THE EASY WAY OUT, DON'T YOU?
SCHULZ

YES, MA'AM..THAT'S MY DOG OUTSIDE..

WELL, HE DOESN'T LIKE BEING ALONE ALL DAY...

10-2
NO, HE'LL JUST WAIT FOR ME OUT THERE ON THE FRONT STEPS..HE'LL FIND SOMETHING TO DO..

YES, MA'AM..MY DOG IS STILL SITTING OUTSIDE ON THE FRONT STEPS..

NO, I TRIED TO EXPLAIN TO HIM THAT DOGS AREN'T ALLOWED ON THE SCHOOL GROUNDS..
10-3

HERE, HE WANTED ME TO SHOW YOU HIS PASSPORT..

SOMETIMES I LIE AWAKE AT NIGHT, AND I ASK QUESTIONS..

IS THERE ANY ONE THING A PERSON CAN DO TO MAKE HIS LIFE SUCCESSFUL?

"BACK EXERCISES!"
10-4

PEANUTS®
by SCHULZ

WHAT ARE YOU DRAWING?
A COW

THAT'S NOT A COW..
WELL, I'VE NEVER SEEN A REAL COW..

IT LOOKS MORE LIKE A DOG..

WHY DON'T YOU JUST CHANGE IT TO A DOG?

HOW CAN I DO THAT?

10-5
ADD A "WOOF!"
SCHULZ

© 1997 United Feature Syndicate, Inc.
"AND THE APOSTLE PAUL ESCAPED WHEN HIS FRIENDS LOWERED HIM OVER THE WALL IN A BASKET.."
WHY DO YOU SUPPOSE HE HAD TO DO THAT?
HE PROBABLY GOT TIRED OF SIGNING AUTOGRAPHS
10-6
SCHULZ

10-7
© 1997 United Feature Syndicate, Inc.
BE PROUD OF ME, MARCIE.. I'VE SPENT A WHOLE HOUR HERE ON THE PUTTING GREEN..
I'M VERY PROUD OF YOU, SIR.. AND YOU'VE ONLY LOST FIVE BALLS..
SCHULZ

IF I PLAY THE KING, I KNOW HE'LL PLAY THE ACE, BUT IF I PLAY THE JACK, HE'LL PLAY THE QUEEN..
www.unitedmedia.com
I JUST WISH I KNEW WHAT HE'S THINKING..
10-8
© 1997 United Feature Syndicate, Inc.
THAT LAST CARD I SWALLOWED TASTED TERRIBLE..
SCHULZ

THIS GOLFER IS HAVING A REAL BAD DAY. SEE...
SO HE DECIDES TO END IT ALL BY GOING OVER NIAGARA FALLS IN A GOLF BAG! HA HA HA!
JUST CARRY THE CLUBS, MARCIE..
© 1997 United Feature Syndicate, Inc.
10-9
SCHULZ

THIS ROUGH IS PRETTY THICK, SIR..
IF WE GET SEPARATED, MAYBE WE'LL MEET AGAIN IN A BETTER WORLD..
JUST FIND THE BALL, MARCIE!
© 1997 United Feature Syndicate, Inc.
SCHULZ
10-10

I THINK IT'S GOING TO RAIN.. I HATE WALKING UP ALL THOSE HILLS.. THE BAG IS TOO HEAVY.. MY FEET HURT.. AND I'M AFRAID OF SNAKES IN THE ROUGH.. SO I DON'T WANT TO CADDIE ANYMORE..
REALLY? WHY?
© 1997 United Feature Syndicate, Inc.
10-11
SCHULZ

PEANUTS
by SCHULZ
I ALWAYS DREAD THIS..

OUR VETERINARIAN JUST CALLED..IT'S TIME FOR YOUR CHECKUP..

HE TOOK THE NEWS SURPRISINGLY WELL, DIDN'T HE ?

HE DIDN'T TRY TO RUN AWAY OR ANYTHING
I WONDER WHY..
© 1997 United Feature Syndicate, Inc.
www.unitedmedia.com

YES, MA'AM, MY DOG IS HERE TO SEE THE VET..
10-12

HE DIDN'T SEEM AT ALL WORRIED, DID HE ?
MAYBE HE'S RECALLED SOME WORDS OF INSPIRATION THAT GIVE HIM STRENGTH..

"HE THAT OUTLIVES THIS DAY, AND COMES SAFE HOME, WILL STAND A-TIPTOE WHEN THIS DAY IS NAMED"
SCHULZ

10-13
HERE, YOU GOT A LETTER FROM YOUR BROTHER SPIKE..

"DEAR SNOOPY.. WHAT HAPPENED TO ANDY AND OLAF? I THOUGHT THEY WERE COMING OUT HERE.."
www.unitedmedia.com

"MY FRIEND, MICKEY MOUSE, CAME BY YESTERDAY, AND LEFT THEM SOME GIFTS"
© 1997 United Feature Syndicate, Inc.

NICE SHOES..
SCHULZ

I HATE TO TELL HIM..YOU'D BETTER TELL HIM..

I CAN'T... YOU TELL HIM..
© 1997 United Feature Syndicate, Inc.

NO, PLEASE..YOU TELL HIM...I DON'T HAVE THE NERVE..
www.unitedmedia.com

10-14
WE THINK MAYBE WE TOOK ANOTHER WRONG TURN..

ANDY! OLAF! WHAT ARE YOU DOING HERE?

WE COULDN'T FIND THE DESERT..
THAT'S RIDICULOUS!

ACTUALLY, WHAT WE FOUND WAS THE WRONG DESERT..
HAVE YOU EVER SEEN THE PYRAMIDS BY MOONLIGHT?
10-15 SCHULZ
© 1997 United Feature Syndicate, Inc.

And so, Andy and Olaf set off once again to find their brother Spike.
www.unitedmedia.com

This time, however, I provided them with an experienced guide to show them the way.
© 1997 United Feature Syndicate, Inc.

10-16
SCHULZ

WHAT'S HE SAYING?
10-17

HE SAID THIS IS AS FAR AS WE CAN GO BECAUSE THE EARTH IS FLAT, AND IF WE GO ANY FARTHER, WE'LL FALL OVER THE EDGE..
www.unitedmedia.com

I WONDER IF HE'S RIGHT..
© 1997 United Feature Syndicate, Inc.

THERE'S ONLY ONE WAY TO FIND OUT!
OLAF!
SCHULZ

10-18
HERE, YOU GOT A POST CARD FROM ANDY..

"DEAR SNOOPY, WE HAD A LITTLE TROUBLE, BUT NOW EVERYTHING IS FINE"
www.unitedmedia.com

"WILL WRITE MORE LATER"
© 1997 United Feature Syndicate, Inc.

"P.S. OLAF SAYS TO TELL YOU THE EARTH IS ROUND!"
SCHULZ

PEANUTS
by SCHULZ
RING!

HI, CHUCK.. DO YOU MISS ME?
10-19

DO I WHAT?

MISS ME! DO YOU MISS ME, CHUCK?! WHAT'S THE MATTER WITH YOU? DON'T YOU UNDERSTAND ANYTHING?!

WHO IS THIS?

WHAT DO YOU MEAN, WHO IS THIS?! IT'S ME, CHUCK! WHO DID YOU THINK IT WAS?!!

OH
www.unitedmedia.com

"OH"? WHAT DOES THAT MEAN? "OH".. IS THAT ALL YOU CAN SAY?!

I'M SORRY.. I WAS THINKING OF SOMETHING ELSE... I HAVE TO FEED MY DOG..

WAIT, CHUCK! DON'T HANG UP! SAY SOMETHING! SAY ANYTHING!

WOOF!

HOW SWEET!
SCHULZ

FIGURE SKATING! THAT'S WHERE THE MONEY IS, MARCIE..
10-20
www.unitedmedia.com

SO WHAT ARE YOU READING?
© 1997 United Feature Syndicate, Inc.

"HOW TO DRIVE A ZAMBONI"
SCHULZ

TWENTY-FOUR!
10/21
www.unitedmedia.com

CHARTREUSE TWENTY-FOUR!
© 1997 United Feature Syndicate, Inc.

BETTER IN COLOR, HUH, MA'AM?
SCHULZ

NO, MA'AM, I DON'T HAVE A BLANKET FOR NAP TIME..
www.unitedmedia.com

MY BROTHER IS THE ONLY ONE IN OUR FAMILY WITH A BLANKET, AND I DON'T WANT TO END UP LIKE HIM..
10-22

I'LL JUST SIT HERE AND READ THE PAPER..
© 1997 United Feature Syndicate, Inc.

"'64 CONVERTIBLE.. HARDTOP..BLACK AND RED INTERIOR..$19,000" YOU SHOULD CHECK INTO IT, MA'AM..
SCHULZ

LET'S SAY YOU AND I ARE MARRIED, SEE, AND YOU'RE DOWN IN THE BASEMENT PLAYING YOUR PIANO...
www.unitedmedia.com

KLUNK!
© 1997 United Feature Syndicate, Inc.

ALL RIGHT, LET'S SAY YOU'RE OUT IN THE GARAGE PLAYING YOUR PIANO..
SCHULZ
10-23

www.unitedmedia.com

© 1997 United Feature Syndicate, Inc.

10-24
NOW WHAT?
SCHULZ

10-25
www.unitedmedia.com

© 1997 United Feature Syndicate, Inc.

THE OTHERS ALL WENT THAT WAY..
SCHULZ

?
PEANUTS
by SCHULZ

© 1997 United Feature Syndicate, Inc.

10-26

www.unitedmedia.com

SCHULZ

WE USED CRAYONS IN SCHOOL TODAY..

WE LEARNED ALL ABOUT COLORS..
LIKE WHAT?

LIKE THE FAT KID NEXT TO ME TAKES ALL THE GOOD COLORS..
10-27
SCHULZ

HEY, KID! GIMME YOUR RED CRAYON!
OKAY, I THREW IT INTO THE TEACHER'S WASTEBASKET..IF YOU WANT IT, GO GET IT!

YOU LOOKING FOR A PUNCH IN THE NOSE, KID?
TRY IT, AND I'LL TRADE YOU ONE FOR TWO!

WELL, MAYBE I LIKE THIS GREEN ONE..
10-28
SCHULZ

YES, SIR, MR.PRINCIPAL..

WELL, THIS BIG KID WAS TAKING ALL THE CRAYONS, SEE?

THEN HE SAID HE WAS GOING TO PUNCH ME IN THE NOSE..
10-29

HIS MOTHER COMPLAINED ABOUT **ME**?!

SIR? YOU KNOW WHAT I THINK?

YOU AND I SHOULD GO OUT TO DINNER SOMETIME, AND TALK ABOUT THIS..

SCHULZ

NO, I CAN'T GO TO SCHOOL.. I'VE BEEN SUSPENDED AGAIN FOR ONE DAY..

ANOTHER WHOLE DAY!

YEARS FROM NOW, YOU KNOW WHAT PEOPLE ARE GOING TO SAY ABOUT ME?

HE'S ONE DAY DUMBER THAN HE SHOULD BE!

WHERE'S THE BIG KID TODAY?
HIS MOTHER TOOK HIM TO ANOTHER SCHOOL..

THEN WHERE ARE ALL THE CRAYONS?

I ALWAYS COLOR THE SKY BLUE..

SOMEDAY DOGS ARE GOING TO LEARN TO FLY..

WE LEARNED TO SWIM.. WHY CAN'T WE LEARN TO FLY?

I CAN SEE IT NOW.. MILLIONS OF DOGS ALL FLYING SOUTH FOR THE WINTER..

BEAGLES LEADING THE WAY!

PEANUTS
by SCHULZ

ASK YOUR DOG IF HE WANTS TO COME OUT AND SHOOT A FEW BASKETS..

11-2

© 1997 United Feature Syndicate, Inc.

www.unitedmedia.com

I COULDN'T FIND HIM, BUT I DOUBT IF HE WOULD HAVE BEEN INTERESTED..
SCHULZ

THIS IS GREAT.. I REALLY LIKE IT..

NOW ALL YOU NEED IS A GOOD TITLE..

Ten Stupid Things Dogs Do To Mess Up Their Lives
11-3

I SUPPOSE YOU REALIZE THAT YOUR MAIN JOB HERE IS BEING A WATCHDOG..
11-4

WHAT I'M WONDERING IS, ARE YOU DOING MORE WRITING THAN WATCHING?

IF A BURGLAR COMES AROUND, HAVE HIM STAND RIGHT HERE, AND I'LL DROP A TYPEWRITER ON HIS HEAD..

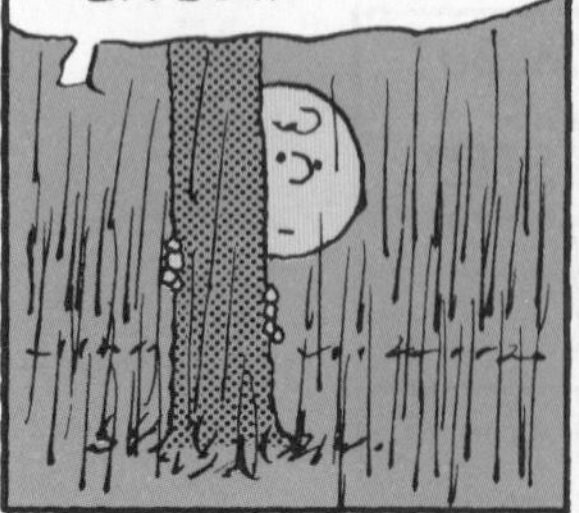
THERE'S THE HOUSE WHERE THE LITTLE RED-HAIRED GIRL LIVES..

WHEN SHE COMES OUT, I'LL SAY, "GOOD MORNING"

THEN SHE'LL SAY, "WHY ARE YOU STANDING HERE IN THE RAIN?"
11-5

THEN I'LL SAY, "OH, IS IT RAINING?"

THEN SHE'LL SAY, "BOY, ARE YOU EVER STUPID!"

DANCING IN THE RAIN IS ROMANTIC.. STANDING IN THE RAIN BEHIND A TREE ISN'T ROMANTIC..

THERE'S A BUNCH OF RABBITS... CHASE 'EM!
www.unitedmedia.com

11-6

© 1997 United Feature Syndicate, Inc.

THEY SAID I NEED AN APPOINTMENT
SCHULZ

NO, MA'AM..I DIDN'T GET MY HOMEWORK DONE
www.unitedmedia.com

WELL, I HAD TO FEED MY DOG, AND TAKE HIM FOR A WALK, AND THEN READ TO HIM..
11-7

YES, MA'AM, I READ TO MY DOG EVERY NIGHT..

..AND I NEVER ASK HIM TO WRITE A BOOK REPORT
© 1997 United Feature Syndicate, Inc.

SORRY, MA'AM.. THAT JUST SORT OF SLIPPED OUT..

11-8
I MIGHT AS WELL TELL YOU NOW...
www.unitedmedia.com

AAUGH!
© 1997 United Feature Syndicate, Inc.

THE SCARIEST WORDS YOU CAN SAY.."I MIGHT AS WELL TELL YOU NOW"
SCHULZ

HA! FOOLED YOU, DIDN'T I? TOO QUICK FOR YOU, WASN'T I?
11-9

IT JUST PROVES ONCE AGAIN THAT WE BLANKET HOLDERS ARE INFINITELY SUPERIOR TO YOU ORDINARY TYPES..

THIS IS A BORDER COLLIE, SEE, AND THESE ARE THE SHEEP HE'S GUARDING..

SUDDENLY, A WOLF COMES, SO THE BORDER COLLIE GETS ON THE PHONE, AND CALLS IN AN AIR STRIKE!

WE'RE SUPPOSED TO BE DOING WATER COLORS OF FLOWERS..
IT ALL TAKES PLACE IN A MEADOW..
SCHULZ
11-10

EVERY VETERANS DAY I GO OVER TO BILL MAULDIN'S HOUSE..
11-11

WE QUAFF A FEW ROOT BEERS..THEN I TELL HIM WHAT HAPPENED YESTERDAY..

I WENT TO A BOOKSTORE TO GET SOMETHING BY ERNIE PYLE.. THEY NEVER HEARD OF HIM..

I DON'T KNOW, BILL.. I JUST DON'T KNOW..
SCHULZ

SIR, YOU KNOW I CAN'T GIVE YOU THE ANSWERS..

11-12
RATS!

COULD I MAYBE JUST RENT SOME?
SCHULZ

Dear Snoopy,
I am still waiting for Andy and Olaf to come here.
11-13

"REMEMBER HOW I TOLD YOU THAT MY WEALTHY FRIEND MICKEY MOUSE LEFT SOME SHOES HERE FOR THEM?"
www.unitedmedia.com

Bad news! Last night somebody stole them!
© 1997 United Feature Syndicate, Inc.

"IF YOU SEE A COYOTE WEARING MICKEY MOUSE SHOES, GRAB HIM!"
SCHULZ

OLAF, HAVE YOU EVER SEEN A COYOTE?
11-14

NOT SINCE I LEFT THE FARM..
I THINK I JUST SAW ONE..
www.unitedmedia.com
© 1997 United Feature Syndicate, Inc.

AND HE WAS WEARING MICKEY MOUSE SHOES!
SCHULZ

Z
I'VE BEEN THINKING ABOUT SOMETHING..IF I SAW THAT COYOTE WEARING MICKEY MOUSE SHOES, COULDN'T THAT MEAN WE'RE GETTING CLOSE TO WHERE SPIKE LIVES?
I DOUBT IT.. IF WE WERE CLOSE, WE'D KNOW IT BECAUSE WE'RE WELL BRED HUNTING DOGS..
11-15
© 1997 United Feature Syndicate, Inc.
SCHULZ

PEANUTS
by SCHULZ
THAT'S WHAT YOU THINK!

OH, YEAH? THAT'S WHAT YOU THINK!
WHAT?

THAT'S MY NEW PHILOSOPHY.. "OH, YEAH? THAT'S WHAT YOU THINK!"

WHY ARE YOU TELLING ME?
© 1997 United Feature Syndicate, Inc.

WHAT?
WHY ARE YOU TELLING ME?
11-16
www.unitedmedia.com

I LIKE IT! THAT'S A GOOD PHILOSOPHY... "WHY ARE YOU TELLING ME?"

"OH, YEAH? THAT'S WHAT YOU THINK! WHY ARE YOU TELLING ME?"
I CAN'T STAND IT..

WHAT?
SCHULZ

"I CAN'T STAND IT!" I LIKE THAT!

AND IT SAYS, "MOSES WAS ON THE MOUNTAIN FORTY DAYS AND FORTY NIGHTS"
THAT'S A LONG TIME TO BE AWAY..
I WONDER WHO HE GOT TO STAY WITH HIS DOG..
SCHULZ
© 1997 United Feature Syndicate, Inc.
11-17

Dear Pen Pal, Did you get my last letter?

HOW DOES SHE KNOW IF THE LETTER SHE GOT WAS YOUR LAST LETTER?

AND IF SHE DOESN'T GET THIS LETTER, HOW WILL SHE KNOW YOU ASKED HER IF SHE GOT YOUR LAST LETTER?

www.unitedmedia.com

11-18
SCHULZ
© 1997 United Feature Syndicate, Inc.

www.unitedmedia.com

?
I'D SAY, "THREE NO-TRUMP."
© 1997 United Feature Syndicate, Inc.

BUT AFTER THIS HAND, I THINK YOU SHOULD ALL GO TO SLEEP..
SCHULZ
11-19

© 1997 United Feature Syndicate, Inc.
OUCH! OO! OW! OUCH!
SCHULZ
11-20

ASK YOUR MOM IF SHE'D LIKE TO BUY SOME HOMEMADE CHRISTMAS CARDS..
11-21
© 1997 United Feature Syndicate, Inc.

THESE ARE KIND OF CUTE
THANK YOU
I DREW ALL THE BUNNIES..
SCHULZ

HOW MANY CHRISTMAS CARDS DID YOU SELL?
I DIDN'T SELL ANY!
www.unitedmedia.com

HOW ARE YOU GOING TO BUY PRESENTS FOR ALL YOUR GIRLFRIENDS?
I DON'T HAVE ANY GIRLFRIENDS.. ALL I HAVE IS A DOG..
© 1997 United Feature Syndicate, Inc.

11-22
DID SOMEONE SAY "DOG"?
SCHULZ

PEANUTS
by SCHULZ

HERE'S THE WORLD FAMOUS PATRIOT SOLDIER STANDING GUARD AT VALLEY FORGE..

SUDDENLY HE RECEIVES WORD THAT GENERAL WASHINGTON WANTS TO SEE HIM..

BUILD A FIRE? YES, SIR..I CAN DO THAT..

IF I CAN JUST GET IT STARTED, I CAN BUILD A GOOD FIRE..

SIGH
© 1997 United Feature Syndicate, Inc.
www.unitedmedia.com

ALL MY OLD COMIC BOOKS..
11-23
SCHULZ

11-24
I'M WORRIED.. I THINK MAYBE HE'S PLANNING A TRICK PLAY..
SCHULZ
© 1997 United Feature Syndicate, Inc.

© 1997 United Feature Syndicate, Inc.
WHY ARE YOU LOOKING AT ME LIKE THAT, MARCIE?
PROBABLY, BECAUSE YOU'RE THE ONLY ONE I KNOW WHO EATS A HOT DOG FROM THE SIDE..
11-25
SCHULZ

11-26
OKAY, GRAMMA, WE UNDERSTAND..HAVE A GOOD GAME..

WE'RE NOT GOING TO GRAMMA'S FOR THANKSGIVING.. SHE'S PLAYING HOCKEY WITH HER IN-LINE SKATING CLUB..
www.unitedmedia.com

© 1997 United Feature Syndicate, Inc.
WHAT ABOUT OUR OTHER GRAMMA?
SHE'S GOING ON AN ALL-DAY RIDE WITH HER MOUNTAIN BIKE CLUB..
SCHULZ

THAT'S SOMETHING NEW.. A THANKSGIVING CLAUS!
RING THE DRUMSTICK!
SCHULZ
© 1992 United Feature Syndicate, Inc.
11-27-97

11-28-97
© 1992 United Feature Syndicate, Inc.

THANKSGIVING IS OVER!
SCHULZ

HEY, STUPID CAT! HOW DO YOU LIKE MY NEW WASTEBASKET?
11-29-97
© 1988 United Feature Syndicate, Inc.

PLEASE FEEL FREE TO USE IT IF YOU HAVE SOMETHING TO THROW AWAY..

I SHOULDN'T HAVE SUGGESTED IT..
SCHULZ

PEANUTS
by SCHULZ
CATCH IT, MARCIE!

YOU KICKED THE FOOTBALL UP INTO THE TREE, SIR..
I KNOW HOW TO GET IT DOWN..

YOU STAND IN FRONT OF THE TREE..I'LL RUN UP AND JUMP ON YOUR SHOULDERS...

MY SHOELACE IS UNTIED AGAIN..
11-30-97
© 1988 United Feature Syndicate, Inc.

WHAM!

OKAY, SIR..I'M READY WHEN YOU ARE!

WHAT ARE YOU DOING DOWN THERE?
FORGET IT, MARCIE! IF THE BALL WANTS TO STAY IN THE TREE, LET IT STAY..

WE'LL PROBABLY NEVER MAKE IT TO THE SPLENDID BOWL ANYWAY, SIR
SUPER BOWL, MARCIE!
SCHULZ

Dear Brother Snoopy,
This year I had a great idea.
© 1987 United Feature Syndicate, Inc.

For my Christmas tree, I decorated a tumbleweed.

It looked really beautiful.
12-1-97

But then it left!
SCHULZ

12-2-97

© 1989 United Feature Syndicate, Inc.

SCHULZ

YES, MA'AM, I'D LIKE TO BUY A CHRISTMAS PRESENT FOR A GIRL I KNOW..
12-3-97

I WAS THINKING MAYBE A PAIR OF GLOVES...
© 1990 United Feature Syndicate, Inc.

WOULD IT HELP IF I DESCRIBED HER?

WELL, SHE HAS TEN FINGERS..
SCHULZ

I WANTED TO BUY PEGGY JEAN SOME GLOVES FOR CHRISTMAS, BUT THEY COST TWENTY-FIVE DOLLARS
12-4-97

SHE'S GOING TO BE DISAPPOINTED WHEN SHE FINDS OUT HER BOYFRIEND IS A CHEAPSKATE

I'M NOT A CHEAPSKATE.. I JUST DON'T HAVE TWENTY-FIVE DOLLARS
PUT IT ON YOUR CREDIT CARD..

I DON'T HAVE A CREDIT CARD..
SO LONG, PEGGY JEAN!
SCHULZ

YOU KNOW WHY I WANT TO BUY PEGGY JEAN THOSE GLOVES FOR CHRISTMAS?

WHEN I FIRST MET HER THIS SUMMER AT CAMP, I NOTICED WHAT PRETTY HANDS SHE HAD... I WANT THOSE PRETTY HANDS TO BE WARM..

12-5-97

BUT I DON'T HAVE TWENTY-FIVE DOLLARS TO BUY THE GLOVES...

SEND HER A NICE CARD, AND TELL HER TO KEEP HER HANDS IN HER POCKETS!
SCHULZ

SEE? THERE THEY ARE... THOSE ARE THE GLOVES I'D LIKE TO BUY PEGGY JEAN FOR CHRISTMAS..

WHERE ARE YOU GOING TO GET TWENTY-FIVE DOLLARS?
THAT'S THE PROBLEM

MAYBE YOU COULD SELL YOUR DOG...

I TAKE IT BACK.. HE'S PROBABLY ONLY WORTH FIFTY CENTS
12-6-97
SCHULZ

PEANUTS®
by SCHULZ

AND SOMETIMES THEY WORSHIPED CATS! CAN YOU BELIEVE IT?
12-7-97

THEY PUT LITTLE GOLD COLLARS ON THEM, AND THEY BUILT CAT SHRINES AND EVERYTHING!

THEN, ONE DAY THEY DECIDED TO WORSHIP SOMETHING BETTER THAN CATS..

THEY DECIDED TO WORSHIP ROCKS!
HA HA HA HA!

HEY, STUPID CAT! DID YOU HEAR THAT? INSTEAD OF WORSHIPING CATS, THEY DECIDED TO WORSHIP ROCKS!!

SLASH!

NEVER DISCUSS THEOLOGY WITH A CAT..
HEE HEE HEE
SCHULZ

LUCY SAID IF I NEED TWENTY-FIVE DOLLARS TO BUY PEGGY JEAN A CHRISTMAS PRESENT, I SHOULD SELL MY DOG...
© 1990 United Feature Syndicate, Inc.

WHAT A GREAT IDEA!

THAT'S THE FIRST TIME I'VE EVER SEEN HIM SPILL HIS WATER DISH..
12-8-97
SCHULZ

YES, MA'AM ... I'M LOOKING AT THOSE GLOVES AGAIN...

I WISH I COULD GET THEM FOR THIS GIRL I KNOW, BUT I CAN'T AFFORD THEM..
12-9-97

I JUST LIKE TO STAND HERE, AND PRETEND I'M BUYING THEM FOR HER..
© 1990 United Feature Syndicate, Inc.

SORRY, MA'AM, I DIDN'T REALIZE I WAS FOGGING UP THE GLASS..
SCHULZ

© 1990 United Feature Syndicate, Inc.
12-10-97
GO AHEAD, ASK HIM..
IS THIS THE BUS STOP?
- FOR SALE - JOE GARAGIOLA AUTOGRAPHED BASEBALL
MAKE ME AN OFFER
ALL I HAVE IS A DIME.. WILL I GET CHANGE?
DO YOU HAVE A BILLIE JEAN KING?
SCHULZ

-FOR SALE-
USED COMIC BOOKS
ARE THESE ALL YOU HAVE?
12-11-97
© 1990 United Feature Syndicate, Inc.
SCHULZ

YES, MA'AM.. I SOLD MY WHOLE COLLECTION OF COMIC BOOKS..SEE? HERE'S THE MONEY! NOW, I CAN BUY THOSE GLOVES FOR THAT GIRL I LIKE...

BROWNIE CHARLES!
PEGGY JEAN! WHAT ARE YOU DOING HERE?
© 1990 United Feature Syndicate, Inc.
12-12-97

I'VE BEEN SHOPPING WITH MY MOTHER..LOOK, I JUST BOUGHT THIS NEW PAIR OF GLOVES!
SCHULZ

AND DID YOU BUY HER THE GLOVES?
SURE..I SOLD MY WHOLE COMIC BOOK COLLECTION TO GET THE MONEY..

THEN I MET HER IN THE STORE, AND SHE SHOWED ME THE NEW PAIR OF GLOVES SHE'D JUST BOUGHT!

© 1990 United Feature Syndicate, Inc.
SO YOU'RE NOT GOING TO GIVE HER THE PAIR YOU BOUGHT?
WHY GIVE HER SOMETHING SHE ALREADY HAS?!

WELL, AT LEAST THEY DIDN'T GO TO WASTE..
SCHULZ
12-13-97

PEANUTS
by SCHULZ

WHY DO I HAVE THE FEELING THAT SOMEONE HAS JUST THROWN A SNOWBALL AT ME?

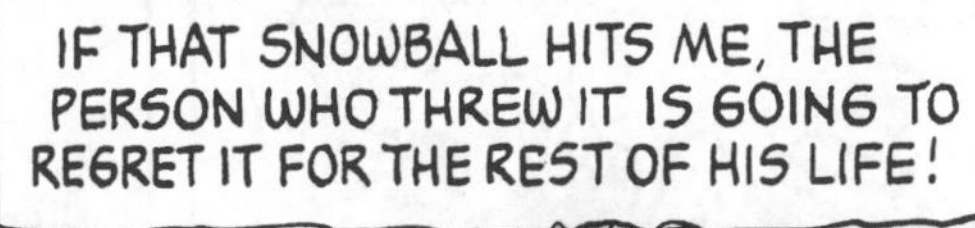
IF THAT SNOWBALL HITS ME, THE PERSON WHO THREW IT IS GOING TO REGRET IT FOR THE REST OF HIS LIFE!

12-14-97
© 1989 United Feature Syndicate, Inc.

SMART! VERY, VERY SMART!
SCHULZ

I DON'T KNOW WHO'S HIDING BEHIND THAT TREE WITH A SNOWBALL...

BUT WHOEVER IT IS BETTER GET RID OF IT BECAUSE IF HE THROWS IT AT ME, I'M GONNA POUND HIM INTO THE GROUND!
© 1991 United Feature Syndicate, Inc.
12-15-97

SCHULZ

DID BEETHOVEN EVER PLAY "JINGLE BELLS"?
12-16-97

HE PROBABLY THOUGHT HE WAS TOO GOOD TO PLAY "JINGLE BELLS"
© 1992 United Feature Syndicate, Inc.

BONK!

IF I HAD BEEN THERE, I WOULD HAVE SAID, "HEY, LUDWIG, PLAY 'JINGLE BELLS'!"
SCHULZ

12-17-97

!
© 1989 United Feature Syndicate, Inc.

SCHULZ

12-18-97
© 1989 United Feature Syndicate, Inc.

SCHULZ

I DON'T THINK YOU'RE THE REAL SANTA CLAUS..

IF YOU'RE THE REAL SANTA, WHERE ARE YOUR HELPERS?

12-19-97
HELP
HELP
HELP
© 1989 United Feature Syndicate, Inc.

THAT'S THE DUMBEST THING I'VE EVER SEEN!
WHO CARES? MERRY CHRISTMAS, SWEETIE! WOOF, WOOF, WOOF!
SCHULZ

SO THEY ALL GO OFF SHOPPING, AND I'M LEFT ALONE IN THE CAR..
12-20-97

THAT'S OKAY..I'LL JUST SIT HERE AND..

ALL RIGHT, GET THAT TRUCK OUT OF THE WAY! WHERE'D YOU LEARN TO DRIVE, IN A CEMETERY? SAME TO YOU, FELLA!!

..BE THE CHAUFFEUR..
© 1987 United Feature Syndicate, Inc.
SCHULZ

PEANUTS
by SCHULZ

"FOUR CALLING BIRDS, AND A PARTRIDGE IN A PEAR TREE.."
THAT SONG DRIVES ME CRAZY!

WHAT IN THE WORLD IS A "CALLING BIRD"?
A CALLING BIRD IS A KIND OF PARTRIDGE..

IN I SAMUEL, 26:20, IT SAYS, "FOR THE KING OF ISRAEL HAS COME OUT TO SEEK MY LIFE JUST AS THOUGH HE WERE HUNTING THE CALLING BIRD..."

THERE'S A PLAY ON WORDS HERE, YOU SEE.. DAVID WAS STANDING ON A MOUNTAIN CALLING, AND HE COMPARED HIMSELF TO A PARTRIDGE BEING HUNTED...

ISN'T THAT FASCINATING?
© 1987 United Feature Syndicate, Inc.

IF I GET SOCKS AGAIN FOR CHRISTMAS THIS YEAR, I'LL GO EVEN MORE CRAZY!
SCHULZ
12-21-97

HAVE I EVER TOLD THE WORLD WAR I FLYING ACE HOW MUCH I ADMIRE HIS BEAUTIFUL SILK SCARF?

PERHAPS THE FLYING ACE MIGHT BE WILLING TO TRADE IT FOR A LITTLE KISS...

12-22-97
SCHULZ

THE FAMOUS WORLD WAR I FLYING ACE LOOKS LONELY..

WOULD IT HELP IF I HELD HIS PAW FOR AWHILE?

12-23-97
LIKE MAYBE UNTIL 1918?
SCHULZ

HE HAS THESE REINDEER, SEE, AND THEY FLY THROUGH THE AIR PULLING HIS SLED...
12-24-97

AND IF YOU BELIEVE THAT, I HAVE A GOLD BIRD NEST THAT I'LL SELL YOU FOR A DOLLAR!

HAHAHAHA!
SCHULZ

MERRY CHRISTMAS, LITTLE FRIEND..

WAKE UP! SANTA CLAUS CAME LAST NIGHT AND DIDN'T LEAVE YOU ANYTHING!
© 1991 United Feature Syndicate, Inc.

12-25-97
APRIL FOOL!
SCHULZ

YES, MA'AM..WE'VE COME TO RENEW HIS DOG LICENSE..
© 1988 United Feature Syndicate, Inc.

bkm
grt
spw
SHE SAID NOT TO WORRY.. YOU DON'T HAVE TO TAKE AN EYE TEST..

12-26-97 SCHULZ
I WASN'T WORRIED.. THIS EYE IS EVEN BETTER..

YES, SIR..THERE SEEMS TO BE A MISTAKE..WE CAME FOR A DOG LICENSE, AND THEY'VE GIVEN HIM A TEMPORARY DRIVER'S PERMIT...
© 1988 United Feature Syndicate, Inc.

DO I THINK HE COULD PASS A DRIVER'S TEST?
12-27-97

"SECTION 203; THE TURN SIGNAL SHOULD BE ACTIVATED BEFORE THE VEHICLE ENTERS THE INTERSECTION"
WELL, YOU NEVER KNOW..
SCHULZ

PEANUTS
by
SCHULZ

© 1990 United Feature Syndicate, Inc.
AN IGLOO! HOW NICE..

IT'S NOT AN IGLOO? THEN WHAT DO YOU CALL IT?

A BEAGLOO?

12-28-97
WHY DO YOU CALL IT A BEAGLOO?

NO, I DON'T THINK IT LOOKS LIKE MY NOSE AT ALL..
SCHULZ

YES, MA'AM.. WELL, ORIGINALLY, I CAME IN WITH MY DOG TO GET HIM A LICENSE...

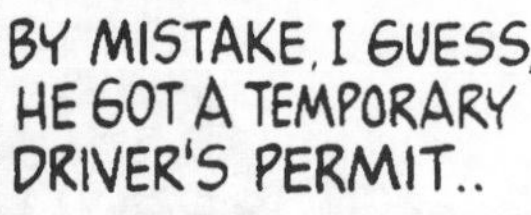
BY MISTAKE, I GUESS, HE GOT A TEMPORARY DRIVER'S PERMIT..

NO, WE HAVEN'T GOT THE DOG LICENSE YET.. I THINK THERE'S BEEN ANOTHER MISTAKE...
12-29-97

ISN'T THIS A FISHING LICENSE?
SCHULZ

YES, MA'AM, WE GOT THE NEW DOG LICENSE..WE ALSO GOT A DRIVER'S LICENSE AND A FISHING LICENSE...

NO, SHE SAYS YOU DON'T NEED A LICENSE FOR THAT..
12-30-97

SCHULZ

12-31-97
WHAT DO YOU MEAN, WE'RE ALL OUT OF HORS D'OEUVRES?!
SCHULZ

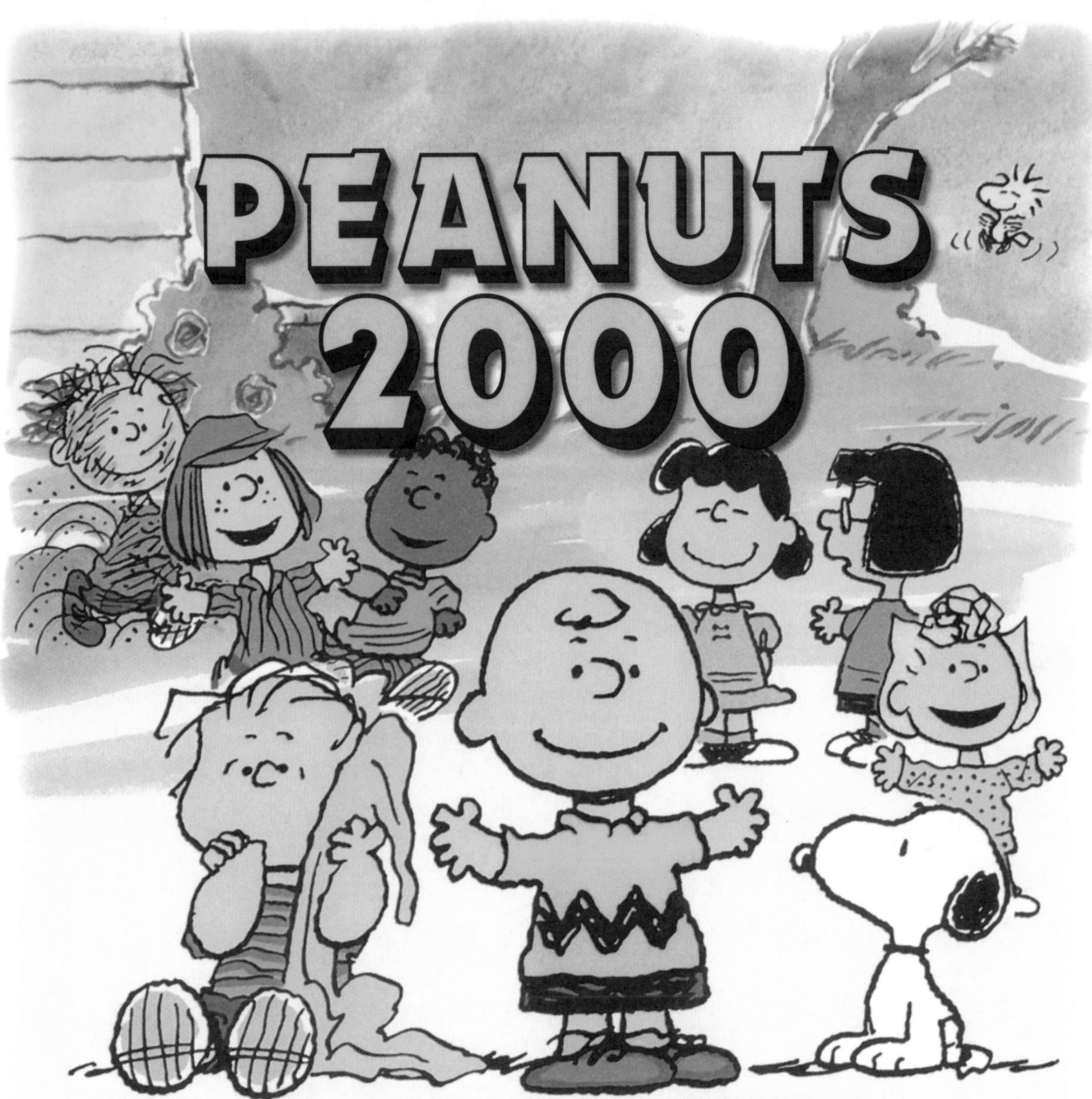
PEANUTS
2000
By Charles M. Schulz

PEANUTS 2000

REMEMBER, IF WE MEET SOMEONE ON THE SIDEWALK, SAY, "HAPPY NEW YEAR"
1-1
www.snoopy.com

IF I SAY, "HAPPY NEW YEAR," WILL THEY GIVE ME A BICYCLE?
NO, THEY WON'T GIVE YOU ANYTHING
© 1998 United Feature Syndicate, Inc.

LET'S GO HOME..
SCHULZ

I'VE DECIDED TO COLLECT A BUNCH OF ROCKS, AND BUILD MYSELF A NICE STURDY HOME
1-2
www.snoopy.com

© 1998 United Feature Syndicate, Inc.

ALWAYS START WITH THE BEDROOM..
SCHULZ

PEANUTS
by
SCHULZ
DO NOT OPEN UNTIL SOMEDAY

YES, MA'AM..I'D LIKE TO RETURN SOMETHING I BOUGHT HERE..

IT'S A CHRISTMAS PRESENT FOR A GIRL, BUT HE WAS TOO SHY TO GIVE IT TO HER..
IT WAS NEVER OPENED..
© 1999 United Feature Syndicate, Inc.

YES, I WAS GOING TO GIVE IT TO A LITTLE RED-HAIRED GIRL IN OUR CLASS..
www.snoopy.com

YOU KNOW HER?
YOU'RE HER MOM?

YOU WORK HERE? IN THIS STORE? YOU'RE HER MOM, AND YOU WORK HERE?
1-3-99

WHEN WE FIRST SAW YOU, WE THOUGHT YOU WERE HER OLDER SISTER..

WHY DID YOU TELL HER THAT?
SHE LET YOU RETURN THE PRESENT, DIDN'T SHE?
SCHULZ

© 1998 United Feature Syndicate, Inc.
I NEVER GOT AROUND TO READING THE BOOK WE WERE SUPPOSED TO READ DURING CHRISTMAS VACATION..
I STARTED TO READ IT, BUT I COULDN'T UNDERSTAND IT..
WHAT BOOK?
BUS STOP
1-4

© 1998 United Feature Syndicate, Inc.

1-5
I HOPE YOU APPRECIATED THE GOOD SERVICE..
THE UMBRELLA WAS THE WRONG COLOR..
SCHULZ

I'M PAINTING WATER LILIES LIKE CLAUDE MONET..
1-6
www.snoopy.com

THEY LOOK MORE LIKE SUBMARINES..
© 1998 United Feature Syndicate, Inc.

THESE ARE SUBMARINES PATROLLING THE ENEMY SHORE..
SCHULZ

"What do dogs think about?" she wondered.

"Someday," thought the dog, "someone is going to leave the gate open, and I'll be out of here like a rocket."

"I suppose," she said, "all they think about is eating."

"Just don't stand too close to that gate," the dog chuckled.

!

RATS! I THOUGHT THEY WERE GIVING AWAY FREE SOCCER BALLS..

I SHOULD CHARGE YOU RENT FOR SHARING THIS BLANKET..
DOGS DON'T PAY RENT..DOGS GUARD THE HOUSE

I WILL ADMIT, HOWEVER, THAT THERE'S A GOOD FEELING TO BE HAD FROM SHARING..
AND A GOOD FEELING THAT COMES FROM KNOWING YOU'RE GUARDING THE HOUSE..
WOOF!

PEANUTS
by
SCHULZ

1-10

IT'S A JIGSAW PUZZLE.. IF THE PIECES DON'T FIT, WE MAKE 'EM FIT!
SCHULZ

HEY, CHUCK, YOU HAVEN'T CALLED ME LATELY..

I CAN'T HEAR YOU.. I'M ON MY CAR PHONE DRIVING ALONG THE AMALFI COAST IN ITALY.. CAN YOU HEAR ME? WHO IS THIS?

YOU'RE JUST ABOUT NINETY PERCENT WEIRD, CHUCK..
1-11

QUICK, MARCIE, SHE'S CALLING ON ME! GIMME THE ANSWER! HURRY! HURRY! HURRY!

YES, MA'AM.. WELL, LET ME THINK ABOUT IT.. THIS IS ONE OF THOSE PROBLEMS THAT REQUIRES REAL THOUGHT...
1-12

SIXTEEN..
SIXTEEN!!

YOU PROMISED YOU'D HELP ME WITH MY HOMEWORK EVERY NIGHT FOR THE REST OF OUR LIVES..

1-13
WHEN DID I PROMISE THAT?

JUST NOW..

THERE! WE FINISHED ALL YOUR HOMEWORK..

I APPRECIATE IT, BIG BROTHER..
GOOD... I'M GLAD YOU DO..
© 1999 United Feature Syndicate, Inc.

I'LL MAKE SURE THAT YOU GET SCREEN CREDIT..
SCHULZ
1-14

NO, I HAVEN'T HEARD ANY DOUGHNUTS CALLING YOU..DOUGHNUTS CAN'T TALK..
1-15
© 1999 United Feature Syndicate, Inc.

MAYBE SO, BUT I'VE HEARD THEM TELL SOME PRETTY FUNNY STORIES
SCHULZ

I WAS WRONG! I DID HEAR A DOUGHNUT CALLING YOU...

1-16

SORRY! I WAS WRONG AGAIN..IT WAS CALLING SOMEONE ELSE..

STUPID DOUGHNUT!
SCHULZ
© 1999 United Feature Syndicate, Inc.

PEANUTS
by SCHULZ

HERE..IT'S A NOTE FROM YOUR DOG..

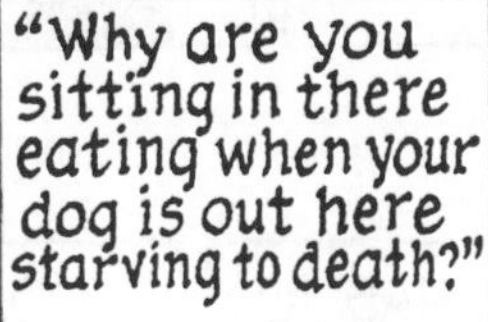
"Why are you sitting in there eating when your dog is out here starving to death?"

TELL HIM HE ISN'T STARVING TO DEATH BECAUSE I JUST FED HIM TEN MINUTES AGO..
© 1999 United Feature Syndicate, Inc.

www.snoopy.com
HE SAYS YOU'RE NOT STARVING TO DEATH BECAUSE HE JUST FED YOU TEN MINUTES AGO..
1-17

"Oh"
SCHULZ

YOU CAN TELL A LOT ABOUT SOMEONE BY FOLLOWING THEIR TRACKS IN THE SNOW..
www.snoopy.com

NOW, WHAT DO YOU THINK WE CAN TELL ABOUT THIS PERSON?

I THINK MAYBE HE WAS A DANCER..
© 1999 United Feature Syndicate, Inc.
1-18
SCHULZ

HERE, EVERYONE HAS TO FILL OUT ONE OF THESE FORMS..

I DON'T KNOW HOW TO FILL OUT A FORM..I'M JUST A LITTLE KID!
www.snoopy.com

JUST PUT CHECK MARKS IN THOSE TINY SQUARES
I CAN DO THAT
1-19
© 1999 United Feature Syndicate, Inc.

SCHOOL WAS GOOD TODAY..WE LEARNED HOW TO FILL OUT FORMS..
SCHULZ

HI, SALLY.. IS CHARLIE BROWN THERE?

"WE'LL ALWAYS HAVE MINNEAPOLIS!".. THAT'S MY NEW PHILOSOPHY..
1-20
www.snoopy.com

IT SOUNDS GOOD.. IS CHARLIE BROWN THERE?

"WE'LL ALWAYS HAVE MINNEAPOLIS"
© 1999 United Feature Syndicate, Inc.

WHO WERE YOU TALKING TO?
PRACTICALLY NOBODY..
SCHULZ

1-21
GRAMPA SAYS HE REMEMBERS WHEN YOU GOT A MOVIE, A NEWSREEL, A SERIAL AND A COMEDY ALL FOR ONLY TEN CENTS..
GRAMPA REMEMBERS EVERYTHING..
I WONDER IF HE KNEW GATSBY..
SCHULZ
© 1999 United Feature Syndicate, Inc.

THIS IS THE HILL WE'RE GOING TO CLIMB..

?
THEN WHAT? THEN WE'LL STAND AT THE TOP, AND SEE THE WHOLE WORLD..
1-22
www.snoopy.com

?
THEN WHAT? THEN WE'LL HIKE BACK DOWN AGAIN..
© 1999 United Feature Syndicate, Inc.

?
STOP SAYING, "THEN WHAT?"
SCHULZ

BEFORE WE GO BACK DOWN THE HILL, LET'S SIT HERE FOR A WHILE..
www.snoopy.com

ACTUALLY, THIS IS A GOOD PLACE TO EAT LUNCH, UNLESS..

..IT'S TOO WINDY
© 1999 United Feature Syndicate, Inc.
1-23
SCHULZ

PEANUTS
by SCHULZ

HERE, PUPPY DOG.. JUMP OVER THE STICK!

© 1999 United Feature Syndicate, Inc.

1-24
www.snoopy.com

I AM NOT A "PUPPY DOG"
SCHULZ

WHERE ARE WE GOING?
© 1999 United Feature Syndicate, Inc.

IT'S A FIELD TRIP..
OH, NO! NOT ME! I'VE HEARD ABOUT THOSE FIELD TRIPS!

THEY TAKE YOU OUT IN THE COUNTRY, AND THEY LEAVE YOU THERE!
1-25
www.snoopy.com

GET ON THE BUS..WE'RE GOING TO AN ART MUSEUM..
SURE, THEY TAKE US TO THE MUSEUM, AND THEN LEAVE US THERE!
SCHULZ

LUCY SAYS WE'RE GOING TO AN ART MUSEUM.. WHAT DO YOU DO IN AN ART MUSEUM?
YOU LOOK AT THE PICTURES..
www.snoopy.com

REALLY? MAYBE THEY'LL HAVE A PICTURE OF MY MOM..
WHY WOULD THEY HAVE A PICTURE OF YOUR MOM?
© 1999 United Feature Syndicate, Inc.

SHE'S VERY PRETTY..
SCHULZ
1-26

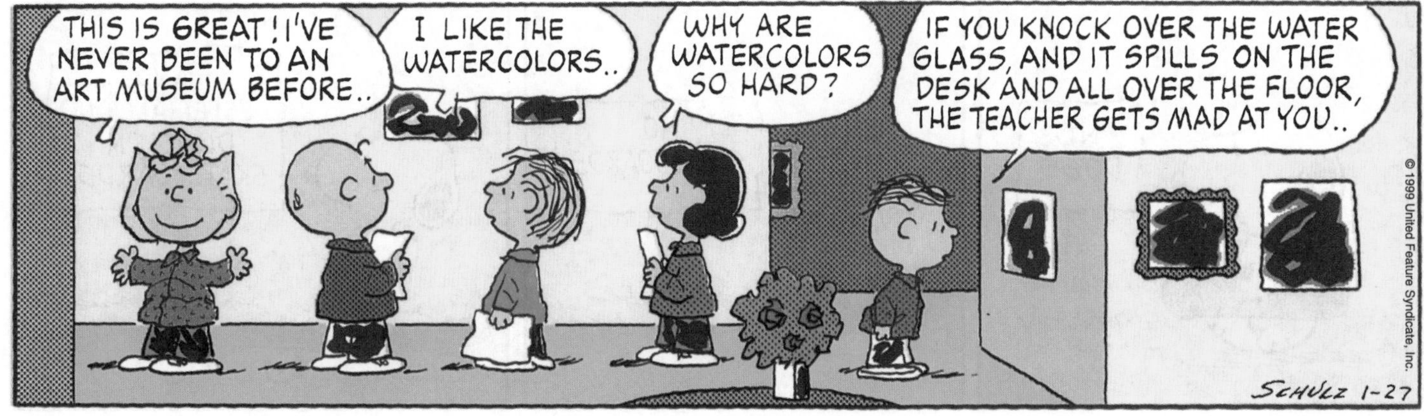
THIS IS GREAT! I'VE NEVER BEEN TO AN ART MUSEUM BEFORE..
I LIKE THE WATERCOLORS..
WHY ARE WATERCOLORS SO HARD?
IF YOU KNOCK OVER THE WATER GLASS, AND IT SPILLS ON THE DESK AND ALL OVER THE FLOOR, THE TEACHER GETS MAD AT YOU..
SCHULZ 1-27
© 1999 United Feature Syndicate, Inc.

I LEARNED A LOT AT THE ART MUSEUM..
I DID, TOO..

I THINK I LEARNED SOMETHING VERY IMPORTANT...

I'LL NEVER BE ANDREW WYETH..

NO DOGS

NO SKATEBOARDS

AND ESPECIALLY NO DOGS ON SKATEBOARDS

PEANUTS
by SCHULZ

1-31
© 1999 United Feature Syndicate, Inc.
www.snoopy.com

I THOUGHT YOU WENT OUT TO BUILD A SNOWMAN..
THE CONDITIONS WEREN'T RIGHT..
SCHULZ

HERE YOU ARE.. SEVEN COOKIES.. ONE FOR EACH DAY OF THE WEEK..
www.snoopy.com

2-1

© 1999 United Feature Syndicate, Inc.

THE DAYS SURE GO BY IN A HURRY, DON'T THEY?
SCHULZ

YES, MA'AM, MY REPORT IS ALMOST READY.. I JUST NEED A LITTLE MORE TIME..
© 1999 United Feature Syndicate, Inc.

LIKE MAYBE TEN YEARS..
2/2
www.snoopy.com

IF I DUCK DOWN LOW, MA'AM, YOU CAN HIT HER WITH AN ERASER..
SCHULZ

I'M THINKING OF STARTING A DISCUSSION GROUP..
2/3
www.snoopy.com

THAT COULD BE VERY INTERESTING..
© 1999 United Feature Syndicate, Inc.

PEOPLE WOULD COME FROM ALL OVER TO LISTEN TO ME..
SCHULZ

HOW CAN YOU PLAY CARDS WITH A DOG?
THIS ISN'T A DOG.. THIS IS "JOE BLACKJACK," THE FAMOUS RIVER BOAT GAMBLER..
www.snoopy.com

HA! I'LL BET HE'S NEVER EVEN SEEN A RIVER BOAT!
2-4
© 1999 United Feature Syndicate, Inc.

HOW ABOUT A STREAM BOAT?
SCHULZ

IF I PLAY THE TWO, HE'LL PROBABLY PLAY THE FOUR, BUT IF I PLAY THE SIX, MAYBE HE'LL PLAY THE NINE..
IF I PLAY ONE OF THESE WITH THE RED SPOTS, HE'LL PROBABLY PLAY ONE OF THE BLACK SPOTS..
2-5
© 1999 United Feature Syndicate, Inc.

I KNOW HE CAN BE VERY CLEVER..
I DON'T HAVE THE SLIGHTEST IDEA WHAT GAME WE'RE PLAYING..
SCHULZ

I GET NERVOUS WHEN I PLAY AGAINST "JOE BLACKJACK," THE WORLD FAMOUS RIVER BOAT GAMBLER..
I NEVER NOTICED IT BEFORE..THE CARDS LOOK THE SAME UPSIDE-DOWN AS RIGHT SIDE UP..
2-6
© 1999 United Feature Syndicate, Inc.
SCHULZ

PEANUTS
by SCHULZ

YOU LOOK PROUD OF YOURSELF..
DID YOU JUST BUY SOMETHING?

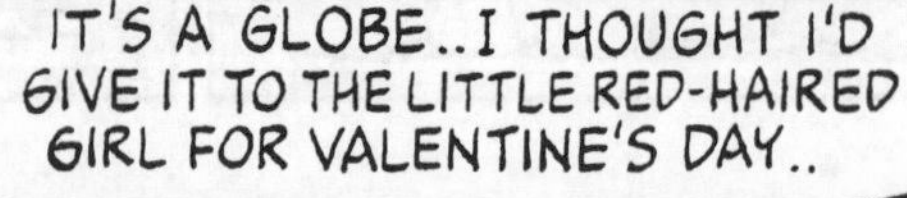

IT'S A GLOBE..I THOUGHT I'D GIVE IT TO THE LITTLE RED-HAIRED GIRL FOR VALENTINE'S DAY..

WHEN YOU TURN IT UPSIDE DOWN, IT SNOWS..
IT SNOWS?
2-7

I DON'T UNDERSTAND..
© 1999 United Feature Syndicate, Inc.

www.snoopy.com

SOMETHING LIKE THAT..
SCHULZ

I'LL HAVE TO ADMIT THAT IN MANY WAYS WE ARE A CLOSE FAMILY..BROTHERS AND SISTERS JUST NATURALLY TEND TO BE THAT WAY..SUCH CLOSENESS IS VERY ADMIRABLE...

HOW WOULD YOU LIKE TO BUY SOME HAND-DRAWN VALENTINES TO GIVE TO YOUR FRIENDS?

I DON'T HAVE ANY FRIENDS..

YOU SHOULDN'T HAVE ANSWERED THE DOOR!

WOULD YOU LIKE TO BUY A HAND-DRAWN VALENTINE?

SEE? IT HAS A HEART ON IT..
IT LOOKS MORE LIKE A BAKED POTATO..

GIVE IT TO SOMEONE ON "BAKED POTATO DAY"

I DON'T SUPPOSE YOU'D LIKE TO BUY SOME HAND-DRAWN VALENTINES, WOULD YOU?

SEE? THEY HAVE BIG RED HEARTS ON THEM..

DOGS DON'T GIVE VALENTINES..

WE'LL TAKE THEM, BUT WE DON'T GIVE THEM..

PEANUTS
by SCHULZ

NO VALENTINES..
2-14
SCHULZ

2-15
HOW CAN SOMEONE NOT GET ANY VALENTINES?
www.snoopy.com

HOW CAN SOMEONE NOT GET EVEN ONE VALENTINE?

IT'S AN AWFUL FEELING, ISN'T IT?
© 1999 United Feature Syndicate, Inc.

I WOULDN'T KNOW..
SCHULZ

2-16
www.snoopy.com

© 1999 United Feature Syndicate, Inc.

CLEAR AIR TURBULENCE
SCHULZ

THIS IS THE BOOK I DIDN'T READ IN NOVEMBER..
www.snoopy.com

THIS IS THE BOOK I DIDN'T READ IN DECEMBER, AND THIS IS THE ONE I DIDN'T READ IN JANUARY..
2-17

SO THIS MUST BE FEBRUARY..

I CAN ALWAYS TELL WHAT MONTH IT IS BY THE BOOK I DIDN'T READ
© 1999 United Feature Syndicate, Inc.

THERE'S A NEW WEIRD LIST OUT, SIR... YOU'RE A TEN..
SCHULZ

Dear Grampa,
I am sending you some golf balls for your birthday.
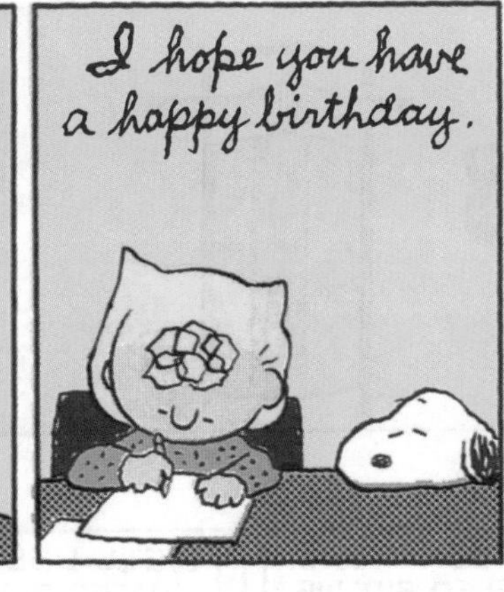
I hope you have a happy birthday.
www.snoopy.com

And I hope you like the golf balls.
© 1999 United Feature Syndicate, Inc.

Try not to hit them into the lake.
SCHULZ
2-18

Leaping onto his horse, he galloped across the prairie.

Gallop
Gallop
Gallop
Gallop
www.snoopy.com

"Don't leave me!" she cried.

Gallop back
Gallop back
Gallop back
Gallop back
© 1999 United Feature Syndicate, Inc.
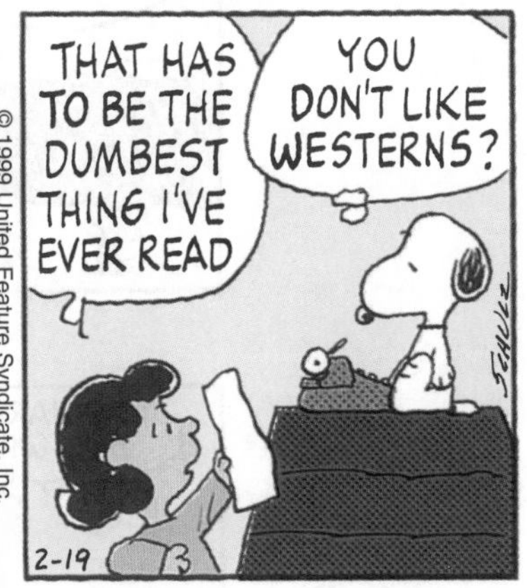
THAT HAS TO BE THE DUMBEST THING I'VE EVER READ
YOU DON'T LIKE WESTERNS?
SCHULZ
2-19

NO, I'M NOT INTERESTED..
2-20

NO, NOT TODAY, THANK YOU..
www.snoopy.com
© 1999 United Feature Syndicate, Inc.

NO, BUT WHY DON'T YOU JUST LEAVE ME YOUR CARD?

SALESBIRDS!
SCHULZ

www.snoopy.com

HEY, CHUCK, YOU DIDN'T SEND ME A VALENTINE THIS YEAR..

WHAT HAPPENED WAS THE PONY EXPRESS LOST THEIR BEST PONY, AND THEN THERE WAS A ROBBERY, AND THEN SOME BAD WEATHER, AND..
2-22

THANKS, CHUCK... I'M HANGING UP FIVE MINUTES AGO..

GOOD EVENING, SIR..I'D LIKE TO SHOW YOU OUR NEW MENU..

THE OLD ONE ALWAYS SAID "DOG FOOD"
2-23

OUR NEW MENU SAYS "DOGGE FOODE"

HOW UPSCALE CAN YOU GET?

ASK YOUR DOG TO COME OUT, AND ROMP IN THE SNOW..

TO "ROMP" MEANS TO PLAY OR FROLIC IN A BOISTEROUS, LIVELY WAY..

2-24

HE SAID, "NO." "NO" MEANS TO DENY OR REFUSE, OR DISAGREE..

I KNOW WHAT IT MEANS!

BEFORE WE KNOW IT, ALL THE SNOW WILL BE GONE, AND I'LL BE STANDING ON MY OL' PITCHER'S MOUND..
www.snoopy.com

AND THIS IS THE YEAR I'M GOING TO HIT SEVENTY-ONE HOME RUNS!

HE'S GOING TO BE SO JEALOUS..
2-25
© 1999 United Feature Syndicate, Inc.

WHO IS?
JOE McGWIRE!
SCHULZ

YOU COULDN'T HIT SEVENTY-ONE HOME RUNS IF YOU PLAYED FOR A THOUSAND YEARS..
www.snoopy.com

AND HIS NAME IS MARK McGWIRE, NOT JOE McGWIRE!
2-26
© 1999 United Feature Syndicate, Inc.

I GET HIM MIXED UP WITH JOE RUTH..
SCHULZ

© 1999 United Feature Syndicate, Inc.
I THINK I LIKED THE MOVIE, BUT I'M NOT SURE..
I THINK IT WAS TOO LONG..
I DIDN'T UNDERSTAND THE ENDING..
I WAS TOO SHORT TO SEE THE SCREEN..
NOW SHOWING
2-27
SCHULZ

PEANUTS®
SCHULZ

I BLOCK THE PASS! THE BALL IS MINE!

I WHIRL..

I DRIBBLE DOWN THE SIDE! WE'RE ONE POINT BEHIND..

I FAKE A PASS, AND WHIRL AGAIN..
© 1999 United Feature Syndicate, Inc.

THREE SECONDS ON THE GAME CLOCK..
2-28

I SHOOT..

IT'S IN!!
www.snoopy.com

THEY LET ME HAVE THE GAME BALL..
SCHULZ

3-1
SO HOW WAS THE MOVIE?
AS SOON AS IT STARTED, IT WAS TOO LONG..
SCHULZ

ASK YOUR DOG IF HE WANTS TO COME OUT AND PLAY..
www.snoopy.com

TELL HIM HE CAN THROW THE BALL, AND I'LL CHASE IT..
3-2

EVERY DAY WE LEARN SOMETHING NEW..

DOGS DON'T HAVE THROWING ARMS..
SCHULZ

IF YOU FIX HIS DINNER AND I SERVE IT, DO WE SPLIT THE TIP?

ABSOLUTELY

3-3

WE'RE NEVER GONNA GET RICH..
SCHULZ

YES, SIR..I'D LIKE TO BUY A NEW KITE..
www.snoopy.com

OH, RED, BLUE, YELLOW... I DON'T CARE..THE COLOR DOESN'T MATTER..
3-4
© 1999 United Feature Syndicate, Inc.

DO YOU HAVE ONE THAT ISN'T AFRAID OF HEIGHTS?
SCHULZ

3-5
© 1999 United Feature Syndicate, Inc.
IS THIS YOURS? I SUPPOSE IT IS, ISN'T IT?
SCHULZ

3-6
© 1999 United Feature Syndicate, Inc.

www.snoopy.com

JOE HOUDINI!
SCHULZ

PEANUTS
by SCHULZ

HERE'S HOW IT WORKS..
© 1999 United Feature Syndicate, Inc.

I'LL TAKE MY CARDS, AND YOU'LL TAKE YOUR CARDS..

THEN WE'LL THROW THEM IN THE AIR..

WHOEVER HAS THE MOST CARDS LAND FACE UP WINS..
www.snoopy.com

3-7
HOW DO YOU DO THAT?
SCHULZ

SOMETIMES I LIE AWAKE AT NIGHT, AND I ASK, "IS LIFE A MULTIPLE CHOICE TEST OR IS IT A TRUE OR FALSE TEST ?"

THEN A VOICE COMES TO ME OUT OF THE DARK, AND SAYS, "WE HATE TO TELL YOU THIS, BUT LIFE IS A THOUSAND WORD ESSAY"
3-8
SCHULZ

I CAN'T BELIEVE IT! HE SAID, "THAT'S ALL THE TIME WE HAVE LEFT.." WHAT'S HE TALKING ABOUT? I'VE GOT PLENTY OF TIME!

HOW CAN HE SAY, "THAT'S ALL THE TIME WE HAVE LEFT"? I'VE GOT MY WHOLE LIFE AHEAD OF ME!

MAYBE YOU SHOULD WRITE HIM A LETTER, AND TELL HIM HOW YOU FEEL..
3-9
I DON'T HAVE TIME..
SCHULZ

AFTER I HIT SEVENTY-ONE HOME RUNS, I'LL SELL THE BALL FOR THREE MILLION DOLLARS
3-10

HOW DOES THE WORST PLAYER IN THE HISTORY OF THE GAME EXPECT TO HIT SEVENTY-ONE HOME RUNS?

I'VE NEVER SEEN A SKY LOOK QUITE SO BLUE, HAVE YOU?
SCHULZ

I'M NOT GOING TO SCHOOL TODAY..GIVE THIS HOMEWORK TO MY TEACHER, WILL YOU?
3-11
www.snoopy.com

IT'S JUST A BUNCH OF SCRIBBLING..
© 1999 United Feature Syndicate, Inc.

WELL, IT'S DARK UNDER HERE..
SCHULZ

YOU WEREN'T HERE YESTERDAY
I WAS HIDING UNDER MY BED
3/12

I DON'T THINK THE TEACHER KNOWS IF I'M HERE OR NOT HERE..
www.snoopy.com

DON'T KID YOURSELF.. SHE HAS A LIST OF OUR NAMES WITH LITTLE CHECK MARKS
© 1999 United Feature Syndicate, Inc.

TWELVE CHECK MARKS, AND YOU'RE BANISHED FOR LIFE..
I NEED A LIGHT UNDER MY BED..
SCHULZ

TELL YOUR FRIENDS THEY CAN'T BUILD A NEST ON MY PITCHER'S MOUND..
www.snoopy.com

??
© 1999 United Feature Syndicate, Inc.

3-13

WHY DO I ALWAYS FEEL LIKE AN OUTSIDER?
SCHULZ

PEANUTS
by SCHULZ
PATS

RERUN! WHAT IN THE WORLD ARE YOU DOING?
I'M PATTING BIRDS ON THE HEAD..

NOBODY PATS BIRDS ON THE HEAD!
LINUS TOLD ME HE USED TO DO IT ALL THE TIME..

YOUR BROTHER IS A BLOCKHEAD! DO YOU THINK I WANT EVERYONE IN SCHOOL SAYING TO ME, "YOUR BROTHER PATS BIRDS ON THE HEAD"?
www.snoopy.com

3-14
STOP IT! STOP IT RIGHT NOW!

AND YOU GUYS GO ON HOME! GET OUT OF HERE! GO FLY WITH SOME DUCKS OR SOMETHING!

© 1999 United Feature Syndicate, Inc.

I CAN'T HELP IT.. HE ALREADY HAD AN APPOINTMENT..
SCHULZ

© 1999 United Feature Syndicate, Inc.
THAT WAS A GOOD MOVIE.. I LIKED IT..
"A BOY AND HIS FAITHFUL DOG"
I THOUGHT IT WAS PRETTY REALISTIC..
THE DOG WAS OVERLY FAITHFUL..
3-15
SCHULZ

IS IT SPRING YET?
YOU CAME OVER HERE TO ASK ME THAT?
www.snoopy.com

YOU HAVE A BROTHER AND A SISTER AT HOME..WHY DON'T YOU ASK THEM?
3-16

THEY GET MAD WHEN I ASK STUPID QUESTIONS
SPRING IS NEXT WEEK
© 1999 United Feature Syndicate, Inc.

THANKS FOR NOT GETTING MAD..
SCHULZ

3-17
© 1999 United Feature Syndicate, Inc.
SORRY WE'RE A LITTLE LATE, MA'AM.. WE WALKED ALL THE WAY TO SCHOOL THIS MORNING..
AGAINST THE WIND..
SCHULZ

THEORETICALLY, MY OLDER BROTHER SHOULD BE MY ROLE MODEL..

BUT THAT BLANKET BUSINESS TAKES CARE OF THAT..
3-18
www.snoopy.com

WHICH FORCES ME TO LOOK ELSEWHERE, AND MAYBE ASK THE QUESTION...

CAN THE NEIGHBOR'S DOG BE A ROLE MODEL?
SCHULZ

AND THAT IS MY REPORT ON MY DOG.. ARE THERE ANY QUESTIONS?

NO, HE'S NOT A SHEEP DOG..WHY IS HE CARRYING THAT "STICK THING"?
www.snoopy.com

AACKK
3-19

ANY MORE QUESTIONS?
SCHULZ

SO HERE'S THE LIST OF PLAYERS WHO ARE ON OUR TEAM THIS YEAR..
HOW ABOUT "YOU KNOW WHO"?

"YOU KNOW WHO" IS IN RIGHT FIELD AGAIN..
I AM?

HOW DO YOU KNOW "YOU KNOW WHO" IS YOU?
YOU KNOW ME..
SCHULZ
3-20

PEANUTS
by
SCHULZ

3-21

© 1999 United Feature Syndicate, Inc.
www.snoopy.com

mf
SCHULZ

WHICH WOULD YOU RATHER DO, EAT BREAKFAST OR HELP ME WITH THE HOMEWORK I SHOULD HAVE DONE LAST NIGHT?
3-22
www.snoopy.com

I THINK I'LL EAT BREAKFAST..
© 1999 United Feature Syndicate, Inc.

I USED ALL THE MILK..
SCHULZ

I LIKE SITTING BEHIND YOU, LINUS..
I'M GLAD
www.snoopy.com

YOU HAVE NICE HAIR..
THANK YOU
© 1999 United Feature Syndicate, Inc.

AND YOU SMELL LIKE ERASERS..
SCHULZ
3-23

I KNOW THE ANSWER! I KNOW THE ANSWER!

SORRY, MA'AM..I WAS JUST BLUFFING..
www.snoopy.com

"BLUFFING"... YOU KNOW.. "GAMESMANSHIP"

THAT'S RIGHT... LOOKING FOR THAT LITTLE EDGE..
3-24
© 1999 United Feature Syndicate, Inc.

YES, MA'AM..I KNOW EVERYTHING BUT THE ANSWERS..
SCHULZ

LOOK, MY DAD BOUGHT ME A BAG OF MARBLES..
www.snoopy.com

3-25
DOGS' DADS CAN'T BUY THINGS..
© 1999 United Feature Syndicate, Inc.

DID YOUR DAD EVER BITE ANYBODY?
SCHULZ

IT'S CALLED "EGGS IN THE BUSH"
© 1999 United Feature Syndicate, Inc.

YOU TRY TO GUESS HOW MANY MARBLES THE OTHER PERSON HAS IN HIS HAND..
www.snoopy.com

3-26
PAWS!
SCHULZ

RERUN AND SNOOPY ATTEMPT TO REVIVE THE ANCIENT ROMAN GAME OF CARDS AND MARBLES..
3-27
© 1999 United Feature Syndicate, Inc.
SCHULZ

PEANUTS
by SCHULZ

DOES ANYONE ELSE IN YOUR FAMILY PLAY THE PIANO?
3-28

MY MOTHER SAYS SHE TOOK LESSONS WHEN SHE WAS LITTLE..

MY DAD PLAYS THE MOUTH ORGAN AT THE BARBERS' PICNIC..

I ALSO HAVE AN UNCLE WHO PLAYS AN ACCORDION..

AND A GRAMPA WHO SORT OF PLAYS THE FIDDLE..
© 1999 United Feature Syndicate, Inc.
www.snoopy.com

I PLAY THE DOG..
SCHULZ

OUR FIRST GAME OF THE SEASON! WHAT DO WE NEED TO WIN?
COURAGE, FORTITUDE AND DEDICATION!

HOW DID YOU KNOW THAT?
3-29

I WROTE DOWN WHAT YOU SAID LAST YEAR..
SCHULZ

PITCH IT TO 'IM, YOU BLOCKHEAD!
3-30

I CAN'T HEAR YOU, MISS KNOW-IT-ALL, WORST PLAYER IN THE HISTORY OF THE GAME, BECAUSE YOU'RE FACING THE WRONG WAY!

PITCH IT TO 'IM, YOU BLOCKHEAD!

IS THAT BETTER?
SCHULZ

IT'S ONLY THE FIRST INNING, AND WE'RE ALREADY BEHIND FORTY TO NOTHING!
3-31

AND NOW IT'S RAINING..

SEE, CHARLIE BROWN? YOU JUST HAVE TO BELIEVE!
SCHULZ

WAKE UP, BIG BROTHER! MARK McGWIRE IS AT THE DOOR! HE WANTS TO PLAY ON YOUR TEAM!

APRIL FOOL!

MARK? MARK?
APRIL FOOL!

MR. McGWIRE? ARE YOU OUT THERE?
APRIL FOOL!

RATS! I GUESS HE LEFT..
4-1

THERE'S A SPIDER ON YOUR BACK! APRIL FOOL!
SCHULZ

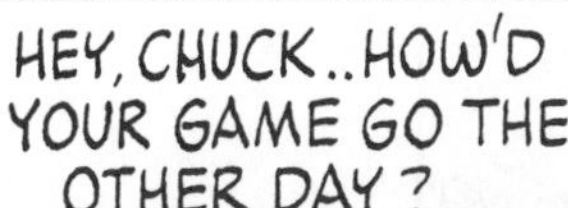

HEY, CHUCK.. HOW'D YOUR GAME GO THE OTHER DAY?

WELL, WE WERE BEHIND FORTY TO NOTHING, BUT THEN IT STARTED TO RAIN SO THE GAME GOT CALLED OFF..
4-2

WOW! GREAT COMEBACK, CHUCK!

IT WASN'T A COMEBACK.. THE GAME WAS CALLED OFF..

FOR YOU THAT'S A COMEBACK, CHUCK! HA! HA! HA!
I'LL BET HE ENJOYS YOUR CALLS, SIR
SCHULZ

ANOTHER TRAFFIC REPORT! WHAT DO I CARE ABOUT A TRAFFIC REPORT? I DON'T DRIVE A CAR!

4-3

PEOPLE DRINK COFFEE WHILE THEY DRIVE..
I DON'T DRINK COFFEE

AND THEY TALK ON THE TELEPHONE..
I COULD DO THAT..
SCHULZ

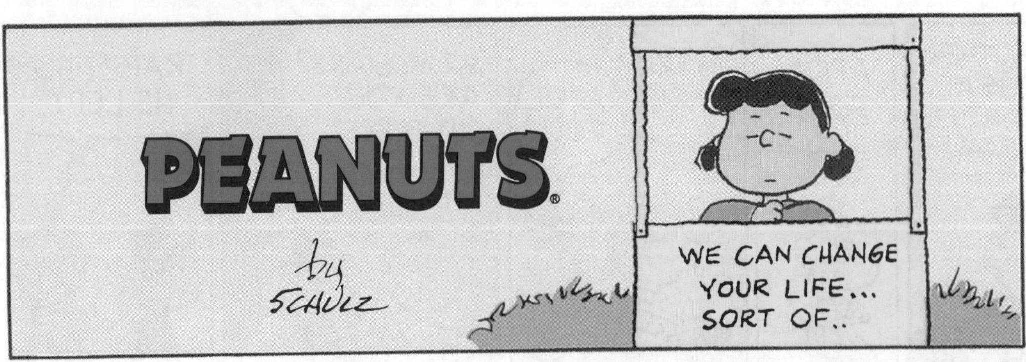
PEANUTS
by SCHULZ
WE CAN CHANGE YOUR LIFE... SORT OF..

PSYCHIATRIC HELP 5¢
SO I'M WONDERING, COULD I EVER LEARN TO BE THE LIFE OF THE PARTY?
THE DOCTOR IS IN

YOU?
© 1999 United Feature Syndicate, Inc.

HA HA HA HA HA!
THE DOCTOR IS IN
4-4

I'M SORRY.. I SHOULDN'T HAVE LAUGHED... WHERE WERE WE? OH, YES, NOW I REMEMBER..
THE DOCTOR IS IN
www.snoopy.com

YOU? THE LIFE OF THE PARTY?

HA HA HA HA!
THE DOCTOR IS IN

WELL, HOW DID YOUR SESSION WITH THE PSYCHIATRIST GO?
I WAS ASKING HER IF I COULD EVER LEARN TO BE THE LIFE OF THE PARTY, AND..

YOU? HA HA HA HA!

ACTUALLY, I'VE NEVER BEEN INVITED TO A PARTY..
SCHULZ

4-5
I HATE TO LEAVE YOU AGAIN, SNOOPY, BUT I'M OFF TO SCHOOL..
www.snoopy.com

THAT'S LIFE.. PEOPLE GO AWAY, AND DOGS STAY HOME..
© 1999 United Feature Syndicate, Inc.

AND STAY HOME, AND STAY HOME, AND STAY HOME AND STAY HOME..
SCHULZ

YOU DID IT, SIR! I'M PROUD OF YOU..
THANK YOU, MARCIE..THANK YOU..
© 1999 United Feature Syndicate, Inc.

I DIDN'T THINK YOU'D DO IT, BUT YOU DID IT!
"THE D-MINUS HALL OF FAME"!
4-6
SCHULZ

YES, MA'AM..NOW THAT I'M IN THE "D-MINUS HALL OF FAME," DO I STILL HAVE TO DO THE SAME WORK AS YOUR ORDINARY STUDENTS?

A ROLE MODEL?
www.snoopy.com

HAHAHAHA!
© 1999 United Feature Syndicate, Inc.

YES, MA'AM, I CAN BE A ROLE MODEL..
4-7
SCHULZ

THE TEACHER GAVE ME THIS CERTIFICATE, CHUCK.. IT SAYS I'M IN THE "D-MINUS HALL OF FAME"

DO YOU THINK MAYBE SHE'S JUST BEING SARCASTIC? IS SHE TRYING TO TELL ME SOMETHING?

WELL...

THANKS, CHUCK..
4-8

YES, MA'AM..HER DESK LOOKS EMPTY DOESN'T IT?

WELL, I KNOW SHE WAS OFFENDED BY THAT "D-MINUS HALL OF FAME" THING

YES, IF I SEE HER, I'LL TELL HER..

SEE? SHE DOESN'T EVEN KNOW I'M UNDER HERE..

HOW WOULD YOU LIKE TO BUY A PICTURE I DREW OF YOUR DOG?
ARE YOU A SALESMAN?

A WHAT?
SALESMEN ARE A DYING BREED..

DID YOU SELL YOUR DRAWING?
I COULDN'T.. I'M A DYING BREED..
4-10

PEANUTS
by SCHULZ
RERUN! ARE YOU COMING OR NOT?

I'M NEVER GOING TO SCHOOL AGAIN..

THE TEACHER ASKED ME IF I THOUGHT I'VE LEARNED EVERYTHING I NEED TO KNOW

I THINK SHE WAS BEING SARCASTIC..
4-11

ANYWAY, I SAID, "YES"...NOW, SHE'S MAD AT ME..

DO YOU THINK YOU'VE LEARNED EVERYTHING YOU NEED TO KNOW?

I THINK I'VE LEARNED ALL I NEED TO KNOW TO LIVE UNDER A BED..
SCHULZ

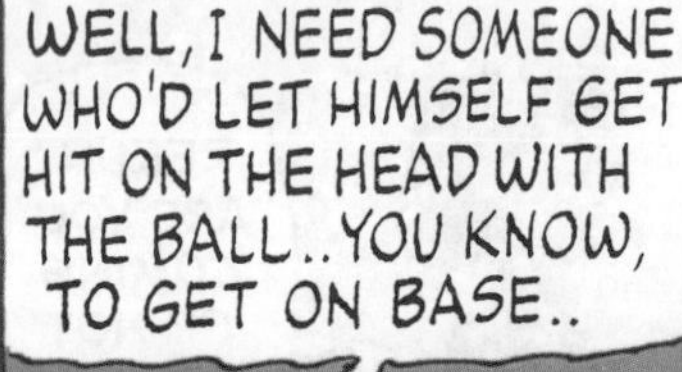
HEY, CHUCK, YOU WANNA PLAY ON MY TEAM THIS YEAR?
WELL, I NEED SOMEONE WHO'D LET HIMSELF GET HIT ON THE HEAD WITH THE BALL..YOU KNOW, TO GET ON BASE..

4-12

NO? WELL, OKAY.. I UNDERSTAND..
© 1999 United Feature Syndicate, Inc.

ANYWAY, GOOD LUCK THIS YEAR WITH YOUR OWN SO-CALLED TEAM..
HAD TO SAY IT, HUH, SIR?
SCHULZ

ONE FINGER WILL MEAN A STRAIGHT BALL..TWO FINGERS WILL MEAN ANOTHER STRAIGHT BALL...
4-13
www.snoopy.com

THREE FINGERS WILL MEAN ANOTHER STRAIGHT BALL..
ANYTHING ELSE?
© 1999 United Feature Syndicate, Inc.

BY THEN IT WON'T MATTER..
SCHULZ

© 1999 United Feature Syndicate, Inc.
4-14

HEY, HOW ABOUT THROWING OUR BALL BACK?

WHO HIT IT?

NOBODY IMPORTANT..

SCHULZ

YOU KNOW, CHARLIE BROWN, BASEBALL IS A REAL THINKING GAME..

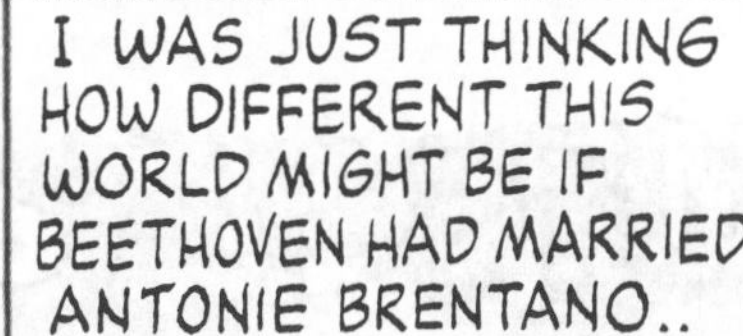
I WAS JUST THINKING HOW DIFFERENT THIS WORLD MIGHT BE IF BEETHOVEN HAD MARRIED ANTONIE BRENTANO..

BUT, THEN, WHAT IF HE HAD MARRIED GIULIETTA GUICIARDI? I JUST DON'T KNOW

4-15

WELL, HOW DID YOUR GAME GO?
WE LOST BY ONE RUN..

4-16
THEY GOT FORTY AND WE GOT ONE..
SCHULZ

SO FAR, YOU'VE HAD A PRETTY SUCCESSFUL LIFE, HAVEN'T YOU?
4-17

I WONDER HOW YOU DID IT..
I WAS LUCKY..

I GOT A FIRST ROUND BYE
SCHULZ

PEANUTS
by SCHULZ

READY TO QUIT THE GAME, HUH? WELL, I DON'T BLAME YOU..

IF YOU'RE GOING TO QUIT, HOWEVER, IT HAS TO BE OFFICIAL..

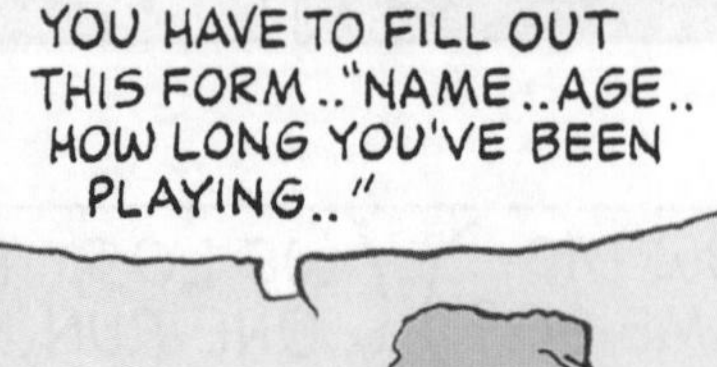
YOU HAVE TO FILL OUT THIS FORM.."NAME..AGE.. HOW LONG YOU'VE BEEN PLAYING.."

"PROMISE NEVER TO PLAY AGAIN.. NEVER TO TAKE ANOTHER LESSON.. NEVER TO WATCH GOLF ON TV.."

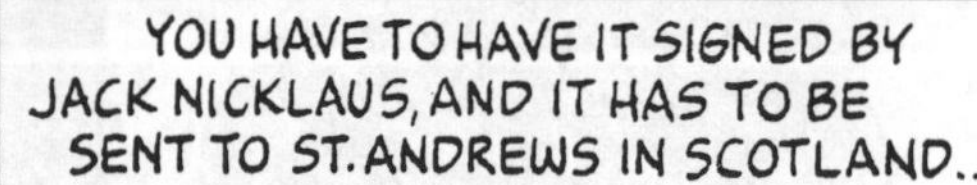
YOU HAVE TO HAVE IT SIGNED BY JACK NICKLAUS, AND IT HAS TO BE SENT TO ST. ANDREWS IN SCOTLAND..

WAIT A MINUTE..THERE'S ONE MORE THING...

"RESIGNING PLAYER MUST REMOVE ALL CLUBS FROM TREES"
SCHULZ
4-18

IF I STAND HERE LONG ENOUGH, DO YOU THINK SOMEONE WILL COME ALONG AND GIVE ME A BICYCLE?
4-19

I DOUBT IT..
THAT'S TOO BAD..

I LIKE TO
THINGS FREE..

IT SAYS HERE, "STOP ACTIVITY IF YOU EXPERIENCE PAIN OR SWELLING..DISCOMFORT SHOULD BE EVALUATED"

4-20
IT WAS A LINE DRIVE..
SCHULZ

I WENT TO YOUR DAD'S BARBER SHOP TODAY..

I DIDN'T KNOW THAT HAIRCUTS HURT..
HAIRCUTS DON'T HURT..
4-21

I FELL OUT OF THE CHAIR..

ROTHER..
O BE
SCHULZ

SO WHAT DO YOU WANT ME TO DO?
www.snoopy.com
© 1999 United Feature Syndicate, Inc.

4-22
ROLE
SCHULZ

DID YOU HEAR THAT? HE SAID IT'S GOING TO RAIN TODAY..

www.snoopy.com
IF IT'S GOING TO RAIN, WHY DIDN'T YOU STAY HOME AND DRIVE YOUR KIDS TO SCHOOL?

YOUR KIDS ARE GONNA GET WET! WHAT KIND OF A FATHER ARE YOU ANYWAY ?!
4-23
© 1999 United Feature Syndicate, Inc.

I YELL AT HIM EVERY MORNING, BUT HE NEVER LISTENS..
SCHULZ

PRETTY SOON THE BACK DOOR WILL OPEN, AND THAT ROUND-HEADED KID WILL COME OUT WITH MY SUPPER..
4-24

I KNOW IT WILL HAPPEN BECAUSE IT ALWAYS HAPPENS
www.snoopy.com

DOGS BELIEVE IF SOMETHING HAPPENS ONCE, IT'LL HAPPEN AGAIN AND AGAIN..THAT'S WHAT DOGS BELIEVE..
© 1999 United Feature Syndicate, Inc.

HA!
SCHULZ

PEANUTS
by SCHULZ
WHO AM I? I AM THE MANAGER

WHAT'S THAT?
4-25

ICE WATER! WHEN WE WIN THE CHAMPIONSHIP, WE'LL POUR IT OVER OUR MANAGER'S HEAD..

I'VE SEEN THEM DO IT AT FOOTBALL GAMES..

WE'RE NEVER GOING TO WIN A CHAMPIONSHIP...WE CAN'T EVEN WIN A GAME!
www.snoopy.com

THAT'S ALL RIGHT.. BUT I CAN'T WAIT FOREVER..

© 1999 United Feature Syndicate, Inc.

ARE YOU OUT OF YOUR MIND?! CHARLIE BROWN IS GOING TO HATE YOU FOR THE REST OF YOUR LIFE!

DID WE WIN?
SCHULZ

I HAVE A GLOVE, CHARLES..NOW, CAN I BE ON YOUR TEAM?
www.snoopy.com

I TOLD YOU, RERUN, YOU'RE TOO YOUNG
4-26

MAYBE NEXT YEAR..
© 1999 United Feature Syndicate, Inc.

NEXT YEAR I'LL BE TOO OLD..
SCHULZ

YOU SEE, THE PROBLEM IS I'M TOO YOUNG... I'M TOO SMALL..
4-27

IT ISN'T AS THOUGH THEY THINK I'M INFERIOR.. LIKE MAYBE I'M A DOG OR SOMETHING..
www.snoopy.com

OKAY, WHERE'S OUR SHORTSTOP?

© 1999 United Feature Syndicate, Inc.

YOU SEE, IT ISN'T AS THOUGH I'M BITTER OR ANYTHING..
SCHULZ

STOP ASKING ME FOR THE ANSWERS, SIR..I DON'T HAVE ALL THE ANSWERS..SOMETIMES I JUST GUESS..
www.snoopy.com

YOU GUESS?! YOU'VE BEEN GIVING ME ANSWERS THAT YOU JUST GUESSED?!!
4-28
© 1999 United Feature Syndicate, Inc.

TIME OUT!
SCHULZ

YES, MA'AM..WE HAVE A LITTLE PROBLEM HERE..

SEE, ON QUESTIONS TWO, NINE, ELEVEN AND TWENTY, I HAD TO ASK MARCIE FOR THE ANSWERS....
4-29

BUT ON NINE AND TWENTY, SHE ADMITS SHE ONLY GUESSED SO ON MY PAPER I WAS WONDERING IF..

DON'T SIGH LIKE THAT, MA'AM..IT BREAKS MY HEART..

SCHULZ

SO THE TEACHER SAID SHE COULD ALWAYS TELL WHEN YOU WERE GUESSING AT THE ANSWERS..

YOU TOLD HER I GUESS AT THE ANSWERS?!
4-30

SURE, MARCIE..I HAD TO PROTECT MYSELF.. YOU MADE MY ANSWERS LOOK STUPID..

YOU UNDERSTAND, DON'T YOU? YOU FORGIVE ME, DON'T YOU?

I GUESS..
SCHULZ

DID YOU NOTICE SOMETHING?

WHEN I BROUGHT YOUR SUPPER OUT, I DIDN'T WALK STRAIGHT FORWARD.. I DID SORT OF A PROMENADE..

I WAS WONDERING IF YOU NOTICED THAT..

I DON'T KNOW WHAT'S WRONG WITH ME..I DIDN'T NOTICE THAT..
SCHULZ
5-1

PEANUTS
by SCHULZ

NEW DECK..

READY..
© 1999 United Feature Syndicate, Inc.
CARTOONISTS DAY MAY 5
www.snoopy.com

5-2
SOMEDAY ONE OF US IS GOING TO HAVE TO LEARN TO SHUFFLE..
SCHULZ

WOLVES ARE MAKING A COMEBACK..
© 1999 United Feature Syndicate, Inc.
5-3

DETAILS AT ELEVEN..
SCHULZ

"WOLVES ARE MAKING A COMEBACK".. THAT'S MY NEW PHILOSOPHY..
www.snoopy.com

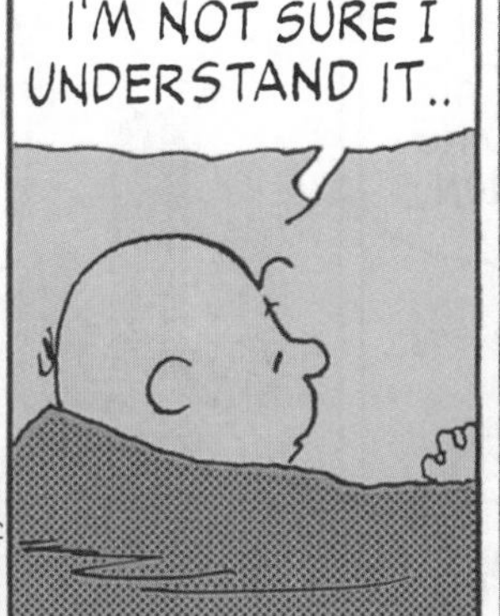
I'M NOT SURE I UNDERSTAND IT..

NO ONE EVER REALLY UNDERSTANDS A NEW PHILOSOPHY..
© 1999 United Feature Syndicate, Inc.
5/4

"WOLVES ARE MAKING A COMEBACK"
YES, THERE'S A LOT OF TRUTH IN THAT..
SCHULZ

5-5

© 1999 United Feature Syndicate, Inc.

www.snoopy.com

SCHULZ
CARTOONISTS DAY MAY 5

I'M ON MY OWN ONE-YARD LINE..THE COUNT IS THREE AND TWO..THE EIGHTEENTH HOLE IS A PAR FIVE WITH WATER IN FRONT..ONE SECOND LEFT ON THE SHOT CLOCK..THE FACE-OFF IS IN OUR ZONE..FORTY-LOVE, MATCH POINT...
5-6

HAVING TROUBLE WITH THE FIRST QUESTION, SIR?
AND A SEVEN-TEN SPLIT IN THE TENTH FRAME!
© 1999 United Feature Syndicate, Inc.
SCHULZ

IF YOU'RE GOING INTO TOWN, BRING ME A PIZZA..
© 1999 United Feature Syndicate, Inc.

5-7
SORRY, I THOUGHT YOU WERE GOING INTO TOWN..

IF YOU EVER DO DECIDE TO GO INTO TOWN, PLEASE BRING ME A PIZZA..
www.snoopy.com

I LEAD A REALLY, REALLY, REALLY, REALLY, STUPID LIFE..
SCHULZ

© 1999 United Feature Syndicate, Inc.
SCHULZ
5-8

PEANUTS

by Schulz

WHAT'S THIS?
I'M DOING A REPORT ON GRAMPA..
www.snoopy.com

THAT'S NICE..DOES IT HAVE A TITLE ?
© 1999 United Feature Syndicate, Inc.

5-10
"WONDERS OF THE ANCIENT WORLD"
SCHULZ

HOW WOULD YOU LIKE TO BUY SOME HOMEMADE FUDGE?
WHO MADE IT?
www.snoopy.com

MY MOM, MY GRAMMA AND MY SISTER..
ARE YOU THE MIDDLEMAN?
5-11
© 1999 United Feature Syndicate, Inc.

NO, THEY'RE ALL TALLER THAN ME..
SCHULZ

www.snoopy.com

5-12
© 1999 United Feature Syndicate, Inc.

NOW, I KNOW WHY YOU WANT TO BE PITCHER..
SCHULZ

AND WHEN THE PELICAN SEES A FISH, HE SWOOPS DOWN ON THE WATER AND GRABS IT..
5-13

www.snoopy.com

SWOOPS..

GRAMPA'S ON THE PHONE.. DO YOU WANT TO WISH HIM A "HAPPY BIRTHDAY"?
www.snoopy.com

I DIDN'T KNOW TODAY WAS HIS BIRTHDAY..

HAPPY BIRTHDAY, GRAMPA..YOU'RE WELCOME..HAVE A NICE DAY..
5-14

WHICH GRAMPA WAS THAT?
SCHULZ

ALL RIGHT, I KNOW WHEN I'M NOT WANTED IN THIS FAMILY!

I DON'T HAVE TO LIVE HERE, YOU KNOW!
www.snoopy.com

I CAN ALWAYS GO LIVE WITH AUNT EDNA..
5-15

..OR LOIS, OR LINDA, OR EUNICE, OR WHATEVER HER NAME IS!
SCHULZ

PEANUTS
by SCHULZ
LINUS?

HERE'S WHAT I WANTED TO ASK YOU..
YAWN

WHAT? I'M SORRY..I WAS YAWNING AND STRETCHING..I CAN'T HEAR WHEN I'M YAWNING AND STRETCHING..

WELL, I WAS ASKING YOU IF..
www.snoopy.com

I COULDN'T HEAR YOU..I WAS CHEWING POTATO CHIPS..WHEN I CHEW POTATO CHIPS, I CAN'T HEAR ANYTHING
5-16

ALL RIGHT, IF YOU CAN'T HEAR ME, I'LL WRITE IT DOWN..

© 1999 United Feature Syndicate, Inc.

I CAN'T READ THIS..IT'S DARK IN HERE..
SCHULZ

YOU MAY NOT REALIZE IT, BUT I FIND THAT YOU'RE VERY INSPIRING..
5-17

I LIKE THE WAY YOU STAND TALL, AND THE WAY YOU SEEM TO BE REACHING FOR THE HEAVENS

IT'S VERY INSPIRING

ON THE OTHER HAND, YOU ALSO LOOK LIKE YOU'RE BEING HELD UP IN A CONVENIENCE STORE..

YES, MA'AM, THIS IS A LIST OF THE COLLEGES I PLAN TO APPLY TO..

I'LL NEED TO HAVE YOU WRITE LETTERS OF RECOMMENDATION FOR ME..
5-18

WHERE'D SHE GO?

I'VE DECIDED TO APPLY ONLY TO COLLEGES THAT HAVE GOLF TEAMS..

DO YOU THINK YOU'LL NEED A GOOD GRADE POINT AVERAGE?
5-19

NO, ALL THEY CARE ABOUT IS CAN YOU REACH THE PAR FIVES IN TWO?

HEY, CHUCK, DO YOU EVER THINK ABOUT COLLEGE?

WELL, NOT REALLY..

THERE'S YOUR PROBLEM.. YOUR LIFE DOESN'T HAVE ANY DIRECTION..

A LIFE SHOULD BE PLANNED LIKE INNING BY INNING..

I TRIED THAT.. THE VISITORS ARE STILL AT BAT..
SCHULZ
5-20

I'M NOT SO SURE ABOUT THIS COLLEGE THING AFTER ALL..

I JUST DISCOVERED SOMETHING..

THEY HAVE CLASSES!
SCHULZ
5/21

5-22

I DON'T KNOW.. SHOULD WE HAVE TRIED TO SEE WHAT THE NOTE SAID?
SCHULZ

PEANUTS
OUI, MON CAPITAINE!

ASK YOUR DOG IF HE WANTS TO COME OUT AND PLAY..
ASK HIM YOURSELF.. HERE HE COMES NOW..

BONJOUR, MONSIEUR..

ODD LOOKING FELLOW..

PROBABLY SAW ONE OF OUR NEW RECRUITING POSTERS...
5-23

I CAN'T BELIEVE WHAT HEADQUARTERS IS SENDING US THESE DAYS..

HERE, PUT THIS ON..

TELL MOM I THINK I MAY BE GONE FOR FIVE YEARS..
SCHULZ

HAVE YOU HEARD ANY ANNOUNCEMENTS? I ALWAYS LIKE THE ANNOUNCEMENTS..
www.snoopy.com

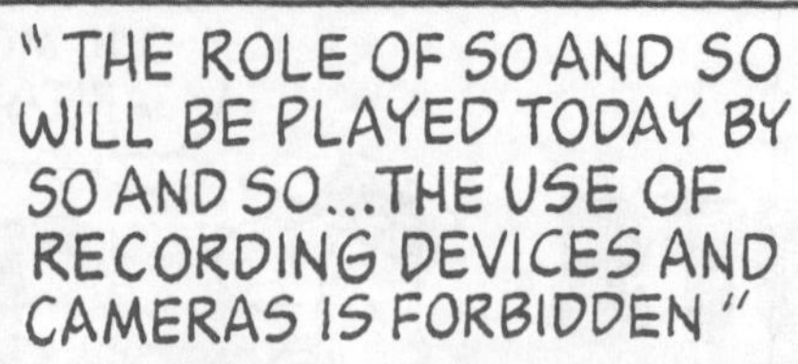
" THE ROLE OF SO AND SO WILL BE PLAYED TODAY BY SO AND SO...THE USE OF RECORDING DEVICES AND CAMERAS IS FORBIDDEN "

5-24

I LOVE THE ANNOUNCEMENTS..
YOU'RE VERY WEIRD, SIR..
SCHULZ

YES, MA'AM..IT WAS A GOOD STORY..THANK YOU FOR READING IT TO US..
Z
5-25
www.snoopy.com

WAKE UP, RERUN..THE STORY'S OVER..YOU MISSED THE GOOD PARTS..

IT HAD GOOD PARTS?
SCHULZ

OUR TEACHER IS MAD AT ME BECAUSE I FELL ASLEEP WHILE SHE WAS READING US A STORY..
www.snoopy.com

BUT AT LEAST I LEARNED SOMETHING..

5-26
ALWAYS SIT IN THE BACK ROW..
SCHULZ

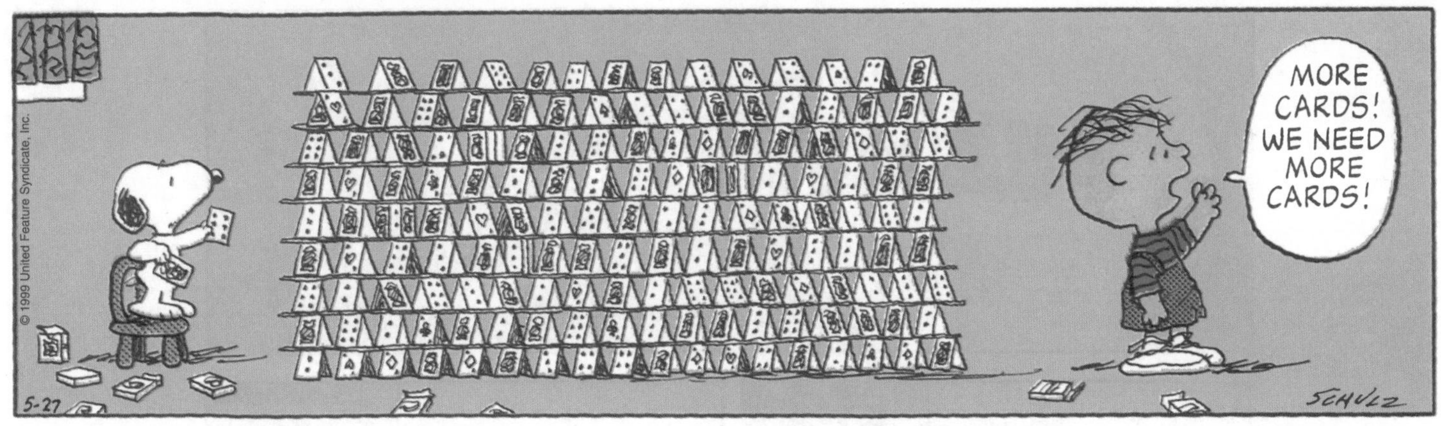
MORE CARDS! WE NEED MORE CARDS!
SCHULZ
5-27
© 1999 United Feature Syndicate, Inc.

WHOOPS!
5-28
SCHULZ
© 1999 United Feature Syndicate, Inc.

KEEP LOOKING UP..THAT'S THE SECRET OF LIFE...
5-29
www.snoopy.com

KLUNK!

I WAS WRONG.. THAT'S NOT THE SECRET OF LIFE..
© 1999 United Feature Syndicate, Inc.
SCHULZ

PEANUTS
by
SCHULZ

© 1999 United Feature Syndicate, Inc.

5-30
www.snoopy.com

YES, MA'AM..I HAVE MY REPORT..

"HOW I WASTED ANOTHER SUNDAY AFTERNOON WATCHING MY DOG SLEEP.."
SCHULZ

YES, MA'AM, I'M FINISHED..

I CUT OUT THE LIONS AND THE ZEBRAS, AND PASTED THEM ALL IN THE JUNGLE, SEE?
5-31
www.snoopy.com

ACTUALLY, I HATE CUTTING AND PASTING..
© 1999 United Feature Syndicate, Inc.

I THINK MY FUTURE IS IN CRAYONS..
SCHULZ

THOMAS PAINE SAID, "THESE ARE THE TIMES THAT TRY MEN'S SOULS"
www.snoopy.com

WHAT WAS HE TALKING ABOUT?
6-1
© 1999 United Feature Syndicate, Inc.

CUTTING AND PASTING..
SCHULZ

SORRY I MISSED THAT BALL, MANAGER.. THE DANDELIONS GOT IN MY EYES..

WHEN THE SUN REFLECTS OFF THE BRIGHT YELLOW DANDELIONS, I CAN'T SEE THE BALL..
www.snoopy.com

THAT'S THE WORST EXCUSE I'VE EVER HEARD!
© 1999 United Feature Syndicate, Inc.

BE PATIENT.. I HAVE TWENTY-THREE NEW ONES!
SCHULZ
6-2

HEY, MANAGER, ARE WE AHEAD YET?
www.snoopy.com

NO, WE'RE NOT AHEAD, AND WE PROBABLY NEVER WILL BE AHEAD!
ARE WE BEHIND?

YES, WE'RE BEHIND, AND WE'LL PROBABLY ALWAYS BE BEHIND!
6-3
© 1999 United Feature Syndicate, Inc.

ANY MORE QUESTIONS?
HOW HAVE YOU BEEN?
SCHULZ

I'M AFRAID TO LOOK AT MY REPORT CARD..

HERE, MARCIE, YOU LOOK AT IT, AND TELL ME HOW I DID..

AAUGHH!!
6-4
© 1999 United Feature Syndicate, Inc.

YOU SHOULD MAYBE WRITE HORROR STORIES, MA'AM..
SCHULZ

AND THEN THE POET SAID, "WHAT IS SO RARE AS A DAY IN JUNE?"
6-5
www.snoopy.com

?
WHICH DAY? I DON'T KNOW WHICH DAY.. WHO CARES?
© 1999 United Feature Syndicate, Inc.

!
YOU DIDN'T LIKE YESTERDAY?
SCHULZ

PEANUTS
by SCHULZ

6-6
© 1999 United Feature Syndicate, Inc.
www.snoopy.com

YOU'RE BACK EARLY.. WHAT HAPPENED?

EVERYWHERE WE WENT.. TALL CREATURES WITH RED HANDS!
SCHULZ

WHEN YOU GO TO A FANCY RESTAURANT, THE WAITER SAYS, "BE CAREFUL, SIR..THE DISH IS HOT"
6-7
© 1999 United Feature Syndicate, Inc.

BE CAREFUL, SIR..THE DISH IS PLASTIC..
SCHULZ

ARE THE DAYS GETTING LONGER OR SHORTER?
6-8
www.snoopy.com

ACTUALLY, THEY'RE GETTING NARROWER

SOME MORNINGS, WHEN YOU GET UP, THE DAY IS SO NARROW YOU CAN HARDLY SQUEEZE IN..
© 1999 United Feature Syndicate, Inc.

I NEVER KNOW WHAT YOU'RE TALKING ABOUT..
TODAY SEEMS TO BE PRETTY WIDE..
SCHULZ

© 1999 United Feature Syndicate, Inc.
THAT WAS A PRETTY GOOD MOVIE..
SUBTITLES ALWAYS BOTHER ME..
FORTUNATELY THEY WERE IN FRENCH..
SCHULZ
6-9

WHERE'D YOU GET THE CAKE?
IN THE KITCHEN
www.snoopy.com

I THINK YOU SHOULD ALWAYS SHARE WITH YOUR SISTER..
I AGREE.. ALWAYS..
6/10

ABSOLUTELY ALWAYS..
POSITIVELY ALWAYS..
© 1999 United Feature Syndicate, Inc.

BUT NOT EVERY TIME..
SCHULZ

HI, MARCIE.. ANY PLANS FOR THE SUMMER?
www.snoopy.com

VIOLIN LESSONS, SPANISH LESSONS, DANCE LESSONS, SWIMMING LESSONS AND READ "DON QUIXOTE"
6-11
© 1999 United Feature Syndicate, Inc.

GO BACK IN AND CLOSE THE DOOR, MARCIE.. I'LL JUST STAND HERE..
SCHULZ

DON'T YOU LIKE TO JUST STARE AT THE CLOUDS, MARCIE?
I CAN'T.. I'M READING "DON QUIXOTE"
6-12
© 1999 United Feature Syndicate, Inc.

HOW ABOUT YOU, CHUCK.. CLOUDS OR "DON QUIXOTE"?
THERE WE WERE.. TEN RUNS BEHIND, AND IT WAS ONLY THE FIRST INNING..
SCHULZ

"LEARNING IS AN EXPERIENCE"
PEANUTS®
by SCHULZ

© 1999 United Feature Syndicate, Inc.
DO YOU MIND IF I STAND HERE BEHIND YOU, CHARLES?

IF I'M GOING TO BE A PITCHER, I WANT TO LEARN FROM THE MASTER..
MASTER?

THIS IS GREAT.. I CAN SEE HOW YOU GRIP THE BALL AND CONCENTRATE
6-13

AND HOW YOU LEAN BACK BEFORE YOU..
www.snoopy.com

POW!

I THINK THIS MUST BE YOUR SHIRT..
YOU CAN LEARN A LOT FROM THE MASTER.. IS THIS YOUR SOCK?
SCHULZ

6-14
www.snoopy.com

BONK!
© 1999 United Feature Syndicate, Inc.

WHY DON'T YOU JUST GET RID OF THE CELL PHONE ?
SCHULZ

HI, CHARLES..MAY I BORROW YOUR DOG FOR THE DAY ?
www.snoopy.com

YOU CAN'T BORROW A DOG.. YOU CAN BORROW MONEY, OR A BASEBALL GLOVE, OR A CAR, BUT YOU CAN'T BORROW A DOG..
6-15

I DIDN'T KNOW THAT..
© 1999 United Feature Syndicate, Inc.

ASK YOUR DAD IF I CAN BORROW HIS CAR..
SCHULZ

© 1999 United Feature Syndicate, Inc.
6-16
SCHULZ

6-17

www.snoopy.com

LET ME ASK YOU SOMETHING...
© 1999 United Feature Syndicate, Inc.

DO YOU KNOW WHY WE'RE OUT HERE?
SCHULZ

I MEMORIZED THE BIBLE VERSE WE WERE SUPPOSED TO MEMORIZE FOR SUNDAY..
WHAT VERSE?
www.snoopy.com

I DON'T KNOW.. NOW YOU MADE ME FORGET..
6-18

MAYBE IT WAS SOMETHING MOSES SAID, OR SOMETHING FROM THE BOOK OF REEVALUATION..
© 1999 United Feature Syndicate, Inc.

FORGETTING IS NOT ALWAYS A BAD THING..
SCHULZ

WHEN SOMEONE WALKS BY, HOW DO YOU DECIDE IF YOU SHOULD BARK AT HIM?
www.snoopy.com

6-19
© 1999 United Feature Syndicate, Inc.

WOOF!
SCHULZ

PEANUTS
by SCHULZ

WHAT ARE YOU DRAWING?
A CARD FOR DAD.. TODAY IS FATHER'S DAY..

REALLY? NO WONDER THERE'S NO SCHOOL..

THERE'S NO SCHOOL BECAUSE TODAY IS SUNDAY..

YOU SAID IT'S FATHER'S DAY..
© 1999 United Feature Syndicate, Inc.

IT'S FATHER'S DAY AND IT'S SUNDAY..
www.snoopy.com
6-20

FATHER'S DAY IS ALWAYS ON A SUNDAY..
www.snoopy.com

GOOD PLANNING, DAD!
SCHULZ

DO YOU THINK SO?

WELL, YOU'RE PROBABLY RIGHT..

WE'RE AS WET AS THE FISH..
SCHULZ
6-21

HEY, MANAGER, HOW COME I ALWAYS HAVE TO PLAY RIGHT FIELD?

BECAUSE YOU'RE SUCH A TERRIBLE PLAYER!

I SUPPOSE YOU THINK YOU'RE SUCH A GREAT PITCHER, HUH?
6-22

AND I SUPPOSE YOU THINK YOU'RE SUCH A GREAT MANAGER?

THIS COULD TURN UGLY..
SCHULZ

LUCY'S ON THE PHONE.. SHE WANTS TO KNOW WHY SHE ALWAYS HAS TO PLAY RIGHT FIELD..

TRADITIONALLY, THE PLAYER WHO IS WEAKEST DEFENSIVELY PLAYS RIGHT FIELD..

HE SAYS THE DUMBEST PLAYER ALWAYS PLAYS RIGHT FIELD..

6-23

THIS COULD TURN REALLY UGLY..
SCHULZ

ALL RIGHT, ANSWER ME THIS.. HOW COME A DOG GETS TO PLAY SHORTSTOP WHILE I HAVE TO PLAY RIGHT FIELD ?
Z
www.snoopy.com

WELL, HE'S QUITE KNOWLEDGEABLE ABOUT THE GAME, AND HE'S USUALLY VERY ALERT, AND..
KLUNK!

INFIELD-FLY RULE? WHO WANTS TO KNOW ABOUT THE INFIELD-FLY RULE ?
© 1999 United Feature Syndicate, Inc.
6-24
SCHULZ

HEY, MANAGER, I'VE DECIDED IF I HAVE TO PLAY RIGHT FIELD ALL THE TIME, I'D RATHER NOT PLAY AT ALL..
www.snoopy.com

REALLY ? WOW! THAT'S GREAT! BOY, WHAT A RELIEF !!
© 1999 United Feature Syndicate, Inc.

OKAY, I'LL PLAY RIGHT FIELD..
SCHULZ
6-25

SO WITH THESE GLASSES I THINK I'LL BE A BETTER OUTFIELDER.. DON'T YOU AGREE?
www.snoopy.com

THE SUN WON'T BE A PROBLEM ANYMORE..YOU'LL APPRECIATE THAT

I'LL CATCH EVERYTHING THAT COMES MY WAY..

NICE TALKING TO YOU, MANAGER..
6-26
© 1999 United Feature Syndicate, Inc.

I CAN'T STAND IT.. I JUST CAN'T STAND IT..
SCHULZ

PEANUTS
by SCHULZ
STICK

FETCH!
www.snoopy.com

I THROW STICK..
6-27
© 1999 United Feature Syndicate, Inc.

YOU FETCH!

FETCH!

I NEED A DOG..
SCHULZ

AT TIMES LIKE THIS I WISH I WERE BACK IN SCHOOL..
I KNOW WHAT YOU MEAN.. DO YOU THINK MAYBE IT'S A LONGING FOR LEARNING THAT WE ALL HAVE?
© 1999 United Feature Syndicate, Inc.

NO, I LEFT
IN MY

YOU CAN TAKE
THE MASK...
GOING TO

DO YOU THINK I SHOULD GO TO CAMP?
ONLY IF YOU WANT TO..
www.snoopy.com

WANT TO?! SINCE WHEN HAVE I EVER HAD A CHOICE ABOUT ANYTHING?
6-29

HOW ABOUT THE PIANO LESSONS?
© 1999 United Feature Syndicate, Inc.

I DIDN'T WANT TO..
SCHULZ

CAMP? NO, I DON'T WANT TO GO TO YOUR CAMP..STOP CALLING ME..
6-30

I TOLD THEM I DIDN'T WANT TO GO TO THEIR CAMP..
GOOD FOR YOU..
www.snoopy.com

REALLY? YOU MEAN THAT? I DID THE RIGHT THING?
ABSOLUTELY!

GOOD FOR ME!
SCHULZ
© 1999 United Feature Syndicate, Inc.

I'M SORRY YOU DIDN'T GET TO DO SOME DIVING.. YOU LOOK LIKE AN EXPERT..

I FELL IN THE POOL ONCE..
SCHULZ
7-1

DO YOU THINK I DID RIGHT BY NOT GOING TO CAMP, BIG BROTHER?
7-2

ABSOLUTELY
I MIGHT HAVE HAD FUN..

NO, YOU WOULDN'T
YOU'RE RIGHT.. I WOULD HAVE HATED IT..

YOU CAN ALWAYS GO NEXT YEAR..
SURE, I CAN THINK ABOUT IT..
SCHULZ

STAY THERE.. I'LL WAKE YOU UP AGAIN NEXT YEAR..

WHEN I GET OLDER, I'M GOING TO LEARN TO PLAY A MUSICAL INSTRUMENT..
7-3

I CAN'T DECIDE IF I SHOULD PLAY THE PIANO, OR THE VIOLIN, OR THE CELLO OR THE HARP..
IT DOESN'T MATTER BECAUSE YOU'LL NEVER GET AROUND TO PLAYING ANY OF THEM..

YOU ARE FORTISSIMOLY WEIRD, MARCIE..
SCHULZ

PEANUTS
by SCHULZ

GRAMPA READ IT TO ME..IT WAS IN A STORY BY LEO TOLSTOY...

THIS WOMAN HAD FOUR CHILDREN, SEE, AND THEY ALL SLEPT TOGETHER IN A BIG CRADLE...

WHEN SHE PUT THEM TO BED, SHE GAVE EACH ONE A "SUCKING RAG."

7-4

ENJOY YOUR "SUCKING RAG"
© 1999 United Feature Syndicate, Inc.
www.snoopy.com

SCHULZ

HOW WOULD YOU LIKE TO BUY A PICTURE OF YOUR DOG?
www.snoopy.com

I DON'T THINK SO.. I WOULDN'T KNOW WHAT TO DO WITH IT..
7-5
© 1999 United Feature Syndicate, Inc.

IF YOU GOT CAUGHT IN THE RAIN, YOU COULD HOLD IT OVER YOUR HEAD..
SCHULZ

What a writer should know...
www.snoopy.com

7-6

© 1999 United Feature Syndicate, Inc.

NEVER LEAN BACK TO READ WHAT YOU'VE WRITTEN..
SCHULZ

GRAMMA SAYS WE LEARN FROM OUR MISTAKES..
www.snoopy.com

NO, YOU LEARN FROM LISTENING TO EVERYTHING YOUR OLDER SISTER TELLS YOU..
© 1999 United Feature Syndicate, Inc.

IS THAT TRUE?
I JUST LEFT
7-7
SCHULZ

THIS IS HOW YOU WALK WHEN YOUR TEAM HAS LOST ANOTHER GAME FORTY TO NOTHING..
www.snoopy.com

THIS IS HOW YOU KICK YOUR GLOVE ALL THE WAY HOME AFTER YOUR TEAM HAS LOST FORTY TO NOTHING..
7-8
© 1999 United Feature Syndicate, Inc.

THIS IS HOW YOU STAND BY THE CURB, AND WATCH A TRUCK RUN OVER YOUR GLOVE AFTER YOU'VE LOST FORTY TO NOTHING..
SCHULZ

YOU CAN TALK TO A CACTUS...
7-9
© 1999 United Feature Syndicate, Inc.

BUT A TUMBLEWEED WON'T LISTEN..
SCHULZ

HAS SCHOOL STARTED YET?
NO, NOT FOR ANOTHER NINE OR TEN WEEKS..
© 1999 United Feature Syndicate, Inc.

SCHULZ 7-10
THAT'S GOOD..I NEED LOTS OF DREAD TIME..

PEANUTS
by SCHULZ

PEGGY JEAN!
BROWNIE CHARLES!

I DIDN'T KNOW YOU WERE HERE AT CAMP.. ACTUALLY, I WAS JUST THINKING ABOUT YOU...
7-11

I WASN'T GOING TO CAMP THIS YEAR, BUT MY BOY FRIEND SAID HE'D BE HERE..

ANYWAY, I PROMISED TO MEET HIM OVER BY THE SOCCER FIELD..
BOY FRIEND?
© 1999 United Feature Syndicate, Inc.

BUT REMEMBER WHEN..REMEMBER WHEN...
www.snoopy.com

REMEMBER...

SALLY? PUT SNOOPY ON THE PHONE, WILL YOU?

WOOF!
SCHULZ

THANKS.. I NEEDED TO HEAR A FRIENDLY VOICE..

SUMMER CAMP? YES, I GOT YOUR BROCHURE..YES, THANK YOU..

NO, I WASN'T PLANNING ON GOING TO CAMP THIS YEAR..
www.snoopy.com

WELL, IF I CHANGE MY MIND, COULD I BRING MY BROTHER'S WOLF WITH ME?

7-12
WOOF!
© 1999 United Feature Syndicate, Inc.

THAT'S ANOTHER CAMP I DON'T HAVE TO GO TO..
SCHULZ

I JUST SAW THE LITTLE RED-HAIRED GIRL DOWN AT THE PLAYGROUND..WE HAD A NICE TALK..
www.snoopy.com

SHE SURE IS CUTE..
DID SHE SAY ANYTHING ABOUT ME?
© 1999 United Feature Syndicate, Inc.

DID SHE WHAT?
I CAN'T STAND IT..
7/13
SCHULZ

THAT SOUNDS LIKE A FIRE ENGINE..
SOMETHING MUST BE ON FIRE..
WELL, IT SURE ISN'T OUR PITCHER!
7-14
www.snoopy.com

HA HA HA HA HA HA!
© 1999 United Feature Syndicate, Inc.

LET HER GET ABOUT TEN FEET AWAY..THEN THROW YOUR GLOVE AT HER..
SCHULZ

WE CAME TO WATCH YOUR GAME, CHARLES.. DO WE NEED TICKETS?

NO, YOU CAN SIT OVER THERE BY THE FENCE..

THESE ARE LOUSY SEATS!

THIS IS THE FIRST TIME I'VE EVER WATCHED A BALL GAME..

WOULD YOU LIKE A COLD DRINK?
THAT WOULD BE NICE..

OVER HERE.. TWO, PLEASE!

IS YOUR GRAMPA STILL PLAYING GOLF?
YES, BUT HE'S GIVEN UP TRYING TO SHOOT HIS AGE.. NOW HE'S TRYING TO SHOOT THE TEMPERATURE..

IT WAS HOT YESTERDAY.. HE SHOT A 102..

PEANUTS
by SCHULZ

HERE'S THE WORLD WAR I FLYING ACE HIGH OVER ENEMY LINES IN HIS SOPWITH CAMEL..

WHAT'S THAT? A FOKKER TRIPLANE DIVING DOWN OUT OF THE SUN!

IT'S THE RED BARON! HE'S RIDDLING MY PLANE WITH BULLETS!

I LEAP FROM THE BURNING AIRCRAFT..
© 1999 United Feature Syndicate, Inc.
7-18
www.snoopy.com

I DASH MADLY ACROSS NO-MAN'S LAND TO SAFETY AND THE AERODROME..

THE GENERAL IS SURE TO AWARD ME A MEDAL FOR MY COURAGE! MAYBE THE BRONZE STAR!

HEY, WHERE HAVE YOU BEEN? I'VE GOT SOMETHING FOR YOU...

THE BRONZE SUPPER DISH!
SCHULZ

YOU'RE RIGHT..
THE DAYS GO
BY TOO FAST..
www.snoopy.com

EVEN THE NIGHTS GO
BY FAST..MAYBE YOU
SHOULD DO WHAT I DO..
© 1999 United Feature Syndicate, Inc.

7-19
SLEEP SLOWER..
SCHULZ

SEE? I PUT GRAPE JELLY
ON MY TOAST...THEN, I'M
EXTRA CAREFUL TO MAKE
SURE IT DOESN'T SLIDE OFF..
www.snoopy.com

BUT IS THAT ENOUGH? NO!
IT FALLS DOWN THROUGH
LITTLE HOLES IN THE TOAST,
AND GETS ON MY SHIRT!
© 1999 United Feature Syndicate, Inc.

7-20
GRAPE JELLY
HATES ME..
SCHULZ

I HAVEN'T HEARD YOU
SING LATELY..
7-21
www.snoopy.com

BIRDS SHOULD SING..
EVERYONE EXPECTS IT...
© 1999 United Feature Syndicate, Inc.

NO, I DON'T
HAVE ANY
REQUESTS..
SCHULZ

HOW CAN YOU SIT THERE BEGGING WHEN YOU DON'T EVEN KNOW WHAT I'M EATING?
© 1999 United Feature Syndicate, Inc.
7-22

SCHULZ
HOW CAN YOU SIT THERE WAITING FOR A LITTLE PIECE, OR A TINY BIT, OR A CHUNK OR WHATEVER?
TRY HANDFUL

NO, I CAN'T COME OUT, SIR.. I HAVE TO PRACTICE THE VIOLIN..
www.snoopy.com

YOU TRY TO DO TOO MUCH, MARCIE.. SOMEDAY YOUR HEAD IS GOING TO FALL OFF..

MAYBE YOU'RE RIGHT.. I'LL COME OUT FOR A WHILE..
© 1999 United Feature Syndicate, Inc.

SEE? IF YOU RELAX NOW AND THEN, YOUR HEAD WON'T FALL OFF..
SCHULZ
7-23

DOG FOOD, I GUESS.. WHY?
© 1999 United Feature Syndicate, Inc.
7-24

NO, I'M NOT EATING, I'M DINING..
SCHULZ

PEANUTS
by SCHULZ

IT'S A RED BALL, SEE? CAN YOU REMEMBER THAT?

I'M GOING TO THROW THIS BALL TO THE EDGE OF THE WORLD SO BE CAREFUL WHEN YOU CHASE IT..

MAKE SURE YOU DON'T FALL OVER THE EDGE OF THE WORLD..

7-25

WELL?
I'M MAKING SURE..
SCHULZ

SCHULZ 7-26
GRAMMA SAYS WHEN YOU WAKE UP IN THE MORNING, YOU SHOULD GIVE THANKS FOR A NEW DAY, AND THEN MAKE PLANS TO DO SOMETHING POSITIVE..
LIKE FEED THE DOG..
© 1999 United Feature Syndicate, Inc.

SHOULD I RUN OUT AND GET THE DOG DISH OR WAIT UNTIL IT STOPS RAINING?
GO NOW

MAYBE I'LL WAIT 'TIL IT STOPS RAINING
NO, GO NOW..
www.snoopy.com

ON THE OTHER HAND, I CAN'T LET MY DOG STARVE TO DEATH..
SO GO NOW..

ON THE OTHER HAND, THERE'S NO SENSE IN GETTING ALL WET..
GO ANYWAY..
7/27
© 1999 United Feature Syndicate, Inc.

LET ME KNOW WHEN IT STOPS RAINING..
SCHULZ

7-28
"AND THE RAIN WAS UPON THE EARTH FORTY DAYS AND FORTY NIGHTS"
UNBELIEVABLE..
WHO WENT OUT IN THE BACK YARD AND GOT THE DOG DISH?
SCHULZ
© 1999 United Feature Syndicate, Inc.

IF IT DOESN'T STOP RAINING, I WON'T BE ABLE TO GO OUT AND GET YOUR DOG DISH..
www.snoopy.com

SO I'LL MAKE THE SUPREME SACRIFICE..I'LL PUT ON MY RAIN OUTFIT AND BRAVE THE ELEMENTS!
© 1999 United Feature Syndicate, Inc.

AFTERWARDS WE CAN HAVE THE AWARDING OF MEDALS..
SCHULZ 7-29

THERE! I WENT OUT IN THE POURING RAIN AND GOT YOUR DISH..
www.snoopy.com

SO HERE'S YOUR BREAKFAST..I HOPE YOU APPRECIATE IT..
© 1999 United Feature Syndicate, Inc.

7-30
DOG FOOD AGAIN?
SCHULZ

SCHULZ 7-31
GRAMMA SAYS BEFORE YOU GO TO SLEEP YOU SHOULD GIVE THANKS FOR ANOTHER DAY..
AND HOPE YOU DON'T DREAM ABOUT CATS ALL NIGHT..
© 1999 United Feature Syndicate, Inc.

HE WANTS US?!
PEANUTS
by SCHULZ

YES, SIR..WE CAN DO THAT..

GENERAL WASHINGTON WANTS US TO DELIVER THIS MESSAGE TO THOMAS PAINE..

"DEAR FRIEND, I AM CONCERNED OF YOUR WELFARE..ARE YOU WELL? TELL ME YOUR THOUGHTS"

MR. PAINE, A MESSAGE FROM THE GENERAL..DO YOU HAVE A RESPONSE?

"THESE ARE THE TIMES THAT TRY MEN'S SOULS"

THAT'S TOO DEPRESSING..

I'LL CHANGE IT A LITTLE..
8-1

HERE YOU ARE, SIR..

SEE? MY MESSAGE MADE HIM FEEL BETTER..

I SAID, "NO PROBLEM.. HAVE A NICE DAY"
SCHULZ

8-2
© 1999 United Feature Syndicate, Inc.

SCHULZ
IT DIDN'T SKIP..

8-3

www.snoopy.com

© 1999 United Feature Syndicate, Inc.
SCHULZ

IT'S MY THEORY THAT THIS WASN'T ALWAYS A DESERT.. I THINK AN ADVANCED CIVILIZATION EXISTED RIGHT HERE..
8-4

THEY HAD ROADS, AND FARMS, SWIMMING POOLS AND EVERYTHING
www.snoopy.com

BUT WHAT HAPPENED?

© 1999 United Feature Syndicate, Inc.
THE SAGUARO KNOWS, BUT HE'S NOT TALKING..
SCHULZ

8-5
© 1999 United Feature Syndicate, Inc.
SCHULZ

Dear Pen Pal,
YOU DON'T HAVE A PEN PAL..
www.snoopy.com

I DON'T?

THEN I DON'T HAVE TO WRITE TO HIM, DO I?
NO, I GUESS NOT..
© 1999 United Feature Syndicate, Inc.

8-6
FORGET YOU, KID!
SCHULZ

HOW WOULD YOU LIKE TO BUY A WATERCOLOR PICTURE OF YOUR DOG?
www.snoopy.com

THERE'S NOTHING ON IT..
© 1999 United Feature Syndicate, Inc.

8-7
I RAN OUT OF WATER..
SCHULZ

"Someday,"
he said.
PEANUTS
by SCHULZ

The
End

© 1999 United Feature Syndicate, Inc.

8-8
www.snoopy.com

I THOUGHT HE'D LIKE
IT.. A MAILBOX WAS
THE HERO..
SCHULZ

THANK YOU, EMILY..
www.snoopy.com

THAT WAS EMILY AT THE DANCE STUDIO..SHE SAYS SHE LIKES TO DANCE WITH ME BECAUSE I DANCE LIKE FRED ASTAIRE..
© 1999 United Feature Syndicate, Inc.

FRED ASTAIRE OR FRED FLINTSTONE?
SCHULZ
8/9

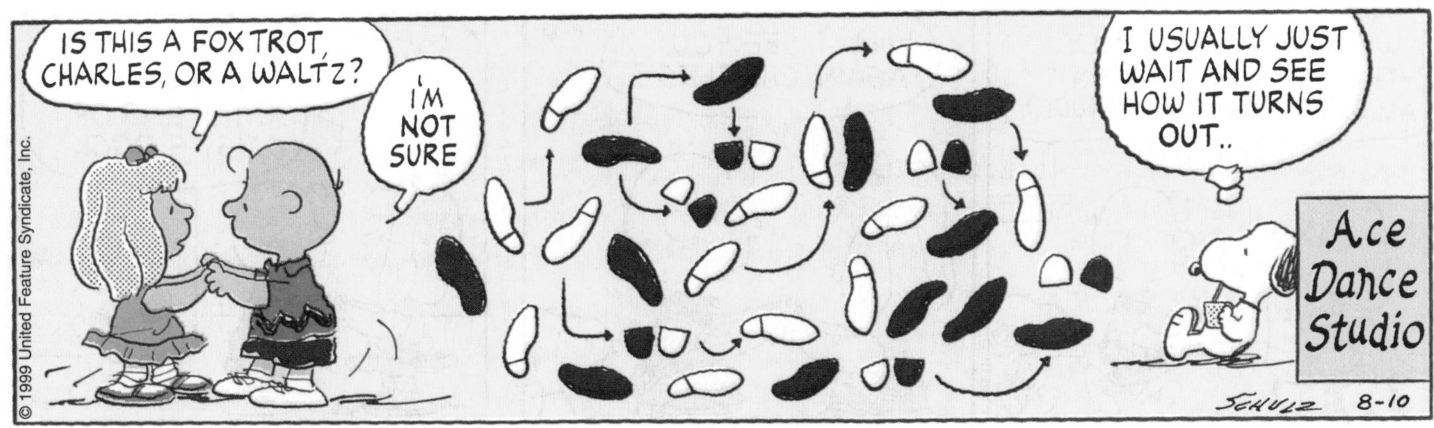
IS THIS A FOX TROT, CHARLES, OR A WALTZ?
I'M NOT SURE
I USUALLY JUST WAIT AND SEE HOW IT TURNS OUT..
Ace Dance Studio
SCHULZ 8-10
© 1999 United Feature Syndicate, Inc.

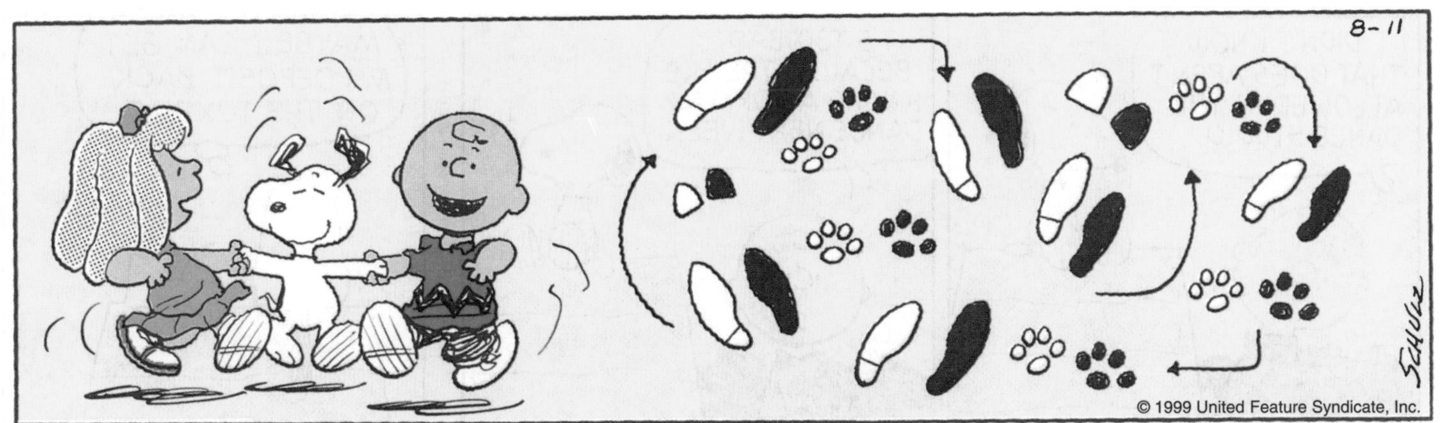
8-11
SCHULZ
© 1999 United Feature Syndicate, Inc.

YES, MA'AM, HE'S MY DOG.. DOGS CAN'T TAKE DANCE LESSONS?
www.snoopy.com

THEN I GUESS WE'LL HAVE TO GO HOME..
8-12

WE HAVE SORT OF AN AGREEMENT..HE GOES WHERE I GO, AND I GO WHERE HE GOES..
© 1999 United Feature Syndicate, Inc.

EXCEPT WHEN HE'S FLYING, BUT DON'T ASK ME TO EXPLAIN THAT..
SCHULZ

WE HAVE TO GO, EMILY.. THEY SAID DOGS AREN'T ALLOWED IN THE DANCE STUDIO..
www.snoopy.com

8-13
WILL I SEE YOU AGAIN, CHARLES?
© 1999 United Feature Syndicate, Inc.

SOMEDAY, EMILY..
WE'LL MEET BY THE GREEN LIGHT AT THE END OF DAISY'S DOCK..
SCHULZ

I DIDN'T KNOW THAT DOGS AREN'T ALLOWED IN THE DANCE STUDIO..
www.snoopy.com

8-14
IT'S TOO BAD BECAUSE THEY'RE HAVING A FORMAL DANCE NEXT WEEK
© 1999 United Feature Syndicate, Inc.

MAYBE I CAN GET MY DEPOSIT BACK ON THE TUXEDO..
SCHULZ

PEANUTS
by SCHULZ
IT'S A NEW BALL, SEE?

© 1999 United Feature Syndicate, Inc.
READY?

I SAID, "ARE YOU READY?"
DOGS CAN'T TALK..

8-15
WHEN I SAY, "READY?" YOU'RE SUPPOSED TO CROUCH DOWN...

..LIKE THIS..

www.snoopy.com

SCHULZ
SORRY.. I THOUGHT YOU WERE READY..

WAKE UP, BIG BROTHER!
8-16

WAKE UP?! WAKE UP?!! WHY ARE YOU WAKING ME UP?
I THOUGHT YOU MIGHT LIKE TO GET AN EARLY START..

FOR WHAT? I'M NOT GOING ANYWHERE..

THAT'S TOO BAD.. YOU COULD HAVE BEEN THE FIRST ONE THERE..
SCHULZ

LOOK WHAT I FOUND.. AN OAR!
8-17

THIS PROVES MY THEORY THAT THIS WHOLE DESERT USED TO BE UNDER WATER..

OR MY OTHER THEORY THAT SOMEONE SOMEWHERE IS MISSING AN OAR..
SCHULZ

SO WHAT I'M WONDERING IS..IF I FOUND ONE OAR, THERE COULD BE ANOTHER ONE AROUND, RIGHT?

AND IF THERE ARE TWO OARS, THERE MIGHT ALSO BE A BOAT, RIGHT?
8-18

THIS SORT OF THING DOESN'T REALLY INTEREST YOU, DOES IT?
SCHULZ

WHY ARE YOU JUST SITTING THERE?!
www.snoopy.com

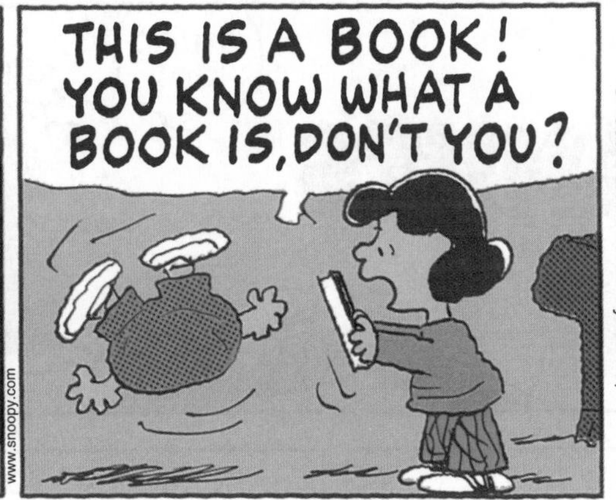
THIS IS A BOOK! YOU KNOW WHAT A BOOK IS, DON'T YOU?
© 1999 United Feature Syndicate, Inc.

NOTHING, MOM.. I'M JUST ENCOURAGING HIM TO READ..
SCHULZ
8-19

WHAT'S THIS?
IT'S A FAMILY SURVEY..
8-20
www.snoopy.com

I'M SUPPOSED TO ANSWER THE QUESTIONS ABOUT BROTHERS AND SISTERS..

HOW DID I DO?
© 1999 United Feature Syndicate, Inc.

I GAVE YOU AN "HONORABLE MENTION"
SCHULZ

SORRY I MISSED THAT ONE, MANAGER
www.snoopy.com

A MANAGER CAN ALWAYS FORGIVE A MECHANICAL ERROR..
8-21

BUT A MANAGER CANNOT FORGIVE A MENTAL ERROR..
I'M IN LOVE WITH YOUR CATCHER..
© 1999 United Feature Syndicate, Inc.

THAT'S A MENTAL ERROR!
SCHULZ

PEANUTS®
by SCHULZ
STUPID KID!

THERE'S A KID DOWN AT THE PLAYGROUND WHO INSULTED ME.. I NEED TO BORROW YOUR DOG TO BITE HIM ON THE LEG..

MAKE SURE HE ROLLS HIS SOCK DOWN..I HATE TO BITE THROUGH A SOCK..

OKAY, KID! EITHER YOU APOLOGIZE, OR THIS MEAN DOG BITES YOU ON THE LEG!

ALL RIGHT, I APOLOGIZE..
YOU DO?

8-22
HE APOLOGIZED..

SCHULZ
I DON'T THINK YOU WANTED TO BITE HIM ON THE LEG ANYWAY, DID YOU?
IT'S TOO FAR TO BEND OVER..

HOW MUCH LONGER BEFORE SCHOOL STARTS AGAIN?
I DON'T KNOW..I THINK SIXTEEN DAYS..
© 1999 United Feature Syndicate, Inc.

8-23
HOW MANY MINUTES?
SCHULZ

WHEN YOU GRADUATE FROM HIGH SCHOOL, DOES SOMEONE GIVE YOU A BICYCLE?
NO, I DON'T THINK SO..
8-24
www.snoopy.com

GRAMPA SAYS WHEN HE GRADUATED, SOMEONE GAVE HIM A FOUNTAIN PEN..
© 1999 United Feature Syndicate, Inc.

A RED BICYCLE WOULD BE NICE..
HE SAID IT WAS A RED FOUNTAIN PEN..
SCHULZ

www.snoopy.com

8-25
© 1999 United Feature Syndicate, Inc.

SCHULZ

I FELL DOWN ON YOUR SIDEWALK AND BUMPED MY KNEE..
FORTUNATELY, WE HAVE A WORLD FAMOUS ORTHOPEDIC SURGEON RIGHT HERE

MAYBE WE SHOULD TAKE HIM TO THE EMERGENCY ROOM..

WE CAN'T... I FORGOT WHERE IT IS..

GOOD NEWS! THE DOCTOR DOESN'T THINK YOU'LL NEED SURGERY..

ACTUALLY, BRUISED KNEES ARE VERY COMMON..

KIDS FALL DOWN ON THE SIDEWALK ALL SUMMER LONG..

COME BACK THIS WINTER WHEN YOU SLIP ON THE ICE..

ALL RIGHT, WHO TOOK THE COMIC BOOK THAT WAS ON THIS TABLE?

HERE, I'M SORRY.. I DIDN'T KNOW IT WAS YOURS..

I SUPPOSE YOU READ ALL THE READING OUT OF IT..

PEANUTS
by SCHULZ
WHO ARE WE PLAYING? WHY ARE WE PLAYING? WHAT ARE WE PLAYING?

HEY, MANAGER.. I HAVE A QUESTION..
www.snoopy.com

WHAT AM I PLAYING TODAY, RIGHT FIELD OR RIGHT WING?
8-29

WELL, I'VE SEEN YOU PLAY RIGHT FIELD SO I THINK YOU'D BE GREAT AT RIGHT WING..

RIGHT WING, HUH? WELL, I GUESS THAT MAKES SENSE..
© 1999 United Feature Syndicate, Inc.

DO YOU HAVE ALL YOUR EQUIPMENT HERE?
SURE, I'M ALWAYS READY FOR ANYTHING..

I WONDER IF HE WAS PUTTING ME ON..
SCHULZ

THE TROUBLE WITH BEING A LITTLE KID IS NO ONE EVER ASKS YOUR OPINION ABOUT ANYTHING
www.snoopy.com

WHY DON'T YOU STOP TALKING AND JUST GO TO BED..
8-30
© 1999 United Feature Syndicate, Inc.

ARE YOU ASKING FOR MY OPINION ?
SCHULZ

GOOD MORNING.. I'M TAKING AN OPINION POLL..
OKAY, WHAT DO YOU WANT TO ASK ME ?
www.snoopy.com

NO, YOU ASK ME SOMETHING, AND THEN I'LL GIVE YOU MY OPINION..
DON'T YOU HAVE ANYTHING BETTER TO DO ?
8-31
© 1999 United Feature Syndicate, Inc.

I DON'T HAVE AN OPINION ON THAT..
SCHULZ

THIS IS MY OPINION..WHEN I THROW THIS BALL, YOU WILL PROBABLY CHASE IT..
www.snoopy.com

THAT'S MY OPINION..
© 1999 United Feature Syndicate, Inc.

IN MY OPINION, IF YOU THROW THAT BALL ONE MORE TIME, YOU'RE NEVER GOING TO SEE IT AGAIN..
SCHULZ
9-1

YES, SIR..I'D LIKE TO BUY SOME SCHOOL SUPPLIES..
www.snoopy.com

MAYBE YOU COULD TRADE IN LAST YEAR'S SEEING AS HOW THEY'VE HARDLY BEEN USED..
9-2
© 1999 United Feature Syndicate, Inc.

YOU SHOULDN'T LET WEIRD PEOPLE IN YOUR STORE, SIR..
SCHULZ

WHAT I WANT TO KNOW IS HOW YOU'RE GOING TO BARK AT A BURGLAR WITH A SUPPER DISH IN YOUR MOUTH..
© 1999 United Feature Syndicate, Inc.

SCHULZ
IF I KNOW A BURGLAR IS COMING, I'LL EAT EARLY..
9-3

9-4
© 1999 United Feature Syndicate, Inc.
SCHULZ

PEANUTS
by SCHULZ
THIS IS SOMETHING I HAVE FINALLY LEARNED..

POSSESSIONS CAN BE A BURDEN, DID YOU KNOW THAT?

THERE'S MORE TO LIFE THAN OWNING THINGS..

SEE THIS HAT? IT'S A FISHING HAT..MY DAD GAVE IT TO ME YEARS AGO..

SEE THESE SHOES? THESE ARE MICKEY MOUSE SHOES..MY FRIEND, MICKEY MOUSE, GAVE THEM TO ME..

THIS HAT AND THESE SHOES ARE THE ONLY THINGS I OWN..

ROCK?

NO, I DON'T EVEN OWN THIS ROCK..
www.snoopy.com

I JUST LEASE IT BY THE MONTH..
SCHULZ
9-5

DO ME A FAVOR ..GO TELL THE WORLD I'M READY TO GET UP..
www.snoopy.com

9-6

© 1999 United Feature Syndicate, Inc.
NOT A SINGLE PERSON CARED..
SCHULZ

WHY AM I STANDING HERE?
IF YOU DON'T KNOW, YOU SHOULDN'T BE HERE..
www.snoopy.com

IF I'M NOT HERE, WHERE SHOULD I BE?
ANYWHERE.. IT'S UP TO YOU..
9-7
© 1999 United Feature Syndicate, Inc.

WHY DID I ASK YOU WHY I'M STANDING HERE?
SCHULZ

YES, MA'AM.. "PIGPEN"
www.snoopy.com

WELL, WHEN I LEFT HOME THIS MORNING, I WAS PRETTY CLEAN..

..SORT OF...RELATIVELY.. ..BORDERLINE...
9-8

© 1999 United Feature Syndicate, Inc.
ABSOLUTELY FILTHY..
SCHULZ

WE'RE SUPPOSED TO BE PAINTING FLOWERS..
NOT ME

THIS IS TARZAN BEATING UP ON MICKEY MOUSE, AND HERE'S DAFFY DUCK BEATING UP ON TARZAN..

I'M INTO BASEMENT COMICS..

9/9

UNDERGROUND
WHATEVER
SCHULZ

YES, SIR..MY TEACHER SAID TO SHOW YOU MY DRAWING..SHE THINKS IT'S TOO VIOLENT..

9-10

IT'S TARZAN, SEE, BEATING UP MICKEY MOUSE, BUT HE'S GOT AN APE AND AN ELEPHANT HELPING HIM..IT WASN'T A FAIR FIGHT..

YES, I HAD TROUBLE DRAWING IT..THE FAT KID WHO SITS NEXT TO ME KEPT THROWING MY CRAYONS ACROSS THE ROOM..
SO WHY DID YOU WISH TO SEE ME.. BECAUSE I PUSHED HIM OUT OF THE CHAIR?
SCHULZ

SCHULZ

9-11

PEANUTS
by SCHULZ

I GOT IT!

IT'S ALL MINE! I GOT IT!

I GOT IT!
© 1999 United Feature Syndicate, Inc.

WHO ARE YOU?
9-12
www.snoopy.com

I'M THE CATCHER..
OH, THAT'S RIGHT...HI!

WHAT ABOUT THE FLY BALL?
THE WHAT?

BONK!

WHAT I THINK I'LL DO IS GO HOME RIGHT NOW, FEED MY DOG, EAT A LIGHT SUPPER, AND GO TO BED EARLY..
SCHULZ

THE TEACHER SAYS WE'RE SUPPOSED TO PAINT THESE FLOWERS..
I DON'T PAINT FLOWERS..I DO UNDERGROUND COMIC BOOKS..
www.snoopy.com

SEE? HERE'S A SPACEMAN ON MARS FIGHTING A PURPLE MONSTER..
9-13
© 1999 United Feature Syndicate, Inc.

WHERE ARE THE WOMEN? I DON'T SEE ANY WOMEN..
THEY HAVE LONG HAIR, RIGHT?
SCHULZ

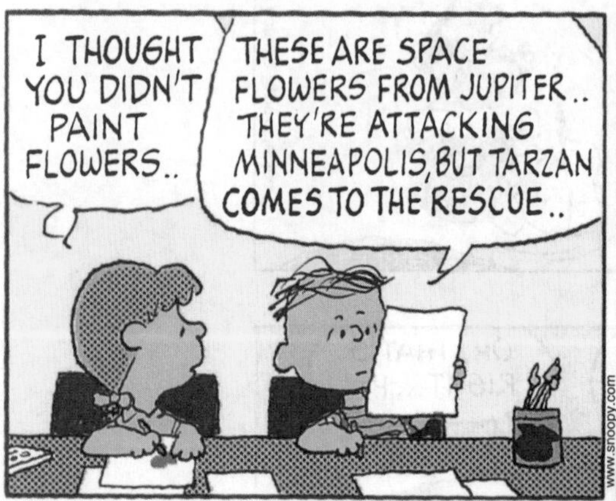
I THOUGHT YOU DIDN'T PAINT FLOWERS..
THESE ARE SPACE FLOWERS FROM JUPITER.. THEY'RE ATTACKING MINNEAPOLIS, BUT TARZAN COMES TO THE RESCUE..
www.snoopy.com

I DIDN'T KNOW TARZAN WAS EVER IN MINNEAPOLIS
HE USED TO ICE SKATE THERE IN THE WINTER..
9/14
© 1999 United Feature Syndicate, Inc.

I THINK YOU'RE SLOWLY GOING MAD..
I MAY HAVE TO HIRE SOMEONE TO DO MY LETTERING..
SCHULZ

SEE? THE TEACHER PUT UP ALL THE FLOWER PAINTINGS OUR CLASS HAS BEEN DOING..
© 1999 United Feature Syndicate, Inc.

9-15
AND WAY OVER HERE, ALL BY ITSELF WHERE NO ONE WILL EVER SEE IT, IS THE UNDERGROUND COMIC YOU DREW..
IT'S UPSIDE DOWN
SCHULZ

THERE! I DID IT!
www.snoopy.com

I ANSWERED EVERY QUESTION!
© 1999 United Feature Syndicate, Inc.

HERE YOU ARE, MA'AM.. FACTORY DIRECT!
9-16

Z
9-17
www.snoopy.com

I'M AWAKE!

Z
© 1999 United Feature Syndicate, Inc.

LAND HO!
SCHULZ

I WAS THINKING OF GIVING YOU A DIFFERENT KIND OF DOG FOOD TONIGHT..
www.snoopy.com

BUT THEN I SAID TO MYSELF, "DOG FOOD IS DOG FOOD..WHAT'S THE DIFFERENCE?"

SO HERE YOU ARE..
SCHULZ
9/18
© 1999 United Feature Syndicate, Inc.

MY AUNT MARIAN WAS RIGHT, BUT I FORGOT WHAT SHE SAID..

PEANUTS
SCHULZ

© 1999 United Feature Syndicate, Inc.

www.snoopy.com

THANK YOU..BUT I DIDN'T EXPECT TO GET IT AUTOGRAPHED
SCHULZ
9-19

DO YOU THINK HE'LL REMEMBER US ?
WE'RE HIS BROTHERS, AREN'T WE ?
www.snoopy.com

HEY! WE'RE BACK!
ANDY! OLAF! I THOUGHT YOU WENT TO LIVE WITH SPIKE..
© 1999 United Feature Syndicate, Inc.

WE KEPT GETTING LOST..
WE MADE TWO RIGHT TURNS AND TWENTY-THREE WRONG ONES..
SCHULZ
9-20

SO WE STARTED OFF TOWARD THE WEST..
HOW DID YOU KNOW WHICH WAY IS WEST ?

SOMEONE SAID THE SUN SETS IN THE WEST..
© 1999 United Feature Syndicate, Inc.

BUT THEN IT GETS DARK..
WE DIDN'T THINK OF THAT..
SCHULZ
9-21

Dear Snoopy, Whatever happened to Andy and Olaf ?

I have been waiting for them.
www.snoopy.com

The weather here has been nice.
© 1999 United Feature Syndicate, Inc.

The sky is blue and the sun is bright.
9-22
SCHULZ

LOOK! A LETTER FROM OUR BROTHER SPIKE!
9-23

HE WANTS TO KNOW WHAT HAPPENED TO YOU GUYS..
www.snoopy.com

HE SAYS THE WEATHER THERE HAS BEEN NICE.. THEN HE SAYS...
© 1999 United Feature Syndicate, Inc.
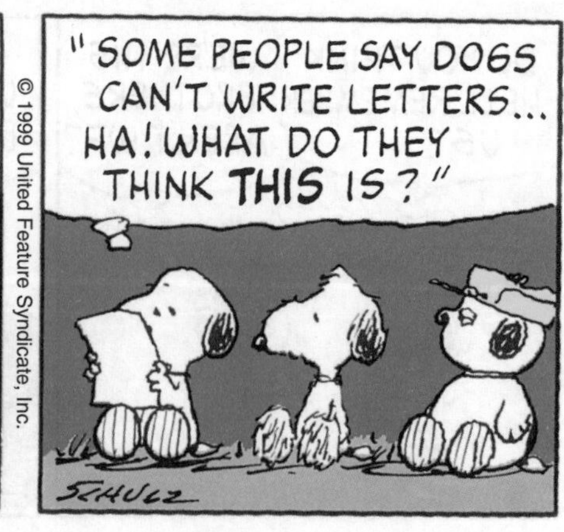
"SOME PEOPLE SAY DOGS CAN'T WRITE LETTERS... HA! WHAT DO THEY THINK **THIS** IS?"
SCHULZ

CHARLIE BROWN! YOU'VE GOT EXTRA DOGS! ARE THEY FREE? I'LL TAKE TWO!
9-24
www.snoopy.com

LOOK, MOM! FREE DOGS!
© 1999 United Feature Syndicate, Inc.

SORRY.. MOM WON'T LET ME HAVE A DOG..
LIFE IS FULL OF DISAPPOINTMENTS
SCHULZ

WE'RE IN TROUBLE.. THE ROUND-HEADED KID SAYS ALL YOU GUYS DO IS PLAY CARD GAMES..
9-25
www.snoopy.com

HE SAID WHAT WOULD THEY DO IF A BURGLAR CAME?
© 1999 United Feature Syndicate, Inc.

WE'D INVITE HIM TO PLAY "SPOONS"
THEN, WHEN HE WASN'T LOOKING, WE'D HIT HIM WITH A SPOON..
SCHULZ

PEANUTS
by SCHULZ
ARE YOU READY?

WELL, ARE YOU GOING TO SCHOOL OR ARE YOU GOING TO HIDE UNDER YOUR BED ALL DAY?

GRAMPA SAYS ALL YOU EVER NEED TO KNOW IS "I BEFORE E EXCEPT AFTER C"

WHAT ABOUT LOUIS THE FOURTEENTH OR FLORENCE NIGHTINGALE?
9-26

GRAMPA SAYS YOU DON'T NEED TO KNOW ANY OF THOSE THINGS.. "I BEFORE E EXCEPT AFTER C" IS ALL YOU HAVE TO KNOW..
www.snoopy.com

I'LL COME OUT WHEN IT'S TIME TO GRADUATE..

ALL RIGHT, I'LL SEE YOU IN TWELVE YEARS..

WHAT ARE YOU DOING HERE? SOMEBODY SAID YOU WERE HIDING UNDER YOUR BED AGAIN..
TWELVE YEARS IS A LONG TIME.. WHO WAS FLORENCE NIGHTINGALE?
SCHULZ

THEY'RE GONE! MY BROTHERS ARE GONE!

WHAT ARE THEY GOING TO DO? THEY CAN'T WANDER AROUND FOREVER..
9-27

STILL, THEY'RE PRETTY SMART.. THEY'LL FIND SOMETHING USEFUL TO DO..
© 1999 United Feature Syndicate, Inc.

YOU KNOW WHAT WE SHOULD DO? WE SHOULD BUY BANJOS..
SCHULZ

QUICK, MARCIE, I NEED SOME ANSWERS!
www.snoopy.com

WHAT'S YOUR HURRY?
I WANT TO BE THE FIRST ONE DONE..

IF YOU GET YOUR PAPER IN FIRST, YOU GET EXTRA CREDIT..
© 1999 United Feature Syndicate, Inc.
9/28

EXTRA CREDIT ON A D-MINUS?
YOU ARE UNCOMMONLY WEIRD, MARCIE!
SCHULZ

WHAT'S THAT?
AN UNDERWATER CAMERA..

IT TAKES PICTURES UNDER WATER..

© 1999 United Feature Syndicate, Inc.
9-29

I DON'T THINK IT'S WORKING..
SCHULZ

WHAT ARE YOU DRAWING NOW?
THESE ARE RABBITS SWINGING THROUGH THE TREES

RABBITS DON'T SWING THROUGH THE TREES
HOW DO THEY GET WHERE THEY WANT TO GO?
www.snoopy.com

9-30
THEY HOP..
© 1999 United Feature Syndicate, Inc.

I CAN'T DRAW HOPPING..
SCHULZ

THANK YOU
www.snoopy.com

THE DENTIST SAID I WAS A GOOD PATIENT AND GAVE ME A FREE TOOTHBRUSH..
© 1999 United Feature Syndicate, Inc.

10-1
I WAS HOPING FOR A DOG OR A BICYCLE..
SCHULZ

I'LL GO OUT FOR A PASS, MARCIE, AND YOU THROW THE BALL..
www.snoopy.com

ARE YOU GOING UPFIELD OR DOWNFIELD?
JUST THROW THE BALL..

10-2
BONK!
© 1999 United Feature Syndicate, Inc.

SORRY, SIR.. I THREW AN UPFIELD PASS WHEN YOU WERE GOING DOWNFIELD..
SCHULZ

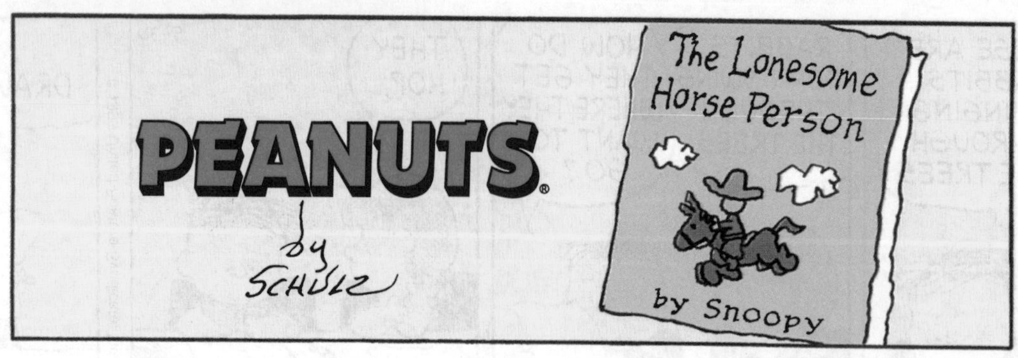
PEANUTS
by SCHULZ
The Lonesome Horse Person
by Snoopy

The sun was setting as the horse person rode back to his cattle place.

Suddenly, he saw some cow takers.

WHAT ARE "COW TAKERS"?
10-3
© 1999 United Feature Syndicate, Inc.
www.snoopy.com

PEOPLE WHO KIDNAP OTHER PEOPLES' COWS..

THIS IS TOO DUMB.. I CAN'T READ ANY MORE!

THE NEXT PART IS THE BEST.. "THE WOUNDED HERO LAY IN THE DUST.."

The robins circled overhead.
SCHULZ

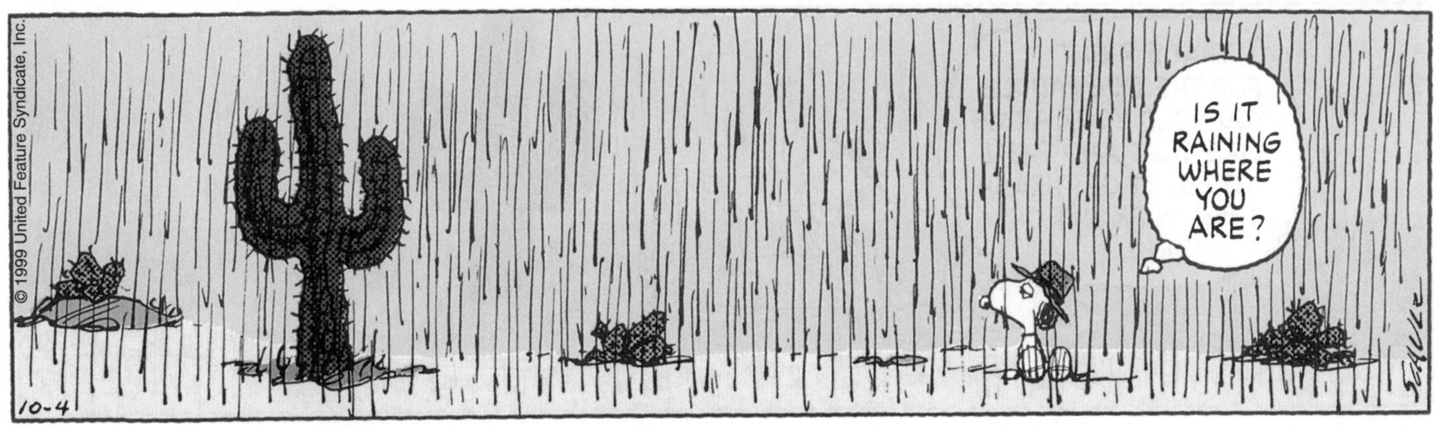
IS IT RAINING WHERE YOU ARE?
© 1999 United Feature Syndicate, Inc.
10-4
SCHULZ

MOM!
© 1999 United Feature Syndicate, Inc.
10-5
SCHULZ

WE NEED MORE PAPER..
© 1999 United Feature Syndicate, Inc.
10-6
SCHULZ

© 1999 United Feature Syndicate, Inc.

© 1999 United Feature Syndicate, Inc.

PEANUTS
by SCHULZ
I CAN DO THIS..

IT'S CALLED "KICK BOXING MADE EASY"

JAB! PUNCH! JAB! PUNCH!

ROUNDHOUSE!

KICK!

JAB! JAB! PUNCH! PUNCH!

JAB! PUNCH! ROUNDHOUSE!

KICK!

NO, ACCORDING TO THIS, IT DOESN'T MEAN YOU WON..
SCHULZ
10-10

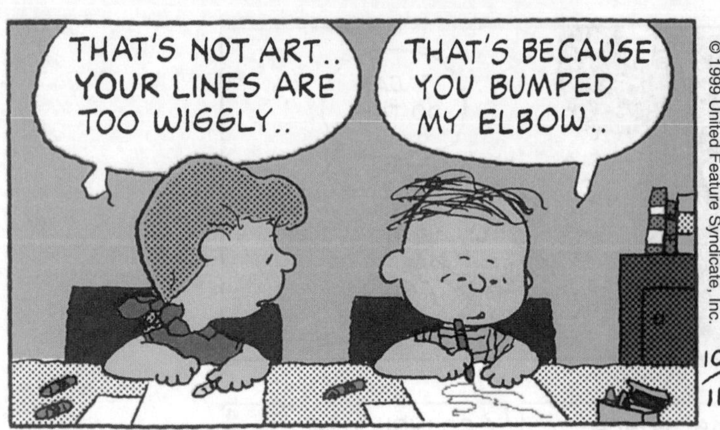
THAT'S NOT ART.. YOUR LINES ARE TOO WIGGLY..
THAT'S BECAUSE YOU BUMPED MY ELBOW..

YOU WERE TAKING UP TOO MUCH ROOM..
THERE'S NO BODY CHECKING IN ART..

I HAVE TO DO A REPORT ON THE NILE RIVER..TELL ME ALL YOU KNOW ABOUT THE NILE RIVER..

OKAY, I GOT THAT..

HOW DOES THIS SOUND? "THE NILE RIVER IS LIKE THE MISSISSIPPI"

"IF YOU'VE SEEN ONE RIVER, YOU'VE SEEN THEM ALL"

"THE NILE RIVER IS ALSO LIKE THE MISSOURI, THE RHINE, THE AMAZON, THE COLORADO, THE VOLGA, THE EUPHRATES, AND THE DANUBE.."

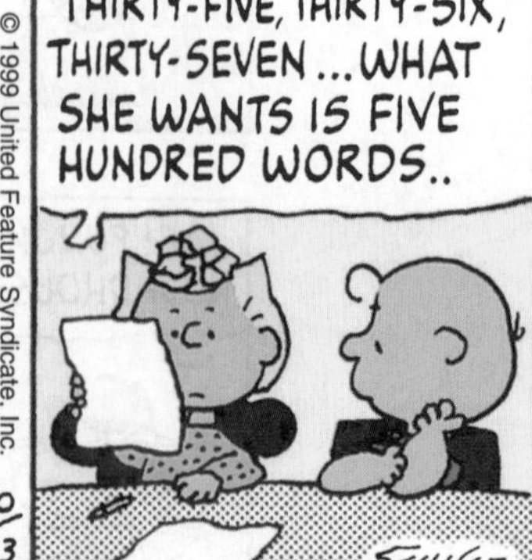
THIRTY-FIVE, THIRTY-SIX, THIRTY-SEVEN ... WHAT SHE WANTS IS FIVE HUNDRED WORDS..

THIS IS MY REPORT ON THE NILE RIVER..
10-14

MY GRAMMA SAYS SHE'S NEVER SEEN THE NILE RIVER SO HOW DO WE KNOW IT'S THERE?
www.snoopy.com

MY GRAMMA SAYS WHEN SHE WAS YOUNG...

MA'AM?
© 1999 United Feature Syndicate, Inc.

YES, I BRING IT ALL TOGETHER NEAR THE END..
SCHULZ

THE TEACHER DIDN'T LIKE MY REPORT..
www.snoopy.com

I HAVE A SNEAKING SUSPICION SHE THOUGHT IT WAS DUMB..
WHY DO YOU THINK THAT?
© 1999 United Feature Syndicate, Inc.

10-15
SHE SAID IT WAS DUMB..
SCHULZ

WELL, FAITHFUL OL' GLOVE, IT'S TIME TO PUT YOU AWAY UNTIL NEXT YEAR..
ANYONE WHO TALKS TO SOMETHING THAT ISN'T ALIVE MUST BE CRAZY..
WHAT ARE YOU DOING HERE? YOU SHOULD BE IN THE KITCHEN..
SCHULZ
10-16
© 1999 United Feature Syndicate, Inc.

PEANUTS
by SCHULZ

BE CAREFUL, DOG..DON'T TOUCH THIS BLANKET, OR..

OR ?

OR WHAT ?

CLOMP!
GOOD GRIEF!

10-17

AAUGH!

DOGS DON'T UNDERSTAND "OR"
SCHULZ

DOES STANDING IN THE RAIN WAITING FOR THE SCHOOL BUS SHOW OUR DESIRE FOR EDUCATION?
NO, IT SHOWS HOW OUR LIVES ARE CONTROLLED BY THOSE IN POWER..
WHAT'S YOUR EXCUSE?
DOGS JUST DO DUMB THINGS..
10-18
SCHULZ
© 1999 United Feature Syndicate, Inc.

QUICK, MARCIE, I NEED AN ERASER AND A RULER..

JUST HAND ME THINGS, MARCIE..
10-19
SCHULZ
© 1999 United Feature Syndicate, Inc.

YES, YOUR HONOR.. THIS YOUNG LADY IS MY CLIENT..

WE'RE HERE TO SUE THE WOLF WHO ATE HER GRANDMOTHER..

YES, SIR, I'LL ASK HER..
10/20
© 1999 United Feature Syndicate, Inc.
HE WANTS TO KNOW WHY YOU'RE WEARING THAT STUPID LOOKING RED RIDING HOOD IN THE COURTROOM..
SCHULZ

DO YOU WANT IT? IT'S A DRAWING I MADE OF A MOUNTAIN..
THANK YOU.. I'LL HANG IT ON OUR WALL..

IT MAY BE WORTH A LOT IN THE FUTURE..
10-21

I'LL LOOK AT IT AGAIN TOMORROW..

DID YOU HANG MY DRAWING ON THE WALL?
NO, WE DECIDED TO THROW IT AWAY..

IT'S STILL IN THE TRASH.. STAY THERE, AND I'LL ROLL IT OUT TO YOU...

10-22

GREAT ART SHOULD NEVER BE ROLLED ACROSS THE PORCH..

10-23

NEVER TRY TO GET SUPPER FIVE MINUTES EARLY..

LUCY!
PEANUTS
by SCHULZ

MOM SAYS TO COME IN FOR LUNCH
SO I'LL HOLD THE BALL, CHARLIE BROWN, AND YOU COME RUNNING UP AND KICK IT..

SHE SAYS RIGHT NOW!
OH, GOOD GRIEF!

THAT'S ALL RIGHT.. WE'LL DO IT SOME OTHER TIME..

NO, RERUN CAN TAKE MY PLACE..
ME?
© 1999 United Feature Syndicate, Inc.

THIS TIME I'LL DO IT! THIS TIME I'LL KICK IT.. RERUN WILL NEVER PULL IT AWAY.. HE JUST WOULDN'T..
10-24

SO HERE WE GO!

WHAT HAPPENED? DID YOU PULL THE BALL AWAY? DID HE KICK IT? WHAT HAPPENED?
www.snoopy.com

YOU'LL NEVER KNOW..
AAUGH!
SCHULZ

SOMEONE SAID YOU WERE A MESSAGE DOG..
THEY DID?

HERE..THE ADDRESS IS ON THE FRONT..

I WANT IT DELIVERED AS FAST AS POSSIBLE..

10-25

10-26

"RETURN TO SENDER"

HEY, CHUCK, GO ASK YOUR DOG WHAT HAPPENED WITH THE MESSAGE HE DELIVERED FOR ME

10-27

WHAT KIND OF A MESSAGE DOG ARE YOU?
10-28

HERE! I WANT THIS DELIVERED RIGHT NOW!

AND DON'T MAKE A PAPER AIRPLANE OUT OF IT!

© 1999 United Feature Syndicate, Inc.

ALL RIGHT, CHUCK, WHERE'S THAT MESSAGE DOG OF YOURS?

NONE OF MY MESSAGES EVER GOT DELIVERED..
HE'S NOT A MESSAGE DOG ANYMORE..HE'S JOINED THE FOREIGN LEGION..
10-29

PARDON, MADEMOISELLE..I HAVE BEEN ORDERED TO FORT ZINDERNEUF... AU REVOIR..HAVE A NICE DAY..

YES..WELL, JUST A MINUTE..I'LL SEE..
10-30

DO YOU HAVE A COUSIN IN ARIZONA?

PEANUTS
by SCHULZ

© 1999 United Feature Syndicate, Inc.
I CAN'T BELIEVE I'M SO STUPID!

WHY DO I BELIEVE HIM?
10-31

BELIEVE WHO?
LINUS! WHY DO I BELIEVE HIM?
COMIX

IF YOU SIT HERE IN THE PUMPKIN PATCH, YOU MAY BE THE FIRST ONE EVER TO SEE THE "GREAT PUMPKIN".

www.snoopy.com

AND YOU BELIEVED HIM?
HOW COULD I HELP IT? WE ACTUALLY HEARD SOMETHING..

LISTEN! DO YOU HEAR THAT? DO YOU SEE ANYTHING?
YES, I SEE SOMETHING

IS IT THE "GREAT PUMPKIN"?

NO! IT'S A ZAMBONI!
SCHULZ

11-1
www.snoopy.com

© 1999 United Feature Syndicate, Inc.

YOU'RE THE LAST ONE.. DID YOU TURN OUT THE LIGHT ?
SCHULZ

I LIKE THE WAY YOU CUT YOUR SANDWICH FROM CORNER TO CORNER, MARCIE.. IT SHOWS REAL CLASS..
www.snoopy.com

CUTTING STRAIGHT ACROSS SHOWS LACK OF BREEDING..
11-2

OF COURSE, THE BEST WAY IS SIMPLY TO FOLD THE BREAD OVER.. THAT KEEPS ALL THE NOURISHMENT IN..
© 1999 United Feature Syndicate, Inc.

YOU ARE SANDWICHLY WEIRD, SIR..
I'M A PURIST, MARCIE..
SCHULZ

I NEED HELP ANSWERING ALL THESE QUESTIONS..
www.snoopy.com

OKAY, READ THE CHAPTER, THEN WE'LL ANSWER THE QUESTIONS
11-3
© 1999 United Feature Syndicate, Inc.

READ THE WHAT ?
SCHULZ

SOMETIMES, IF YOU STARE AT THE BACKDOOR, YOUR SUPPER COMES EARLY..
www.snoopy.com
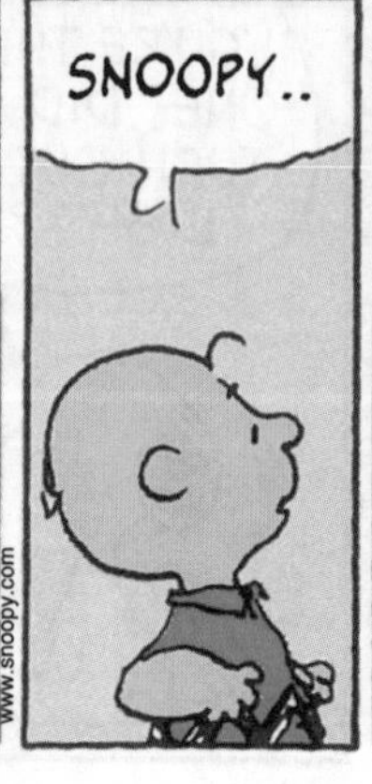
SNOOPY..

IT WORKED!
IT WORKED!
IT WORKED!
IT WORKED!
11-4
© 1999 United Feature Syndicate, Inc.

I JUST CAME OUT TO TELL YOU THAT SUPPER WILL BE A LITTLE LATE TONIGHT..
IT DIDN'T WORK..
SCHULZ

PSST, FRANKLIN.. WHAT DID YOU PUT DOWN FOR THE FIFTH QUESTION?
THERE IS NO FIFTH QUESTION..THAT WAS YESTERDAY
www.snoopy.com

REALLY? I THOUGHT I DID THAT TEST
MAYBE YOU DIDN'T HAND IT IN..

YOU'RE RIGHT.. HERE IT IS..
© 1999 United Feature Syndicate, Inc.

THIS IS THE ONE WHERE I SPELLED MY NAME WRONG..
SCHULZ
11-5

11-6
THIS GUY ON TV SAYS SPORTS ARE ALL FATHERS AND SONS TALK ABOUT..
WHAT ELSE IS THERE TO TALK ABOUT?
"TESS OF THE D'URBERVILLES"
SCHULZ
© 1999 United Feature Syndicate, Inc.

PEANUTS
by SCHULZ

♠ 8 3
♡ Q 5 4
◇ K J 2
♣ Q J 10 9 8
♠ J 10 5 4 2
♡ K 8 3
◇ 10 6
♣ A 7 4
N
W E
S
♠ Q 9 7 6
♡ J 10 9 6
◇ 8 4 3
♣ K 6
♠ A K
♡ A 7 2
◇ A Q 9 7 5
♣ 5 3 2
OKAY.. THREE NO TRUMP..
© 1999 United Feature Syndicate, Inc.
11-7

SORRY, MEN.. WE'LL FINISH THAT HAND WHEN I RETURN..

FLYING ACE SNOOPY REPORTING, MON CAPITAINE

YES, SIR..EVERYTHING WENT BAD..PERHAPS THE CAPTAIN COULD TELL ME WHAT I DID WRONG..

HE SAID I SHOULD HAVE LED A LOW HEART TO THE QUEEN..
www.snoopy.com
SCHULZ

Dear Harry Potter,
I am your biggest fan.

Would you like to come to our house for dinner?
www.snoopy.com

"HARRY POTTER" IS A FICTITIOUS CHARACTER..
© 1999 United Feature Syndicate, Inc.
11/8

SOME OTHER TIME, HARRY..
SCHULZ

11-9
© 1999 United Feature Syndicate, Inc.
WHERE'S RERUN?
HE'S KIND OF SICK..HE SAID IF HE WERE A DOG, HE'D CRAWL UNDER THE PORCH..
THAT'S WHAT OUR GRAMPA ALWAYS TOLD US..IF YOU DON'T FEEL GOOD, CRAWL UNDER THE PORCH..
SCHULZ

I HEARD YOU WERE SICK YESTERDAY..
YES, BUT TODAY I'M BACK..
www.snoopy.com

THE FAT KID TRIED TO SIT HERE IN YOUR PLACE WHILE YOU WERE GONE..
11/10

© 1999 United Feature Syndicate, Inc.
I HIT HIM WITH A BOX OF WATERCOLORS
I WAS WONDERING WHY HE WAS WEARING A RED, BLUE, GREEN AND YELLOW SHIRT..
SCHULZ

ANOTHER C-RATION HAS BEEN CONSUMED IN YOUR HONOR, ERNIE..WE'LL NEVER FORGET YOU..
© 1999 United Feature Syndicate, Inc.
11-11 ERNIE PYLE - TO REMEMBER -

I'M WONDERING IF YOU'D LIKE TO ADDRESS ALL MY CHRISTMAS CARDS FOR ME
11-12
www.snoopy.com

AND MAYBE DO ALL MY SHOPPING, AND WRAP ALL THE PRESENTS FOR ME..
I DON'T THINK SO..
© 1999 United Feature Syndicate, Inc.

NO CHRISTMAS SPIRIT, HUH?
SCHULZ

ONE INCH CLOSER TO THIS BLANKET, DOG, AND YOU'LL REGRET IT FOR THE REST OF YOUR LIFE..

TWO INCHES.. ONE AND A HALF..

ONE AND A QUARTER..

HALF AN INCH..
SCHULZ
11-13
© 1999 United Feature Syndicate, Inc.

PEANUTS
by SCHULZ

© 1999 United Feature Syndicate, Inc.

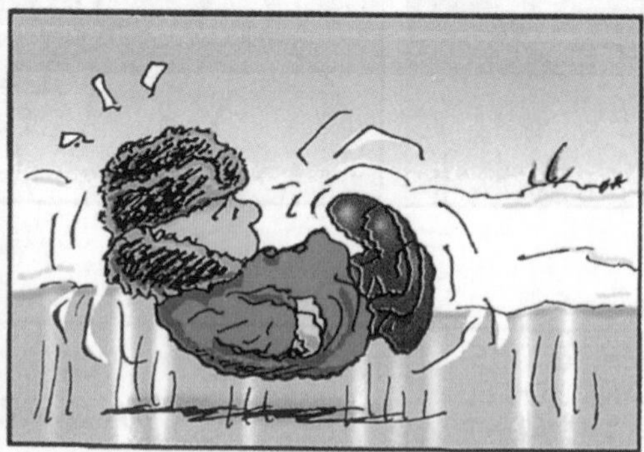

11-14

www.snoopy.com

SCHULZ

The dog wasn't happy the way things were going in the family.

"The next time there's an election," he thought, "I'll run for Head of the Family."

Unfortunately, when the election was held, he only got one vote.

HOW WAS SCHOOL TODAY?
I FAILED STORY LISTENING..
SCHULZ

The dog knew if he could get to the top of the stairs before the rest of the family, he could hold them off forever.

"The house should be mine anyway," he thought.

"The old man wanted me to have it. I was always his favorite."

"Oh, well," he thought, "Where did I put my ball?"

SCHULZ

THIS IS MY GRAMPA'S NEW CAR.. IT HAS BELLS, AND LIGHTS, AND BUTTONS FOR EVERYTHING..
WHAT'S THIS LIGHT FOR?
REMINDS YOU TO FEED THE DOG..
SCHULZ 11-18
© 1999 United Feature Syndicate, Inc.

© 1999 United Feature Syndicate, Inc.
11-19
SCHULZ

HEY, CHUCK..YOU READY FOR ANOTHER GREAT FOOTBALL GAME?

WELL, I DON'T KNOW..OUR BEST PASS RECEIVER HAS A CONCUSSION, A SPRAINED WRIST, A BRUISED ELBOW, AND TWO BROKEN LEGS..
© 1999 United Feature Syndicate, Inc.

PUT SOME ICE ON IT..
SCHULZ
11-20

PEANUTS
by SCHULZ
NO, I THINK HE'S WRITING..

The Dog Who Never Did Anything

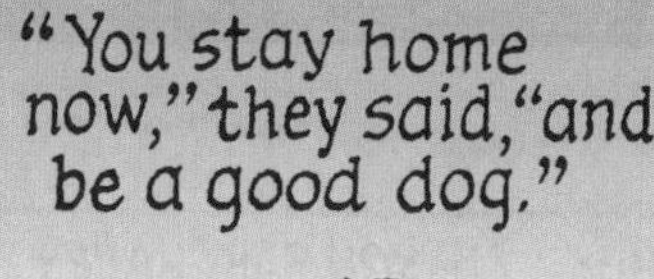
"You stay home now," they said, "and be a good dog."

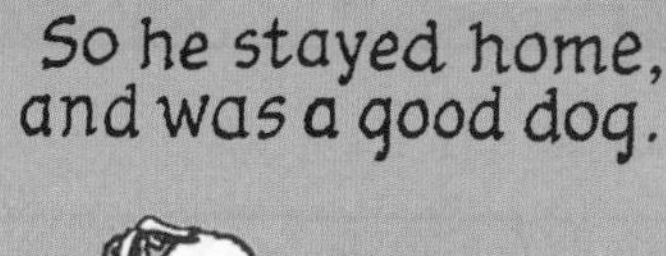
So he stayed home, and was a good dog.

Then he decided to be even a better dog so he barked at everyone who went by.

And he even chased the neighbor's cats.

"What's happened to you?" they said. "You used to be such a good dog."
11-21

So he stopped barking and chasing cats, and everyone said, "You're a good dog."
www.snoopy.com

The moral is, "Don't do anything, and you'll be a good dog."
SCHULZ

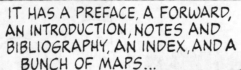

HEY, MARCIE, ABOUT THIS BOOK WE'RE SUPPOSED TO BE READING.. HAVE YOU LOOKED AT IT ?

IT HAS A PREFACE, A FORWARD, AN INTRODUCTION, NOTES AND BIBLIOGRAPHY, AN INDEX, AND A BUNCH OF MAPS...

ARE THEY OUT OF THEIR MINDS ?!
11-22
SCHULZ

WILL THEY GIVE ME A TURKEY ?

SOMETIMES I THINK YOU LIVE IN A DIFFERENT WORLD
OR MAYBE A PUMPKIN PIE..

WHEN I WAS WALKING HOME TODAY, I MET A LADY ON THE SIDEWALK..

I DID JUST WHAT YOU TOLD ME.. I SAID, "HAPPY THANKSGIVING!".. SO SHE YELLED AT ME..

SHE THOUGHT I WAS BEING SARCASTIC..
11-24
SCHULZ

GO BACK TO SLEEP.. THERE'S NO SCHOOL TODAY..
www.snoopy.com

SAY THAT AGAIN..
GO BACK TO SLEEP..THERE'S NO SCHOOL TODAY..
© 1999 United Feature Syndicate, Inc.

11-25
WORDS TO LIVE BY..
SCHULZ

YOU ATE A WORM AND PRETENDED IT WAS A TURKEY?
www.snoopy.com

WHO GOT THE DRUMSTICK AND WHO GOT THE WISHBONE?

HAHAHAHAHA
© 1999 United Feature Syndicate, Inc.

11-26
boot!
SCHULZ

FIRST YOU CATCH A SNOWFLAKE ON YOUR TONGUE..
www.snoopy.com

© 1999 United Feature Syndicate, Inc.

THEN YOU PUT IT IN THE OL' MICROWAVE..
SCHULZ
11-27

PEANUTS

TWO ROOT BEERS, S'IL VOUS PLAÎT..

PARDON, MADEMOISELLE..COULD MY BROTHER HAVE A STRAW?

11-28

© 1999 United Feature Syndicate, Inc.

www.snoopy.com

ALWAYS THE ROWDY ONE, AREN'T YOU, SPIKE?
I GOT CARRIED AWAY..

I SHOULD TAKE THIS BOTTLE CAP OVER TO THAT LITTLE RED-HAIRED GIRL..

IF SHE HAS A BOTTLE CAP COLLECTION, SHE'LL THROW HER ARMS AROUND ME, AND SAY, "THANK YOU! THANK YOU! THANK YOU!"

11-29

A BOTTLE CAP COLLECTION?

Dear Snooty Claus,

"SNOOTY" CLAUS?
HE THINKS HE'S SO SMART.. HE DIDN'T BRING ME ANYTHING I WANTED LAST YEAR..

WELL, DON'T BURN YOUR BRIDGES..
BRIDGES? WHAT HAVE BRIDGES GOT TO DO WITH IT?

NOW I FORGOT WHAT I WAS WRITING..
11/30

I JUST DON'T THINK YOU SHOULD WRITE TO SANTA CLAUS AND CALL HIM "SNOOTY."

WHY NOT? HE MADE ME MAD LAST YEAR.. I REFUSE TO CALL HIM MR. CLAUS!
12-1

WELL, GIVE IT SOME THOUGHT..
I WILL

Dear Shorty,

LOOK! A CHRISTMAS STAR!

IF WE PUT IT ON TOP, EVERYONE WILL BE ABLE TO SEE IT..
www.snoopy.com
12-2

© 1999 United Feature Syndicate, Inc.

COULD YOU MAYBE FLEX YOUR KNEES A LITTLE?
SCHULZ

NO, I GUESS NOT..IT MAKES YOU LOOK LIKE A SHERIFF..
12-3
SCHULZ
© 1999 United Feature Syndicate, Inc.

OUCH! OW! OOO! OUCH!
12-4
www.snoopy.com

OUCH! OW! OUCH! OUCH!

OUCH! OUCH!
OW! OUCH!
© 1999 United Feature Syndicate, Inc.

"JOY TO THE WORLD" OUCH!
SCHULZ

PEANUTS®
by
SCHULZ

© 1999 United Feature Syndicate, Inc.

12-5
www.snoopy.com

I WAS RIGHT..
YOU DIDN'T HAVE
IT IN "PARK"
SCHULZ

12-6
IF WE TAKE READING, MATH, AND HISTORY, SIR, WHICH SHOULD WE TAKE IN THE MORNING?
HISTORY SHOULD ALWAYS BE STUDIED IN THE MORNING, MARCIE, BEFORE ANYTHING ELSE CAN HAPPEN..
© 1999 United Feature Syndicate, Inc.
SCHULZ

12-7
A GOOD WATCHDOG DOESN'T JUST GO, "WOOF!"
www.snoopy.com

A GOOD WATCHDOG GOES, "ROWRGHR!"
© 1999 United Feature Syndicate, Inc.

ALL CAPITALS?
SCHULZ

THERE'S A WHOLE BUNCH OF BURGLARS OUTSIDE..YOU SHOULD GO BARK AT THEM..

WOOF!
www.snoopy.com

THAT WAS GOOD.. YOU SCARED THEM AWAY WITH ONE "WOOF"
© 1999 United Feature Syndicate, Inc.

12-8
IT WAS A QUALITY "WOOF"
SCHULZ

YES, MA'AM.. I WALKED TO SCHOOL IN THE RAIN..
www.snoopy.com

THEN MY WET HAIR DRIPPED ON MY HOMEWORK, AND RUINED IT..
12-9

HERE YOU ARE, SIR.. CONGRATULATIONS
WHAT'S THIS?
© 1999 United Feature Syndicate, Inc.

THE NOBEL PRIZE FOR FICTION..
SCHULZ

WE'RE SUPPOSED TO DRAW EACH OTHER'S FACE..
WELL, TURN YOUR HEAD..I CAN ONLY DRAW A SIDE VIEW FACE..
www.snoopy.com

I'M TRYING TO HAVE AN EXPRESSION OF SOMEONE LOOKING TO THE FUTURE WITH HOPE..
© 1999 United Feature Syndicate, Inc.

THAT'S ALL RIGHT.. I'M JUST DRAWING YOUR EAR..
12/10
SCHULZ

THEY CALL IT "SNOW"
12-11
www.snoopy.com

IT COMES FROM UP THERE..

AND THEN IT FALLS DOWN HERE..
© 1999 United Feature Syndicate, Inc.

?
I'M SORRY.. I THOUGHT YOU WANTED A SCIENTIFIC EXPLANATION..
SCHULZ

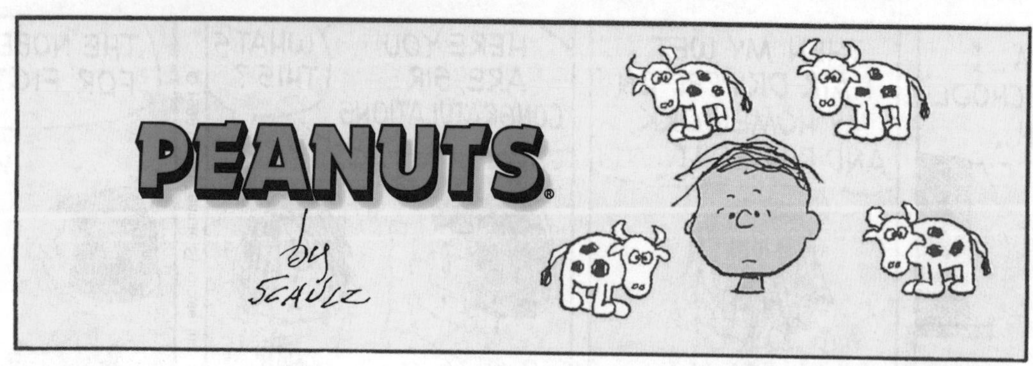
PEANUTS
by SCHULZ

THEY DON'T TEACH US ENOUGH..
12-12

"TWO TIMES TWO IS FOUR..THREE TIMES THREE IS NINE.."
© 1999 United Feature Syndicate, Inc.

THAT'S ALL WE LEARNED TODAY..THAT'S NOT ENOUGH..

WHAT IF I HAVE FOUR COWS, AND I WANT TO BUY EACH COW FOUR BAGS OF FEED, HOW MANY BAGS DO I BUY? HOW WOULD I KNOW?

THEY DON'T TEACH US ENOUGH..

"TWO TIMES TWO.. THREE TIMES THREE" WHO CARES?

I NEED TO KNOW MORE..

"SIXTEEN"
www.snoopy.com

WHAT IF I HAVE FIVE SHEEP?
SCHULZ

CLANG CLANG
CLANG CLANG

SEASON'S GREETINGS..

DON'T SLUMP..

I WANT TO SEND MY TEACHER A CHRISTMAS CARD, BUT I DON'T KNOW HER NAME..
www.snoopy.com

HOW CAN YOU NOT KNOW HER NAME? DON'T YOU EVER TALK TO HER?

WHEN SHE CALLS YOUR NAME IN CLASS, WHAT DO YOU SAY?
© 1999 United Feature Syndicate, Inc.

"WHO, ME?"
SCHULZ
12-16

Two people and a dog walking through the snow.
www.snoopy.com

She removed one of her mittens, and placed her hand in his.

He touched her cheek.
© 1999 United Feature Syndicate, Inc.

"Sooner or later," the dog thought, "one of them is going to forget and drop the leash."
SCHULZ
12-17

12-18
www.snoopy.com

© 1999 United Feature Syndicate, Inc.

SO WHEN YOU GET OLDER, MAYBE I'LL TAKE YOU TO A NICE WARM GYMNASIUM..
SCHULZ

PEANUTS
by SCHULZ

www.snoopy.com

© 1999 United Feature Syndicate, Inc.
12-19

RATS! WE'RE TOO LATE..

I WAS HOPING WE COULD GET A RIDE INTO TOWN..
SCHULZ

HEY, MARCIE..I'M GONNA BE MARY IN THE CHRISTMAS PLAY..WHAT DO YOU THINK I SHOULD WEAR?
www.snoopy.com

THERE IS NO CHRISTMAS PLAY, SIR... THAT WAS LAST YEAR..

YOU'RE KIDDING! WHY DIDN'T ANYONE TELL ME?

EVERYBODY IN THE WHOLE WORLD PROBABLY TOLD YOU, BUT YOU NEVER LISTEN..
© 1999 United Feature Syndicate, Inc.

YOUR KIND HATES MY KIND, DON'T YOU, MARCIE?
SCHULZ
12-20

© 1999 United Feature Syndicate, Inc.
12-21
HEEL!
SCHULZ

LOOK, GRAMMA SENT US A CHRISTMAS CARD WITH A DOLLAR IN IT..
www.snoopy.com

12-22
HOW NICE..

© 1999 United Feature Syndicate, Inc.
ENJOY YOUR FIFTY CENTS..
SCHULZ

I'M GOING OVER TO YOUR DAD'S BARBER SHOP, CHARLIE BROWN..
www.snoopy.com

DOES HE GIVE AWAY A BICYCLE WITH EVERY HAIRCUT?
NO, I DON'T THINK SO..

HE'D HAVE KIDS LINED UP AROUND THE BLOCK FOR HAIRCUTS IF HE GAVE AWAY BICYCLES..
12-23
© 1999 United Feature Syndicate, Inc.

SHOULD I TELL HIM THAT?
NO, JUST TELL HIM TO TRIM THE SIDES AND TAKE A LITTLE OFF THE TOP..
SCHULZ

WE SHOULD MAKE SOME CHRISTMAS COOKIES..
I DON'T KNOW HOW TO MAKE CHRISTMAS COOKIES..
www.snoopy.com

I DON'T KNOW HOW TO BAKE OR FRY OR ANYTHING..
WELL, WE SHOULD MAKE SOMETHING..
12/24
© 1999 United Feature Syndicate, Inc.

HOW ABOUT CHRISTMAS COLD CEREAL?
SCHULZ

12-25
www.snoopy.com

© 1999 United Feature Syndicate, Inc.

NO, YOU SHOULD HAVE JUMPED, AND YELLED, "ABANDON SNOWMAN!"
SCHULZ

PEANUTS
by SCHULZ

12-26

SCHULZ

THIS IS MY JOE TORRE LOOK.. I'M GOING TO USE IT NEXT SEASON..
www.snoopy.com

I'LL MANAGE THE TEAM FROM THE BENCH LIKE JOE TORRE, AND I'LL STARE AT EVERYBODY LIKE THIS, AND WE'LL WIN EVERY GAME
© 1999 United Feature Syndicate, Inc.
12/27

NO, HE CAN'T COME TO THE PHONE NOW.. HE'S CRACKING UP..
THIS WILL BE MY JOE TORRE LOOK..
SCHULZ

Dear Gramma, Thank you for the Christmas cookies. They were good.
www.snoopy.com

Thank you, Thank you, Thank you.
© 1999 United Feature Syndicate, Inc.

12-28
What else can I say?
SEND SOME MORE..
SCHULZ

SO AFTER YOU BUILT YOUR NEST IN THIS TREE, THE TREE FELL DOWN..
12-29
www.snoopy.com

© 1999 United Feature Syndicate, Inc.

SO AFTER YOU BUILT YOUR NEST IN THIS TREE, THE TREE FELL DOWN..
SCHULZ

SOMETIMES IF YOU SIT IN THE RAIN, A RICH LADY WILL COME BY IN A LIMOUSINE AND TAKE YOU HOME..
www.snoopy.com

RICH LADIES IN LIMOUSINES DON'T DRIVE THROUGH OUR BACK YARD..
12-30
© 1999 United Feature Syndicate, Inc.

IF YOU SIT OUT FRONT BY THE CURB, THEY SPLASH WATER ALL OVER YOU..
SCHULZ

THAT PHONE CALL WAS FOR YOU.. I TOLD THEM YOU DON'T TAKE PERSONAL CALLS..
www.snoopy.com

I TOLD THEM YOU LEAD A SECLUDED LIFE, AND PREFER NOT TO BE PART OF THE OUTSIDE WORLD..
12-31
SCHULZ
© 1999 United Feature Syndicate, Inc.

I VOLUNTEERED TO BE THE ONE IN OUR FAMILY TO TAKE ALL THE PHONE CALLS..
I'D SAY SOMETHING, BUT I AM OUT OF THIS WORLD..

1-1-00
© 1999 United Feature Syndicate, Inc.
SCHULZ
SUDDENLY THE DOG REALIZED THAT HIS DAD HAD NEVER TAUGHT HIM HOW TO THROW SNOWBALLS..

PEANUTS
by SCHULZ

HEY, CHUCK, IT'S A GREAT GAME, ISN'T IT?

WE'RE HAVING FUN, AREN'T WE, CHUCK?

IT'S STILL YOUR BALL..
1-2-2000

FOURTH DOWN..
© 2000 United Feature Syndicate, Inc.

WHAT ARE YOU GONNA DO, CHUCK?

YOU GONNA RUN OR PASS?

EVERYBODY'S GONE HOME, SIR..

YOU SHOULD GO HOME, TOO.. IT'S GETTING DARK..
WE HAD FUN, DIDN'T WE, MARCIE?
www.snoopy.com

YES, SIR.. WE HAD FUN..

NOBODY SHOOK HANDS AND SAID, "GOOD GAME"
SCHULZ

PEANUTS
by SCHULZ

ASK YOUR DOG IF HE WANTS TO COME OUT AND ROMP IN THE SNOW, AND LAUGH, AND ACT LIKE WE DON'T HAVE THE SENSE WE WERE BORN WITH..

1-9

HAHAHAHAHA!

HOW COULD IT EVER GET BETTER THAN THIS?
IF YOU WERE A GOLDEN RETRIEVER
SCHULZ

PEANUTS
by SCHULZ
ME?

YES, SIR.. WE'LL DO IT..

GENERAL WASHINGTON WANTS TO KNOW IF WE CAN CHOP UP SOME FIREWOOD FOR HIS CABIN..

1-16
www.snoopy.com

© 2000 United Feature Syndicate, Inc.

YES, SIR..WOODSTOCK THINKS MAYBE YOU SHOULD JUST TURN UP THE THERMOSTAT..
SCHULZ

PEANUTS
by SCHULZ
GIFT CERTIFICATE

WHAT'S THIS? A GIFT CERTIFICATE?

I'M SORRY, SIR..THIS IS A GIFT CERTIFICATE FOR PIZZA..WE DON'T SERVE PIZZA HERE..

© 2000 United Feature Syndicate, Inc.

WHAT'S THIS? A GIFT CERTIFICATE FOR DOG FOOD?
1-23

WHY CERTAINLY, SIR... WE'LL TAKE CARE OF THIS RIGHT AWAY..

HERE YOU GO..
www.snoopy.com

I CAN'T BELIEVE IT TOOK ME THREE YEARS TO THINK OF THAT..
SCHULZ

PEANUTS
by SCHULZ

WE'RE SUPPOSED TO BE PAINTING FLOWERS TODAY
I DON'T DO FLOWERS..I DO UNDERGROUND COMICS..

SEE? HERE'S BILLIE JEAN KING AND DAFFY DUCK THROWING LONG JOHN SILVER OFF THE PIRATE SHIP..

I HAVE BIG PLANS FOR MY WORK..

YES, MA'AM..THESE WILL BE CONSECUTIVELY NUMBERED LIMITED EDITION PRINTS..

EACH PRINT WILL BE SIGNED AND ACCOMPANIED BY A CERTIFICATE OF AUTHENTICATION..
1-30

© 2000 United Feature Syndicate, Inc.
YES, MA'AM.. I UNDERSTAND..

www.snoopy.com
WHAT DID SHE SAY?
SHE SAID TODAY WE'RE PAINTING FLOWERS..
SCHULZ

PEANUTS
by SCHULZ

2-6

THE INSIDE OF A MAILBOX SHOULD ALWAYS BE KEPT CLEAN IN CASE YOU GET A LOVE LETTER..

© 2000 United Feature Syndicate, Inc.

AREN'T YOU GOING OUT TO GET THE MAIL?
NOT WHILE IT'S RAINING..

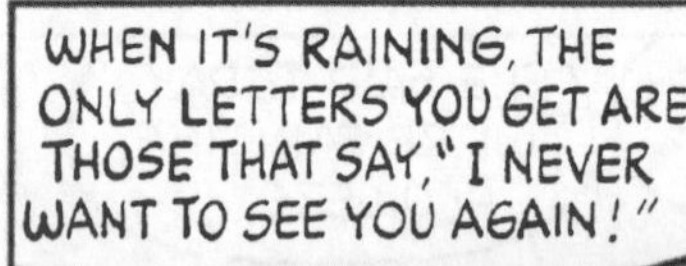
WHEN IT'S RAINING, THE ONLY LETTERS YOU GET ARE THOSE THAT SAY, "I NEVER WANT TO SEE YOU AGAIN!"

YOU SEEM TO KNOW A LOT ABOUT LOVE LETTERS..
www.snoopy.com

IF I EVER GOT ONE, I DON'T KNOW WHAT I'D DO..
SCHULZ

PEANUTS
SCHULZ
NO, I THINK HE'S WRITING..

Dear Friends...

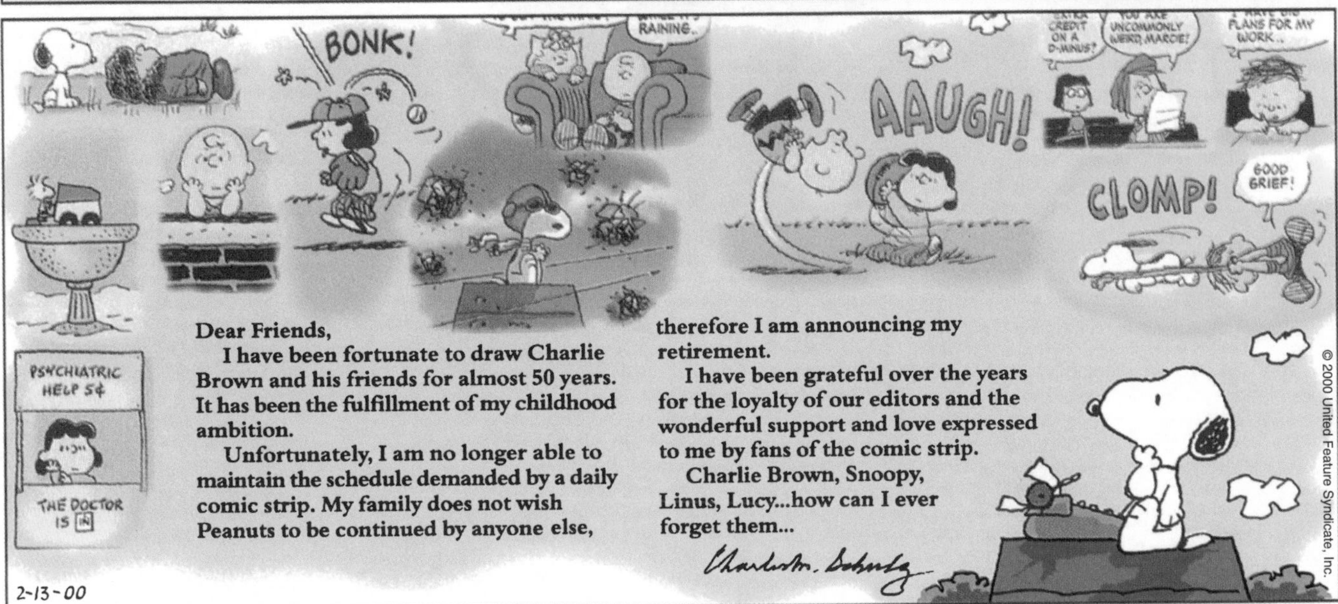
BONK!
RAINING..
CREDIT ON A D-MINUS?
UNCOMMONLY WEIRD, MARCIE!
PLANS FOR MY WORK..
AAUGH!
CLOMP!
GOOD GRIEF!
PSYCHIATRIC HELP 5¢
THE DOCTOR IS IN
Dear Friends,
I have been fortunate to draw Charlie Brown and his friends for almost 50 years. It has been the fulfillment of my childhood ambition.
Unfortunately, I am no longer able to maintain the schedule demanded by a daily comic strip. My family does not wish Peanuts to be continued by anyone else, therefore I am announcing my retirement.
I have been grateful over the years for the loyalty of our editors and the wonderful support and love expressed to me by fans of the comic strip.
Charlie Brown, Snoopy, Linus, Lucy...how can I ever forget them...
Charles M. Schulz
2-13-00
© 2000 United Feature Syndicate, Inc.